Vegetable Production

With Special References to Western Crops

Vegetable Production

With Special References to Western Crops

By

John H. MacGillivray, Ph.D.

Professor of Vegetable Crops and Olericulturist,
University of California

New York • The Blakiston Company, Inc. • Toronto

Preface

The material found in this volume was first prepared in mimeograph form for the use of students in the beginning vegetable course at the University of California. Since most students are interested primarily in the state where they go to school, western production methods and practices were emphasized. Eventually it was found desirable to increase the scope of the material, until a wide coverage has been obtained. The subject matter has been planned from the viewpoint of presenting the important aspects of vegetable production in concise form. References for further reading are given at the end of each section.

The objectives of an elementary course in vegetable production might be stated as follows: To become familiar with the procedures and scientific principles used in vegetable production that assure high yields and good quality. Important considerations are: (1) Choosing the best environment, the best cultural practises—including modifying the environment for maximum production; (2) choosing the best vegetables and varieties; (3) botanical relationships and adaptations; (4) harvesting, packing, and shipping under conditions to prevent the rapid deterioration of quality; (5) realizing the importance of vegetables as a source of food and their contribution to the nutritional health of our people; and (6) an appreciation that productive skill cannot be obtained through classroom work.

The publication consists essentially of two parts. The first covers the general principles of production, such as physiology, plant breeding, and irrigation. The second treats of the application of these principles to the production of different crops. Vegetables are produced over a wide range of climatic conditions as well as of soil types. Procedures will vary to some extent both with crop and local techniques; therefore, the principles are emphasized rather than production practises. Temperature and soil moisture are two factors of production that have been emphasized in the text. The student should keep in mind, however, that there are many important factors—and that success depends upon the integration of all these factors.

A publication of this type represents help and suggestions from many people. The author takes pleasure in acknowledging the assistance and advice of his colleagues in the Department of Vegetable Crops, the University

v

of California. In addition to this group the following persons have been very generous with their contributions: W. E. Berg, L. J. Clemente, Dave Cuthbertson, M. W. Gardner, Harold Goss, E. A. Grensted, W. H. Lange, Joe Mullin, W. Nixon, H. W. Peterson, L. H. Pollard, G. W. Scott, and R. Whipple. Various people have been generous with the loan of pictures for which credit is given in the text. Especial thanks are given, moreover, for the many illustrations made available by the University of California, most of which were supplied by members of the Department of Vegetable Crops. I wish also to express my appreciation to Mrs. Betty Pearson for typing the manuscript, to Mrs. Jean Hahn and Mrs. Vivian Burgy for typing the tables, and to Mrs. Beverly Kepner for the drawings. The author is responsible for the treatment of the material.

THE AUTHOR

Autumn, 1952

Contents

Production Principles

Chapter 1

Types of Vegetable Production

Vegetable crops are a vital source of food, and all of our food comes from land or water areas of the world. *Agriculture* is spoken of as the cultivation or husbandry of land areas and, similarly, *Aquiculture* is concerned with the productivity of water areas for food. The science of Aquiculture is not pursued intensively yet, but it is possible for water to be as productive as land.

Agriculture produces not only food, but also materials used for shelter and clothes, as well as miscellaneous crops such as tobacco. Both animals and plants furnish food. Since a vegetable is a plant food, we need only to distinguish it from other plant foods.

Educational agencies usually have grouped the study of agricultural plants into Agronomy, Pomology, Vegetable Crops or Truck Crops, Floriculture, Landscape Gardening, and Forestry. *Floriculture* and *Landscape Gardening* have to do with the artistic aspects of a man's home. *Forestry* is the economic development of our forest or wood resources. *Agronomy, Pomology,* and *Vegetables* deal primarily with our food resources. Most educational agencies classify Pomology, Vegetable Crops, Floriculture, Landscape Gardening, and sometimes Forestry as the science of *Horticulture*, referring to the fact that they are frequently garden crops.

WHAT IS A VEGETABLE?

The production of food crops for livestock, such as hay and grain, is considered a part of Agronomy. Fiber crops, such as cotton and flax, as well as tobacco and oil-bearing crops are in this same field. The grain crops are more frequently considered a direct source of human food. From a botanical standpoint, these are fruits—low in water content (10 to 20 per cent), and almost always processed to produce flour or some similar material before being used as food. Dry beans possess characteristics similar to the grains, except that these are threshed but not otherwise processed. Agronomic food crops will store for a year or longer with little loss of food value, and may be held in ordinary farm buildings.

Horticultural food crops have three things in common: the edible part is high in water content (85 to 95 per cent) ; crops are more frequently eaten

3

fresh than processed; and they store for varying lengths of time, though rarely for over a period of nine months. Good storage conditions usually require either a naturally or mechanically cooled building. Most pomological crops are produced on woody, perennial plants—frequently trees. The food is a ripe fruit; and, in the case of deciduous trees, ripens over a short period of time. In contrast, most vegetables are annuals, some are perennials grown as annuals, some are biennials, and in only a few cases are they perennials. Asparagus, rhubarb, and globe artichoke are examples of perennials. In vegetables, the botanical parts of the plant used as food are root, stem, leaf, immature flower parts, and both immature and mature fruits. Most of the vegetable fruit plants produce a crop over a longer period of time than deciduous fruits, and thus there are frequently blossoms and marketable fruits on the plant at the same time. Vegetables are grown on herbaceous, not woody, plants. Vegetables are defined on the basis of these general characteristics. The lack of an accurate, simple definition also holds for other groups of crops and other biological material.

GENERAL TYPES OF VEGETABLE PRODUCTION

About 89 per cent of the per capita consumption of our vegetables[8] are eaten in the fresh state, and the remainder are processed. These data are on the retail store basis which eliminates marketing and canning wastes. When farm tonnages are compared, about 80 per cent are used for fresh consumption. Most of the processed vegetables are marketed in tin cans, but there are also frozen, dried, and pickled vegetables. Besides the previously mentioned types of production, there is also the vegetable-seed industry. There are several subdivisions under these three main groups. All these types of vegetable production are found in the West; however, modern transportation has tended to break down many of the former boundaries between the different types of fresh-vegetable production.

The Fresh-vegetable Industry. Usually the industry has been separated into (a) home and farm gardening, (b) market gardening, (c) truck farming, and (d) greenhouse and forcing crops.

Home and Farm Gardening. The home or farm garden reduces living expenses because the vegetables are grown for the home table. A wide selection of crops is grown even though the local climate is not exactly ideal for all of them. Land, fertilizer, and seed may be expensive compared to commercial growing, but the quality of the product is usually more desirable.

Market Gardening. This refers to commercially grown vegetables produced near large cities or other local markets. A variety of vegetables is grown in spite of the high land rental, expensive labor, and sometimes the lack of labor-saving devices. Low cost of transportation, and the possibility of quick adjustment of supply and variety to the demands of a local market have made this type of vegetable growing profitable. As cities have grown in size, market-garden areas have been in demand for building sites, and the gardens have moved to the outer boundaries of the cities.

Truck Farming. Truck farming was characterized formerly as a few crops grown a long distance from market on low-priced land, with cheap labor. These factors have tended to make profitable the growing of vegetables in spite of high transportation costs. Under such conditions, the cost of transportation may be greater than the cost of production. The data in Table 1 illustrate the high cost of transportation to eastern markets when compared to the growing costs. In the case of lettuce, growing costs are 13 per cent of the total while transportation is about double or 25 per cent. Retail distribution costs are about equal to the transportation costs from the West. This high cost of transportation is typical for Truck Crops. Another point is worth illustrating from Table 1. Since growing costs are only about 13 per cent of the total, the grower is more likely to disk up and destroy his crop in a period of low prices than will the market gardener who is close to his market. In recent years, truck farming has been conducted successfully on high-priced land, with expensive labor, where climatic conditions are ideal, and there is no competition of quality products in volume from areas nearer the market. Imperial and Salinas Valleys in California and areas in Texas and Florida might be considered examples of truck-farming areas. This terminology has led to vegetables in some states being called Truck Crops.

Fig. 1. Head lettuce is an important truck crop. Most of this crop is shipped to eastern markets and is grown in large fields.

Table 1*

COST OF PRODUCTION FOR VEGETABLES GROWN IN THE
SOUTHWEST AND SHIPPED TO NEW YORK CITY IN 1948

Type of Expense	Carrots		Celery		Lettuce	
	Per Bunch Cents	Per Cent	Per Pound Cents	Per Cent	Per Head Cents	Per Cent
Growing	0.9	9.0	2.0	18.5	1.6	13.3
Harvesting	1.1	11.0	1.0	9.3	0.5	4.2
Packing	1.9	19.0	2.1	19.4	2.6	21.7
Transportation	2.5	25.0	2.0	18.5	3.0	25.0
Wholesale distribution	1.1	11.0	1.2	11.1	1.3	10.8
Retail distribution	2.5	25.0	2.5	23.1	3.0	25.0
Total costs or per cent	10.0	100	10.8	100	12.0	100

* Courtesy, *Western Grower and Shipper*, vol. 20, No. 5, 1949.

Greenhouse and Forcing Crops. Where winters are severe, vegetables may be grown in greenhouses and are referred to as the *greenhouse* and *forcing crops.* Greenhouse growers specialize in a few crops like cucumbers and tomatoes. They are rather numerous in the area between Chicago, Illinois, and Albany, New York; particularly in Ohio near Lake Erie. Cost of production is relatively high owing to the expense of greenhouses, winter heat, and poor climatic conditions for growing in the winter. Hours of sunlight are too short in winter for good production. Transportation cost is usually low to the nearby markets; but the main advantage is a high-quality crop in sufficiently low volume to command high prices. In some areas, the normal outdoor season is extended by producing a few crops in hotbeds or coldframes. Since each of the last three types of production has differing advantages and disadvantages, it is natural that different economic conditions will favor one type over another in different years.

Processed Vegetables. Vegetables are preserved by the following methods: (a) canning, (b) freezing, (c) dehydration or drying, and (d) pickling.

Canned vegetables are preserved by heat to kill a sufficient number of organisms to prevent spoilage at ordinary temperatures. The few organisms in frozen vegetables are not harmful because their growth is inhibited by low-temperature storage. Dehydration represents another principle, where the low-water content discourages the development of spoilage organisms. In pickling, conditions are made unfavorable for the growth of damaging micro-organisms. The salt and vinegar used in pickling, and the lactic acid formed by fermentation act as preservatives of the food.

Canning. Processing has been practised for many years with a few fruits and vegetables. Over a period of 75 years, the canning industry has grown until the average person consumes about 10 per cent of his vegetables in this form.

Canning crops usually are grown in areas of good climatic conditions for the crop and relatively cheap cost of production. Two examples from the West are: California leads in tomato canning, and Washington is second only to Wisconsin in the production of canned peas. Canning factories are centrally located in order to preserve the vegetables promptly. Unfortunately, the weather sometimes disrupts harvesting timetables; therefore, canned goods are not always preserved as promptly or as timely as they should be. The canning industry uses vegetables in such a large volume that high quality is sometimes difficult to obtain. This problem will occur in the freezing and perhaps the dehydration industry, after their volume has increased. Canned goods may be stored cheaply, transportation is cheaper since all waste has been removed, and the range of distribution is much larger than with fresh vegetables. Methods of producing frozen vegetables are similar to those of canning up to the time of freezing.

Freezing. Frozen products generally have been rewarded with good con-

Fig. 2. A 35-acre greenhouse range near Terre Haute, Indiana. Cucumbers and some tomatoes are grown exclusively in these houses; and winter heating requires 20,000 tons of coal per year. (Courtesy, J. W. Davis Co.)

Fig. 3. A self-propelled lima bean viner which picks up the plants from a windrow and shells out the beans. Labor-saving machinery is essential to any processing industry.

sumer acceptance, although storage and transportation are more expensive than for canned goods. Some vegetables, such as broccoli, Brussels sprouts, and spinach have very good quality after freezing, and this method of preservation is preferred. Green lima beans are another item which might be added to this list. At the present time, some 15 vegetables are processed by freezing. Six of these crops are frozen in quantities of 10 million pounds each year. In 1948, a little over half of the frozen vegetables were processed in the western states.

Dehydration. This industry was increased greatly during World War II, because of the need for conserving shipping space. The data in Table 2 indicate that weight is decreased greatly compared to canning or the fresh prod-

Table 2*

RELATION BETWEEN FRESH WEIGHT AND THE PROCESSED
WEIGHTS OF CANNED AND DRIED VEGETABLES PACKED FOR SHIPMENT

	Weight 1000 lb. Fresh		
Crop	*Canned and Packed (Pounds)*	*Dehydrated and Packed (Pounds)*	*Drying Ratio*
Cabbage	1,700	150	14:1
Onions	2,000	180	9:1
Potatoes, white	2,000	400	5:1
Tomatoes	1,500	85	15:1

* Courtesy, *Calif. Agr. Exp. Sta. Bull. 680*, 1943.

uce. In the case of canned tomatoes, the weight is increased over the fresh produce because of the weight of cans and heavy package for overseas shipment. Dried tomatoes, on the other hand, have less than one-tenth of the original weight of fresh produce. The drying ratio indicates the amount of fresh vegetable required to produce a pound of the dried product. Fourteen pounds of cabbage are required to produce one pound of dried product. Certain vegetables seem to make better dehydrated products than others. Onions have been an important dried vegetable for many years. Fresh onions are unpleasant to prepare in a food factory, and also, the dried product is desired because the powder is uniform in pungency or onion taste. Many dried vegetables are valued because they may be blended with other food products which have a characteristic flavor.

Pickling. Pickling accounts for a minor tonnage of vegetables. Cucumber pickles and sauerkraut are the two most important crops in this respect. Cabbage for kraut and cucumbers for pickles usually are produced in areas of high yield and low cost of production.

Seed Industry. Each year about one-quarter of a million acres are required to produce the vegetable seed for the vegetable industry. This figure excludes the seed needs for white and sweet potatoes. While seed acreage is not segregated as to states, there is considerable evidence that some 80 to 90 per cent of this acreage is located in the western states. The irrigated areas of the West are ideal for some crops. The dry weather during harvest permits the curing of seed without rain damage, and some areas are relatively free from certain seed-borne diseases. The mild winters along the Pacific Coast make possible early winter planting, and sometimes a shorter period of time between planting and harvesting of the seed crop. The importance of good vegetable seed is discussed more fully in Chapter 7.

The word *Olericulture* is used sometimes to designate vegetable production with the same meaning as Vegetable Crops. The culture portion of the word is self-evident as to meaning, but the first part is more difficult. In the next chapter, there will be found some seven vegetables whose species name is *oleracea*. This word was applied to these crops by Linnaeus who lived in the middle of the eighteenth century. In those days, most of the vegetables were cooked and consequently called potherbs. *Oleracea* means vegetable-garden herb used in cooking. At the present time, many of our vegetables are used in salads, but the meaning of the word Olericulture is traced back to the meaning of two hundred years ago.

HOME GARDEN CIRCULARS OF WESTERN STATES

1. Bouquet, A. G. B.: Farm and home vegetable garden, *Ore. Agr. Ext. Bul. 614,* 8 p., 1944.
2. Dietz, Carl F.: Vegetable gardening, *Ida. Agr. Ext. Ser. Bul. 139,* 24 p., 1941.
3. Dodge, John C., David Brannon, and M. R. Harris: Home gardens, *Wash. Agr. Ext. Ser. Bul. 422,* 24 p., 1950.
4. Drage, Charles M.: Gardening by the month, *Colo. Agr. Ext. Ser. Bul. 386-A,* 16 p., 1945.
5. Fite, A. B.: Growing a home garden in New Mexico, *N. M. Agr. Ext. Cir. 142,* 39 p., Revised, 1944.
6. MacGillivray, John H.: Home vegetable gardening, *Calif. Agr. Ext. Ser. Cir. 26,* 30 p., Revised, 1950.
7. Menke, Mark W.: The Nevada home gardener's handbook, *Nev. Agr. Ext. Ser. Bul. 87,* 80 p., 1944.
8. The national food situation, *U.S.D.A. Bur. of Agr. Econ., N.F.S. -53,* 22 p., July–Sept., 1950.

Chapter 2

Classification of Vegetables

The number of vegetables used commonly in the United States would probably number some 20 to 30. If minor crops were also considered, the number would be increased to over 50. The latter number seems large, but the total number of plants used as vegetables in the world is probably more than 240. Classification is essential as an aid in orderly arrangement of such a large number of plants. There are numerous methods of classification, but one's choice depends upon the helpfulness of the basis used, and its success as a method of classification. Some of the bases that may be used are as follows: (a) Number of seasons a plant may live—thus a life of one year is an annual plant, a life of two is a biennial, and a life of three or more is a perennial; (b) relative resistance of plants to frost or low temperatures, as given in the table on Thermo classification; (c) optimum soil acidity for growth; (d) part of the plant eaten—root, stem, leaf, immature flower parts, and fruits both mature and immature; (e) optimum growing temperatures (Thermo classification)—cool and warm season crops; (f) most desirable temperature for storage; (g) usual economic duration of storage period; (h) depth of rooting as given in the section on irrigation; and (i) botanical method or arrangement according to flower type—grouping plants into families, genera, species, and botanical varieties.

From the standpoint of correlating our knowledge of vegetables, both the Thermo and botanical classifications are of value. The botanical method was developed primarily by botanists for the purpose of identifying plants and usually is based on the plant's flowers. Where a vegetative part of a plant is eaten, flowers are not formed in production of the vegetable for market. The botanical method is useful in vegetable production and research, because the plants of some families have similar adaptations—insects and diseases frequently affect the plants of close botanical relationship. Plants of the same family have similar flowers; thus plant breeders frequently use identical methods of crossing flowers within the same family. The characteristics of the botanical families to which the various vegetables belong are given in the chapters on each crop.

METHOD OF BOTANICAL CLASSIFICATION

All plants are considered as one community. The following botanical classification gives the four subcommunities of plants according to Bailey, a prominent American horticulturist and botanist. These four main groups of plants are: (a) algae and fungi, (b) mosses and liverworts, (c) ferns, and (d) seed plants. Vegetables are primarily seed-bearing plants, but also include mushrooms, a fungus. The following scheme gives the main divisions in plant classification, illustrated by a vegetable example, namely, Zucchini squash.

Vegetable community—plants
    Subcommunity—Spermatophyta (seed plants)
        Division—Angiospermae (angiosperms)
            Class—Dicotyledoneae (dicotyledons)
                Family—Cucurbitaceae (gourds)
                    Genus—*Cucurbita*
                        Species—*Pepo* L.
                            Botanical variety—*Melopepo* Alef.
                            Horticultural variety—Zucchini
                                Horticultural strain—Dark Green Zucchini
                                Horticultural lot number—No. 675

The above method of classification is familiar to botanists down to the horticultural variety. Zucchini, a variety name, indicates a certain type of summer squash which may be further separated as to strain. Thus, seedsmen sometimes list two strains—Zucchini and Dark Green Zucchini. Furthermore, the seedsmen may have several selections of Dark Green Zucchini which are listed under seed lot number; in this case it is No. 675. There is considerable detailed work in the production of seeds, and this illustrates a rather uniform method of handling seed stocks. The scientific name of the Zucchini would be *Cucurbita Pepo* L. var. *Melopepo* Alef. The botanical variety should be given when it is a part of the scientific name. The letter *L.* indicates this species was first described and named by Linnaeus, a Swedish botanist. Similarly, the botanical variety was added to distinguish summer squash from pumpkin (*C. Pepo*). This was suggested by Friedrich Alefeld, a German botanist (1820 to 1872), so his name accompanies the word *Melopepo* Alef.

The following botanical classification as given by Bailey[1] gives the four main groups of plants, and lists the various vegetables which belong under each of these subcommunities. The remainder of the classification is skeletonized, so it includes only families with vegetables and only the major and important minor crops.

BOTANICAL CLASSIFICATION OF VEGETABLE PLANTS

I. Algae and fungi (Thallophyta)
    Mushroom family—Agaricaceae
    Mushroom *Agaricus campestris* L.
II. Mosses and liverworts (Bryophyta)
III. Ferns (Pteridophyta)
IV. Seed plants (Spermatophyta)
    A. Gymnosperms (Cone-bearing plants)
    B. Angiosperms (Flowering plants)
      a. Monocotyledonous plants
        Grass family—Gramineae
          Sweet corn—*Zea Mays* L.
        Lily family—Liliaceae
          Chive—*Allium Schoenoprasum* L.
          Garlic—*A. sativum* L.
          Leek—*A. Porrum* L.
          Onion—*A. Cepa* L.
          Shallot—*A. ascalonicum* L.
          Asparagus—*Asparagus officinalis* L.
        Yam family—Dioscoreaceae
          Yam—*Dioscorea alata* L., and other species
      b. Dicotyledonous plants
        Buckwheat family—Polygonaceae
          Rhubarb—*Rheum Rhaponticum* L.
        Goosefoot family—Chenopodiaceae
          Beet—*Beta vulgaris* L.
          Swiss chard—*B. vulgaris* L. var. *Cicla* L.
          Spinach—*Spinacia oleracea* L.
        Carpet-weed family—Aizoaceae
          New Zealand spinach—*Tetragonia expansa* Murr.
        Mustard family—Cruciferae
          Cabbage—*Brassica oleracea* L. var. *capitata* L.
          Cauliflower—*B. oleracea* L. var. *botrytis* L.
          Kale, collard—*B. oleracea* L. var. *acephala* D. C.
          Brussels sprout—*B. oleracea* L. var. *gemmifera* Zenker
          Sprouting broccoli—*B. oleracea* L. var. *italica* Plenck
          Kohlrabi—*B. caulorapa* Pasq.
          Turnip—*B. Rapa* L.
          Rutabaga—*B. Napobrassica* Mill.
          Chinese cabbage, pe-tsai—*B. pekinensis* Rupr.

Pak-choi—*B. chinensis* L.
Mustard—*B. Juncea* Coss; *B. hirta* Moench.
Water cress—*Nasturtium officinale* R. Br.
Horseradish—*Armoracia lapathifolia* Gilib.
Radish—*Raphanus sativus* L.
Pea family—Leguminosae
Pea—*Pisum sativum* L.
Broad bean—*Vicia Faba* L.
Bean, snap—*Phaseolus vulgaris* L.
Bean, lima—*P. lunatus* L.
Mallow family—Malvaceae
Okra or gumbo—*Hibiscus esculentus* L.
Roselle—*H. Sabdariffa* L.
Parsley family—Umbelliferae
Florence fennel—*Foeniculum vulgare* Mill. var. *dulce* Fiori
Carrot—*Daucus Carota* L.
Parsley—*Petroselinum crispum* Nym.
Celery—*Apium graveolens* L. var. *dulce* Pers.
Celeriac—*A. graveolens* L. var. *rapaceum* D. C.
Parsnip—*Pastinaca sativa* L.
Morning glory family—Convolvulaceae
Sweet potato—*Ipomoea Batatas* Lam.
Nightshade family—Solanaceae
Potato—*Solanum tuberosum* L.
Eggplant—*S. Melongena* L.
Pepino, melon shrub—*S. muricatum* Ait.
Tomato—*Lycopersicon esculentum* Mill.
Tomato, currant—*L. pimpinellifolium* Mill.
Pepper—*Capsicum frutescens* L.
Gourd family—Cucurbitaceae
Field pumpkin—*Cucurbita Pepo* L.
Pumpkin or cushaw—*C. moschata* Duchesne
Summer squash, bush pumpkins—*C. Pepo* L. var. *Melopepo* Alef.
Winter squash—*C. maxima* Duchesne
Watermelon—*Citrullus vulgaris* Schrad.
Cucumber—*Cucumis sativus* L.
Cucumber, English forcing—*C. sativus* L. var. *anglicus* Bailey
Gherkin—*C. Anguria* L.
Cantaloupe, muskmelon—*C. Melo* L. var. *reticulatus* Naud.

Fig. 4. A carrot seed field. The man is holding an umbel in his hand from which comes the name of the family—Umbelliferae. (Courtesy, Pieters-Wheeler Seed Company.)

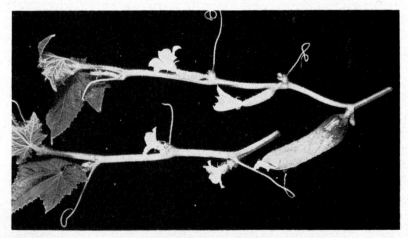

Fig. 5. Members of the Cucurbitaceae Family have separate male and female flowers (small cucumbers) as in this cucumber plant.

Casaba, Honeydew—*C. Melo* L. var. *inodorus*
   Naud.
Chayote—*Sechium edule* Sw.
Composite family—Compositae
Chicory, French endive—*Cichorium Intybus* L.
Endive—*C. Endivia* L.
Salsify—*Tragopogon porrifolius* L.
Lettuce—*Lactuca sativa* L.
Artichoke, globe—*Cynara Scolymus* L.
Cardoon—*C. Cardunculus* L.

THERMO CLASSIFICATION OF VEGETABLES

Vegetables may be separated into cool and warm season crops. Cool season crops require cool weather for their proper development. Likewise, warm weather is essential for warm season crops. The Thermo classification groups vegetables together according to their average monthly temperature requirements. Such a procedure can be related to many of the important principles of vegetable production. One important consideration is the rule which may be used to separate cool and warm season crops. *Cool season crops are those in which the edible part is root, stem, leaf, or immature flower part. Warm season crops are those in which the edible part is a fruit. There are, however, four exceptions—pea and broad bean (fruits) are cool season crops; sweet potato (a root) and New Zealand spinach (a leaf and stem) are warm season crops.* This rule separates vegetables into two large groups, and further temperature requirements are given in the Thermo classification which follows. Vegetables which will survive slightly freezing weather (Group A) are placed in the first group, and those requiring continuous warm weather are placed in the last group (E). Each group requires warmer weather than the preceding group. The above definition of cool and warm season crops plus their Thermo classification forms a framework for our scientific knowledge of vegetables.

The importance of temperature is discussed more fully in Chapter 5, but some of the relationships between crops regarding temperature responses need to be discussed at this point. Many factors affect plant growth, but none of these are any more important than temperature. Temperature affects such plant processes as absorption of water and plant nutrients, photosynthesis, transpiration, respiration, translocation of food, and metabolism—all of which are associated with growth. Death of plants may result from high or low temperatures. Vegetables are planted when the soil temperature and air temperature are suitable for growth of the crop. Crops in Group E are planted when the temperature is much warmer than is necessary for Group A. Some cool season crops are subject to premature seeding, and many warm season crops are subject to chilling injury. The effects of photoperiodism may be modified by temperature. Where a botanical family contains several crops, they are usually of one climatic group. The nightshade and gourd families consist primarily of warm season crops. A preponderance of cool season crops are found in the lily, goosefoot, mustard, parsley, and composite families. Many cool season crops are relatively small in size and are shallow-rooted. A few are moderately deep-rooted. Shallow-rooted crops need more careful and frequent irrigation than do deep-rooted crops. Nitrification occurs slowly in cool soils; so cool season crops are more likely to respond to nitrogen fertilization. Temperature is an important factor affecting the set of fruit, and too low or too high temperatures may make plants unfruitful. Cool season crops—with one exception—should be stored at 32° F. The food chapter indicates that vegetables, whose vegetative part is eaten, are more efficient food producers when you consider nutrients per pound, acre, and man-hour. This Thermo classification is useful wherever average monthly temperatures are available. These relationships make desirable a thorough understanding of temperature relationships between crops.

BOTANICAL PART OF PLANT EATEN AS A VEGETABLE

Root Beet, carrot, celeriac, chicory, horseradish, parsnip, radish, rutabaga, salsify, sweet potato, turnip.

Stem Asparagus, kohlrabi, white potato.

Leaf Brussels sprout, cabbage, cardoon, celery, Chinese cabbage, chive, collard, endive, Florence fennel, French endive, garlic, kale, leek, lettuce, mustard, New Zealand spinach, onion, pak-choi, parsley, perennial onion, rhubarb, shallot, spinach, Swiss chard, water cress.

Immature flower part Cauliflower, globe artichoke, roselle, sprouting broccoli.

Fruit immature Broad bean, chayote, cucumber, lima bean, okra, pea, snap bean, summer squash, sweet corn.

mature Eggplant, muskmelon (cantaloupe), pepper, pumpkin, tomato, watermelon, winter squash.

The following outline is based on average monthly temperatures.[2] Numbers after the crops indicate number of days needed to produce the crop after field planting under good growing conditions for medium maturing varieties.

I. COOL SEASON CROPS

Group A. Prefer average monthly temperatures of 60° to 65° F. Intolerant of 70° to 75° F., and tolerant of slightly freezing weather:

Spinach—45	Broccoli—75, 150
Cabbage—100	

Minor crops: Beet, broad bean, Brussels sprout, collard, horseradish, kale, kohlrabi, parsnip, radish, rhubarb, rutabaga, salsify or vegetable oyster, turnip, water cress.

Group B. Prefer 60° to 65° F. Intolerant of 70° to 75° F. Damaged near maturity by freezing weather:

Cauliflower—65	White potato—110
Globe artichoke—perennial	Celery—135
Lettuce—75	Carrot—110
Pea—60	

Minor crops: Cardoon, celeriac, chicory, Chinese cabbage, endive, Florence fennel, mustard, pak-choi, parsley, Swiss chard, witloof chicory or French endive.

Group C. Adapted to 55° to 75° F. Tolerant of frost:

Onion—140	Asparagus—perennial

Minor crops: Chive, garlic, leek, perennial onions, shallot.

II. WARM SEASON CROPS

Group D. Adapted to 65° to 80° F. Intolerant of frost:

Sweet corn—80	Pepper—120
Bean, snap—55, 80	Squash—60, 110
Bean, lima—80	Cucumber—75
Tomato—120	Cantaloupe—135

Minor crops: Chayote, New Zealand spinach, pumpkin, roselle.

Group E. Long season crops, which thrive above 70° F.

Watermelon—115	Sweet potato—150

Minor crops: Eggplant, hot peppers, okra.

A careful study of this chapter will be a great aid to the reader in correlating the material in the crop chapters. The general rule for identifying cool and warm season crops is dependent upon knowing what portion of the plant is eaten. This information immediately makes available considerable general knowledge about the crop. The second important consideration is the Thermo classification of the crops. Vegetables are listed according to the temperatures under which they can be grown successfully, and further details are given concerning the temperature requirements of cool and warm season crops in the last five chapters of this book.

REFERENCES

1. Bailey, L. H.: "Manual of Cultivated Plants," 1116 p., New York, The Macmillan Company, 1949.
2. Boswell, V. R. and H. A. Jones: Climate and vegetable crops, p. 373–399, *U.S.D.A. Yearbook, 1941.*

Chapter 3

Economic Importance and Production Areas

The economic importance of vegetable crops can be measured in acres, tons of product, and value of the product. Acres differ in productivity, and vegetables are not always sold on a weight basis; so the monetary value has been chosen as a desirable basis for measuring their economic importance. Values are based on shipping point or farm value, and therefore do not include the income received by wholesalers and retailers for the crop.

RELATIVE IMPORTANCE OF AGRICULTURAL PRODUCTS

The U.S. Department of Agriculture maintains offices in each state, usually in the capital, to collect statistics regarding agricultural crops. The Agricultural Estimates group in the Bureau of Agricultural Economics makes available the following data: (1) Annual summaries of acreage, production, and value by states and seasonal groups; (2) monthly acreage and production forecasts for truck crops for fresh market; and (3) periodic reports on the prospective acreage and production of truck crops grown for processing; and (4) weekly or biweekly local reports on truck crop conditions and supplies. The Division of Market News of the Production and Marketing Administration (U.S.D.A.) makes available market conditions and F.O.B. wholesale prices as follows: (1) Reports are issued by field representatives located at important shipping points and on terminal wholesale markets in larger cities; (2) daily reports providing price ranges and general market conditions; and (3) collects and disseminates information relative to daily rail and truck shipments and wholesale market receipts of perishable commodities. Some of these crop data have been summarized in this chapter and in the crop sections. A twelve-year average does not give yearly fluctuations and the above sources will need to be consulted where more recent data are desired. These statistical data are confined to the important vegetable crops and in the case of sweet corn only three of the several states growing the crop are listed.

The values of the important crops and livestock are given in Table 3, for the United States. In the country as a whole, livestock represents 56.2 per cent of the value of agricultural products. Part of this value is the result of

Table 3*

AVERAGE ANNUAL CASH RECEIPTS FROM FARMING BY CLASSES
OF FARM PRODUCTS FOR THE UNITED STATES AND THE ELEVEN
WESTERN STATES, 1939–1950

Class of Farm Products	United States		Eleven Western States	
	Cash Receipts (Million dollars)	Per Cent of Total	Cash Receipts (Million dollars)	Per Cent of Total
Vegetable crops†	1,267	6.2	437	12.0
Fruits and nuts	1,091	5.3	641	17.6
Agronomic and other crops	6,620	32.3	1,004	27.6
Total all crops	8,978	43.8	2,082	57.2
Livestock and livestock products	11,521	56.2	1,558	42.8
Total cash receipts‡	20,499	100.0	3,640	100.0

* Courtesy, California Crop and Livestock Reporting Service, Sacramento, California.
† Includes potatoes and sweet potatoes.
‡ Does not include Government payments.

feeding livestock grains, forage crops, and by-products from crops. Agronomic and miscellaneous crops are worth 32.3 per cent of the total; vegetables, including white and sweet potatoes, are 6.2 per cent, with fruits and nuts providing 5.3 per cent of the total. The 1939–1950 yearly average for crops and livestock was 20.5 billion dollars. The percentages of farm products grown in the West, indicate that vegetables and fruits are higher than the national average. Almost one-third of all the commercial vegetables produced in the United States have their origin in the eleven western states.

The average yearly value of potatoes (1939–1951) in millions is as follows: Maine, 63.7; California, 46.4; New York, 39.4; Idaho, 34.9; Pennsylvania, 26.6; Michigan, 21.6; Colorado, 20.2; Minnesota, 19.4; Wisconsin, 16.0; Oregon, 14.2; New Jersey, 12.7; Washington, 12.1; Ohio, 12.0; North Dakota, 11.9; Virginia, 11.6; North Carolina, 11.2; Florida, 8.3; Indiana, 7.0; Texas, 6.7; Utah, 3.5.

In several of the western states, such as Arizona, California, and Washington, the value of all crops is greater than livestock. This situation is also true in many of the southern states. In the important farming states of the middle west, livestock is considerably more valuable than the crops raised in those areas.

IMPORTANT VEGETABLE STATES

California is the most important vegetable state and produces a value as great as the total of the next three most important states—New York, Florida, and Maine. The value of vegetables in the more important states is found in Table 4. White potatoes rank high in some states since much of the vegetable value is from this crop. In the case of Colorado, Idaho, Montana, Nevada, Wyoming, and several states east of the Rockies, over one-half of the total vegetable value is from white potatoes. The major and minor crops in the United States are listed in the order of their importance, in Table 4, together with their value in millions of dollars.

In eight of the eleven western states, white potatoes are the most important vegetable, while in California and Arizona lettuce ranks first. Sweet potatoes are not grown to any extent in any of the western states. Some 20 vegetables are important in the West and a considerable proportion of this food is shipped to eastern markets. A few of these crops such as globe artichokes, garlic, Brussels sprouts, and late cauliflower are not generally produced throughout the United States, whereas they are grown extensively in the southwest.

Table 4

FRESH AND PROCESSED FARM VALUES FOR STATES AND CROPS IN
MILLIONS OF DOLLARS

Rank of States, 1940–1951

1. California	265.5	8. Pennsylvania	43.0	15. Minnesota	28.7
2. New York	92.7	9. Idaho	38.3	16. Indiana	27.9
3. Florida	84.8	10. Wisconsin	36.9	17. Washington	27.2
4. Maine	65.6	11. Arizona	35.2	18. Virginia	25.1
5. Texas	54.5	12. Colorado	34.6	19. Ohio	24.2
6. New Jersey	54.4	13. North Carolina	31.2	20. Georgia	22.2
7. Michigan	44.7	14. Oregon	29.3	21. Maryland	21.6

Rank of Vegetables, 1940–1951

1. White potato	491.7	8. Pea	42.1	15. Watermelon	22.6
2. Tomato	159.0	9. Cantaloupe	37.4	16. Spinach	14.6
3. Sweet potato	102.3	10. Cabbage	37.6	17. Cauliflower	14.0
4. Lettuce	82.9	11. Carrot	34.1	18. Pepper	11.4
5. Snap bean	55.5	12. Asparagus	29.3	19. Lima bean	10.0
6. Onion	47.9	13. Sweet corn	28.1	20. Beet	4.3
7. Celery	45.1	14. Cucumber	22.7	21. Globe artichoke	2.3

INCREASE IN PRODUCTION OF VEGETABLES IN UNITED STATES

The per capita consumption in the United States of several vegetables are compared in Fig. 6. White potatoes, sweet potatoes, and other vegetables are given by five year periods beginning in 1909–1913. During this time the consumption of sweet potatoes has decreased 39 per cent and white potatoes 33 per cent while other vegetables have increased 35 per cent. Some of this change of diet can be attributed to the fact that office and city workers prefer a light diet, low in calories. There are several other causes for the increase in consumption of leafy vegetables, and decrease in consumption of starchy vegetables. The availability of many vegetables the year round, whereas even a few years ago they were scarce, may be noted. Then too, there is the wide publicity in advertising of the importance of avoiding excess fat through diet. This comes from insurance companies, medical sources, and the numerous "low calorie" cookbooks presently on the market. All such factors, plus many others, tend to widen our diet, and very frequently, at the expense of starchy foods. The annual per capita consumption of several vegetables is given in

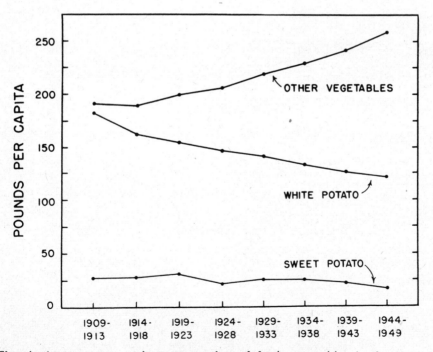

Fig. 6. Average per capita consumption of fresh vegetables in the United States, by five-year periods.

Table 5. Sweet corn, spinach, kale, potatoes, and sweet potatoes are the only vegetables that show decreased consumption in the 1946–1950 period. Most other vegetables show small to large increases. Canned vegetables have more than doubled in this period. Statistics are available only for frozen foods since 1937, therefore the increase in pounds has been small but the percentage increase has been large. The average person eats about 1600 pounds of different kinds of food in a year. In recent years the average person has consumed about 400 pounds of vegetables or one-fourth of his total intake of food. The per capita consumption of most vegetables has increased in the last 25 year period.

Table 5

THE AVERAGE ANNUAL PER CAPITA CONSUMPTION OF FRESH, CANNED AND FROZEN VEGETABLES FOR TWO PERIODS IN POUNDS (RETAIL WEIGHT)

Crop	1918–22	1946–50	Crop	1918–22	1946–50
Potato	143.8	106.8	Spinach	3.6	2.5
Cabbage	30.7	32.6	Peppers	1.7	2.3
Tomato	19.4	23.6	Asparagus	0.7	1.4
Watermelon	19.6	22.8	Lima bean (unshelled)	0.6	1.1
Onion	18.5	21.4	Eggplant	0.3	0.4
Lettuce	7.2	17.5	Kale	0.3	0.2
Sweet potato	24.1	13.1	Artichokes	—	0.2
Sweet corn	14.2	12.2	Garlic	—	0.2
Carrot	6.7	11.5	Shallots	—	0.1
Celery	4.5	10.6	Minor Crops	15.0	24.7
Cantaloupe	8.6	9.2			
Snap bean	7.3	8.8	Sub Total	337.7	338.3
Beet	3.7	3.9	Canned vegetables	19.1	40.6
Green pea (unshelled)	2.8	3.9	Frozen vegetables	0.5*	3.0
Cucumber	3.0	3.9			
Cauliflower	1.4	3.4	Total†	357.3	381.9

* Data for the 1937–1941 period.
† Vegetables from non farm-home gardens were 18.2 for 1918–1922 and 21.0 pounds for 1946–1949.
Courtesy, *U.S.D.A. Misc. Pub. 691,* 1949 and 1950.

VEGETABLE AREAS OF THE UNITED STATES

Boswell and Jones[1] have listed five major regions for vegetable production. In two of these areas, crops usually are grown without irrigation, and both are large in extent. Three areas use irrigation as an important farm practise to produce high yields. The nonirrigated areas are the Atlantic and Gulf region, extending from Massachusetts to Texas; and the Great Lakes region, which extends from upper New York State around the Lakes, up into Minnesota. The irrigated areas are a small area in Texas called the Rio Grande Valley; the intermountain states of Colorado, Utah, and Idaho; and the

Pacific Coast and intermountain valleys of Arizona, California, Washington, and Oregon.

VEGETABLE AREAS OF WESTERN STATES

There is insufficient rainfall in many sections of the West to produce profitable crops of vegetables. Consequently, it is necessary to grow the vegetables in valleys where rivers furnish an adequate source of water, or in areas where there is sufficient underground water for pumping. However, there are a few areas in western Washington and Oregon, northern Idaho, and northwestern California where rainfall is sufficient for the production of some crops.

In Washington, there are important areas along the Columbia, Yakima, and Snake rivers. Vegetable districts in Oregon are along the Willamette, Columbia, and Snake rivers, as well as other minor streams. Most of the Idaho production is along the Snake River in the southern part of the state, but some seed production of peas is located in the clay-farm section to the north. Colorado has four areas: Along the Platte (northeast); Arkansas (southeast); Rio Grande (south, or San Luis district); and the Colorado (west) rivers. In Utah, the vegetable districts occur along the east side of the Great Salt Lake and extend southwest to the Arizona-Nevada border. There are several areas in New Mexico, generally on the Rio Grande River or its tributaries. The Arizona regions are on the Gila River near Yuma and Phoenix, with some production in the southeastern part of the state. California has the following vegetable districts: Imperial Valley, irrigated from the Colorado River; the Sacramento and San Joaquin valleys with their deltas west and north of Stockton; small production areas along the coast from San Francisco south to the Mexican border, with important districts along the Salinas River and around Los Angeles. The important crops grown in each of these states have been listed subsequently in this chapter.

Figure 7 indicates the regions without regard to their economic importance. The crops of the various areas are listed below.

Arizona

1. Yuma (Yuma County): Cantaloupe, carrot, lettuce, and watermelon.
2. Phoenix (Maricopa County): Broccoli, cabbage, cantaloupe, celery, carrot, cauliflower, lettuce, onion, sweet potato, white potato, and watermelon.
3. Eloy (Pinal County): Asparagus, carrot, cauliflower, lettuce, and white potato.
4. Duncan Valley (Greenlee County): Cantaloupe, onion, and white potato.
5. Cochise County: Chili pepper.
6. Santa Cruz County: White potato, and miscellaneous vegetables.

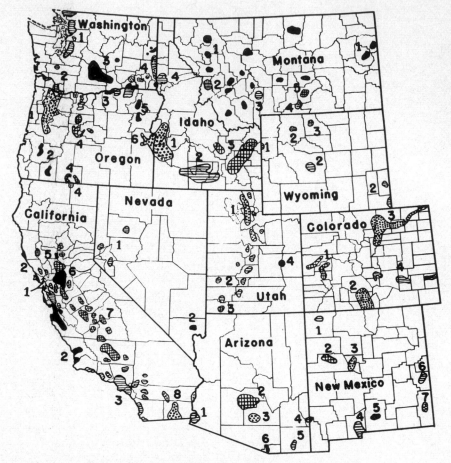

Fig. 7. The vegetable areas of the western states.

California

1. San Francisco Bay (Alameda, Contra Costa, Napa, Santa Clara, and Sonoma counties): Broccoli, Brussels sprout, cabbage, cauliflower, celery, cucumber, garlic, green lima bean, globe artichoke, lettuce, pea, pepper, rhubarb, snap bean, spinach, sweet corn, tomato, and white potato.

2. Central Coast (Marin, Mendocino, Monterey, San Benito, San Luis Obispo, San Mateo, and Santa Cruz counties): Broccoli, Brussels sprout, cabbage, carrot, cauliflower, celery, endive, garlic, globe artichoke, green lima bean, lettuce, onion, pea, snap bean, spinach, tomato, and white potato.

3. South Coast (Los Angeles, Orange, Riverside, San Bernardino, San Diego, Santa Barbara, and Ventura counties) : Asparagus, beet, broccoli, cabbage, cantaloupe, carrot, cauliflower, celery, cucumber, green lima bean, onion, parsley, pea, pepper, snap bean, spinach, summer squash, sweet corn, sweet potato, tomato, watermelon, and white potato.
4. Tulelake (Modoc and Siskiyou counties) : Onion and white potato.
5. Sacramento Valley (Butte, Colusa, Lake, Sacramento, Solano, Sutter, Yolo, and Yuba counties) : Cantaloupe, green lima bean, pea, snap bean, spinach, tomato, watermelon, and winter squash.
6. Delta (Contra Costa, Sacramento, San Joaquin, Solano, and Yolo counties) : Asparagus, broccoli, carrot, celery, cucumber, garlic, onion, pea, spinach, sweet corn, tomato and white potato.
7. San Joaquin Valley (Fresno, Kern, Kings, Madera, Merced, San Joaquin, Stanislaus, and Tulare counties) : Asparagus, broccoli, cabbage, cantaloupe, carrot, celery, cucumber, green lima bean, lettuce, pea, pepper, snap bean, spinach, summer squash, sweet corn, sweet potato, tomato, watermelon, white potato, and winter squash.
8. Desert valleys (Imperial and Riverside counties) : Broccoli, cabbage, cantaloupe, carrot, cucumber, endive, lettuce, onion, pea, pepper, snap bean, summer squash, sweet corn, sweet potato, tomato, and watermelon.

Colorado

1. Western slope (Delta, Mesa, and Montrose counties) : Lettuce, onion, pea, snap bean, tomato, and white potato.
2. San Luis Valley (Alamosa, Conejos, Costilla, Rio Grande, and Saguache counties) : Cabbage, cauliflower, lettuce, pea, spinach, white potato, and bunch vegetables.
3. Platte River or northeastern Colorado (Adams, Arapahoe, Boulder, Jefferson, Larimer, Logan, Morgan, Sedgwick, and Weld counties) : Beet, cabbage, cantaloupe, celery, lettuce, onion, pea, snap bean, spinach, tomato, turnip, and white potato.
4. Arkansas Valley (Custer, Crowley, Fremont, Otero, Prowers, and Pueblo counties) : Cantaloupe, carrot, celery, cucumber, onion, pea, snap bean, spinach, tomato, and watermelon.

Idaho

1. Ada, Adams, Canyon, Elmore, Gem, Owyhee, Payette, and Washington counties: Carrot, lettuce, onion, pea, sweet corn, white potato, and small vegetable seeds.
2. Cassia, Elmore, Gooding, Jerome, Lincoln, Owyhee, and Twin Falls

counties: Bean seed, corn, onion, white potato, and small vegetable seed.

3. Bannock, Bingham, Bonneville, Butte, Custer, Fremont, Jefferson, Madison, and Power counties: Pea and white potato.

4. Latah, Lewis, and Nez Perce counties: Pea.

Montana

1. Beaverhead, Blaine, Broadwater, Cascade, Dawson, Deer Lodge, Flathead, Lake, Lewis and Clark, Madison, Missoula, Musselshell, Powell, Richland, Teton, and Wheatland counties: White potato.

2. Ravalli County: Pea, sweet corn, and white potato.

3. Gallatin County: Pea and white potato.

4. Carbon County: Pea.

5. Yellowstone County: Sweet corn.

Nevada

1. Lyon, Pershing, and Washoe counties: Onion and white potato.

2. Clark County: Celery and tomato (plants).

New Mexico

1. Farmington (San Juan County): White potato.

2. Bluewater Valley (Valencia County): Cabbage, carrot, lettuce, snap bean, and white potato.

3. Middle Rio Grande Valley (Bernalillo and Valencia counties): Cantaloupe, carrot, and chili pepper.

4. Mesilla Valley (Dona Ana County): Cantaloupe, chili pepper, lettuce, onion, and white potato.

5. Cloudcroft (Otero County): Cabbage, carrot, and lettuce.

6. Portales (Roosevelt County): Onion, snap bean, sweet potato, and tomato.

7. Lovington (Lea County): Lettuce and onion.

Oregon

1. Willamette and Lower Columbia valleys (Benton, Clackamas, Clatsop, Columbia, Lane, Linn, Marion, Multnomah, Polk, Washington, and Yamhill counties): Asparagus, cabbage, cantaloupe, carrot, cauliflower, celery, cucumber, lettuce, onion, pea, snap bean, spinach, squash, sweet corn, tomato, watermelon, and white potato.

2. Southwestern (Douglas and Jackson counties) : Asparagus, cantaloupe, cauliflower, onion, tomato, watermelon, and white potato.
3. Mid-Columbia Valley (Hood River, Morrow, Umatilla, and Wasco counties) : Asparagus, cabbage, cantaloupe, lettuce, onion, pea, spinach, tomato, watermelon, and white potato.
4. Central and Klamath (Crook, Deschutes, Jefferson, and Klamath counties) : Onion and white potato.
5. Baker and Union counties: Pea and white potato.
6. Snake River (Malheur County) : Cantaloupe, carrot, lettuce, onion, pea, sweet corn, watermelon, white potato, and vegetable seeds.

Utah

1. Provo and Salt Lake (Box Elder, Cache, Davis, Morgan, Salt Lake, Utah, Wasatch, and Weber counties) : Cabbage, cantaloupe, celery, onion, pea, snap bean, sweet corn, tomato, and white potato.
2. Central (Beaver, Garfield, Iron, Juab, Millard, Piute, Sanpete, and Sevier counties) : Cabbage, carrot, pea, and white potato.
3. Southwest (Washington County) : Carrot, onion, pea, and white potato.
4. East Central (Emery and Grand counties) : Cantaloupe.

Washington

1. Puget Sound (King, Lewis, Pierce, Skagit, Snohomish, and Whatcom counties) : Beet, broccoli, cabbage, carrot, cauliflower, celery, lettuce, onion, pea, radish, rhubarb, snap bean, spinach, sweet corn, tomato, and white potato.
2. Vancouver (Clark County) : Market vegetables.
3. Central and southeastern (Asotin, Benton, Grant, Kittitas, Spokane, Walla Walla, and Yakima counties) : Asparagus, cabbage, cantaloupe, carrot, lettuce, onion, pea, rutabaga, snap bean, spinach, sweet corn, sweet potato, tomato, watermelon, and white potato.
4. Eastern (Columbia, Garfield, Spokane, Walla Walla, and Whitman counties) : Processing and dry peas.

Wyoming

1. Teton County: Pea.
2. Fremont, Goshen, Laramie, and Park counties: White potato.
3. Big Horn County: Beet, corn, pea, snap bean, and pumpkin.

References

1. Boswell, V. R., and H. A. Jones: Climate and vegetable crops, p. 373–99, *U.S.D.A. Yearbook, 1941.*
2. *United States Census of Agriculture, 1945,* vol. 1, pt. 27–33, U.S. Government Printing Office, Washington, D.C., 1946.
3. Parker, C. O., and R. Royston: Usual dates of planting and harvesting commercial truck crops for fresh market, *U.S.D.A. Bur. of Agr. Econ.,* 65 p., 1945.
4. Preliminary survey of major areas requiring outside agricultural labor, *U.S.D.A. Ext. Farm Labor Cir. 38,* 207 p., 1947.
5. *Agricultural Statistics, 1950,* U.S. Department of Agriculture, Government Printing Office, Washington, D.C., 791 p., 1951 and mimeographed reports.

Chapter 4

Soils for Vegetable Production

As pointed out previously, the word *agriculture* refers to the cultivation of the soil for food. This serves to emphasize the importance of soil in agricultural production, but unfortunately ignores the fact that part of the plant grows in the air, which is also essential. The air environment in any area is very similar for all plants, and is not subject to much modification by the farmer. The soil, on the other hand, may vary to a considerable extent in a climatic area, and may be affected through fertilization, irrigation, and other practices; therefore it is subject to some modification by the agriculturist.

THE SOIL AS A HOME FOR PLANT ROOTS

The soil furnishes the plant with anchorage to hold it up, as well as with water and nutrients. Most cultural operations are performed on the soil. Among these might be listed (a) fertilization or the addition of plant nutrients, (b) irrigation, (c) seeding or transplanting of the crop, (d) plowing and cultivating, and (e) harvesting of crops whose edible portion grows in the soil. Farm operations practised on that portion of the plant which is in the air include (a) pruning, (b) pest control of insects and diseases, and (c) harvesting portions of the plant which are in the air. The numerous soil operations emphasize the importance of the soil. The grower finds it easy to observe the aerial parts of the plant, but the roots are just as important; though they are either hidden from view or require extra work to observe. Poor soil conditions are frequently indicated by poor growth of the aerial parts of the plant. The grower may take soil samples with a soil tube or examine the soil at different depths with a shovel or other equipment. Such a procedure is helpful in determining moisture content of the soil. There are many changes going on in the soil that can be determined only by research methods or by the effect on top growth of plants.

A soil is discussed usually in terms of a surface measurement such as acreage. A more accurate method of describing it would be in terms of volume of soil. As the depth of good soil increases, there is a greater storage of available soil moisture and plant nutrients; both of which are essential for good yields. The volume of usable soil may be limited by hardpan or high-water table; both decrease the depth to which the roots may penetrate. *Hardpan* is a layer of soil whose particles are cemented together and do not become soft when wet with water. Real estate agents sometimes sell farms indirectly on a volume basis, as they will sell a soil 2 feet deep considerably cheaper than a soil 4 feet deep, and justly so.

FORMATION OF A SOIL

A soil is made up of minerals, organic matter, water, and air. These components exist there as three states of matter—solid, liquid, and gas. A large amount of a soil's fertility comes from the minerals of the soil. The soil particles are weathered, disintegrated particles from the parent rocks. The breakdown into small particles has occurred over centuries, and in any field may have occurred in place, or elsewhere with movement to the field by water and/or wind. Some parent rocks or portions of them disintegrate rapidly; others more slowly. Soils are classified to some extent by the size of soil particles. Gravel and sand particles are coarse, while clay is made up of very fine particles. Through the disintegration of soil particles, phosphorus, potassium, and other minerals are made soluble for plant growth. The relative proportion of soil constituents is shown in Figs. 8A, B.

The organic matter of a soil comes from the decayed parts of plants and animals. These materials are plant roots, green and animal manures, fungi, bacteria, worms, insects, and sometimes rodents. Certain tissues of these organisms disintegrate faster than others, so the soil humus is made up of slowly decaying material. Through decay, plant nutrients are made available to plants. In mineral soils, the organic matter varies from less than 1 per cent to from 7 to 10 per cent. Hilgard and Loughridge in California have shown the average humus content of surface soils was lowest in the desert areas (0.5 per cent). Other areas are San Joaquin Valley with 0.8

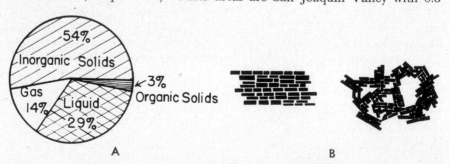

Fig. 8. (A) Proportions of various constituents in a typical cubic foot of mineral soil. (Courtesy, U. S. Department of Agriculture.) (B) The arrangement of soil particles in a dispersed soil (*left*) and in a flocculated soil (*right*), after drying.

per cent, Sacramento Valley with 1.1 per cent, and the Coast Range valleys with 1.7 per cent. Organic matter furnishes food for soil organisms, nutrients for crop plants, and improves the physical condition of the soil. *Peat* and *muck* are organic soils, or soils which contain sufficient organic content to dominate the soil characteristics. Such soils are formed slowly under the following conditions. In shallow-water areas, there is frequently a large growth of plants, and this may continue until the depression is filled completely with decaying organic matter from dead plants or plant parts, thus forming an organic soil. Peat usually contains over 65 per cent organic matter, and muck from 25 to 65 per cent. Muck is decomposed more thoroughly than peat.

Areas between the particles are occupied by water and air after the excess water has been removed by drainage. The water is held in the soil by cohesive and adhesive forces. As the soil dries out, the water is held more tightly, and the energy required to remove water increases. The water held with less force (that below about 15 atmospheres tension) is used by the plant and is called *available water*. Soil moisture usually contains nutrients, carbon dioxide, and oxygen. The remaining pore space is filled with gases, such as nitrogen, oxygen, and carbon dioxide. The relative volume used for water and air varies with the type of soil. Sands usually contain a smaller amount of water but considerable air space. Clays are typically the reverse of this condition. Water needs to have some oxygen mixed with it to facilitate absorption by roots. Thus, air is essential for growth of the plant, for the growth of aerobic microörganisms, and for bacteria on the roots of legumes to fix nitrogen.

CHARACTERISTICS OF A SOIL

A soil has three characteristics. Among the physical characteristics of soil important in crop production are color, texture, and structure. The color of sand is almost a light gray; and that of muck or highly organic soil, nearly black. *Texture* refers to the size of the mineral particles. *Structure* is concerned with the arrangement of the different types of particles to produce a kind of soil (Fig. 8B).

Color. A dark-colored soil usually is associated with a high-humus content, which in turn indicates a favorable structure and supply of nitrogen. Sometimes dark soils are associated with inadequate drainage such as undrained mucks. The reddish or reddish-brown soils are less fertile than the black or dark-brown soils, but more productive than yellow, gray, or white soils.

Texture. The mineral particles of a soil are classified as to size into sand, silt, and clay. Any mineral soil can be described in terms of these three kinds of material. There are several sands with different-sized particles, and this is true to a lesser extent of silts and clays. The classification of soils on this basis has been simplified here by presenting only the three main kinds of separates as shown below.

	Millimeters
Sand (roughly)	2.0 to 0.05
Silt	0.05 to 0.002
Clay	less than 0.002

One millimeter is approximately 1/25 of an inch, and 0.3 millimeter is about 1/80 of an inch. Thus, as the diameter of the particles decrease in size, there are many more contained in a cubic foot of soil. The total surface of the small particles per cubic foot of soil is much greater than that of large particles. The surface area of the particles in a cubic foot of medium sand is equal to about 3000 square feet, or 1/14 of an acre; and similarly, the surface area in heavy clay is equal to 900,000 square feet per cubic foot, or 20 acres. This same thing is true of cantaloupes with 27 or 45 fruits filling a crate. The cantaloupes with 27 per box have a smaller total surface than those with 45 fruits per box.

The physical characteristics of sand, silt, and clay determine the qualities of soils spoken of as sands, loams, and clays. Thus, as shown below, a soil may be described in terms of textural grades, based on the relative amounts of different particles.

	Per cent sand	*Per cent silt*	*Per cent clay*
Sand	85	15	15
Loam	30 to 50	30 to 50	20
Clay	50	50	20

Sand is loose and single-grained. The individual grains can be seen or felt. If squeezed when moist, it will form a cast, but will crumble when touched. Since the particles are fairly large and sometimes irregular, there is less particle surface and considerable air space. Sand, therefore, is low in water-holding capacity, and the large size of air spaces aids water drainage. Sands exhibit low plasticity and cohesion. Clay particles are highly plastic and sticky when wet. When moist, a clay soil can be pinched out between the thumb and fingers to form a long, flexible "ribbon". Fine-textured soils like clays usually form very hard lumps or clods upon drying. The absorptive capacity of clay particles is very high for water, gases, and soluble salts. Silt possesses a smaller amount of fine particles than clay— thus has the clay characteristics to a lesser degree. A *loam* is a soil having a mixture of the different grades of sand, silt, and clay in such proportions that the characteristics of none are predominant.

Structure. Whereas texture refers to individual soil grains, structure refers to their arrangement in a soil mass. The grains are held together in aggregates of different sizes and shapes to form the structure of soil, which may greatly influence its physical condition and productivity. Soils with fine particles may have them arranged in a dispersed or flocculated condition. The latter condition is to be preferred, since the soil is open and loosely packed; this permits the permeation of water and air more rapidly, and results in better plant growth. If clay soils are plowed too wet, clods are formed which interfere with tillage and productivity for several years. Another unfavorable condition is soil which contains excess water and is referred to by farmers as a "water-logged" soil. This condition is found with poor drainage, and under such conditions, the air-pore space is small or nonexistent. Soils with high water content (clays) are slow to warm up in spring because of the greater amount of water needed to be warmed. Sands usually are considered as earlier or warmer soils than clays in the spring. This can be explained in terms of specific heat of soils and water. The specific heat of dry soil is 0.2; or, it requires 1/5 of a B.T.U. (British thermal unit) to warm 1 pound of soil 1° F. Water has a specific heat of 1.0; Therefore it requires 1 B.T.U. to warm 1 pound of water 1° F. Thus, 17 B.T.U. will warm a cubic foot (85 pounds) of dry soil 1° F. On the other hand, there are 4 pounds of water in a cubic foot of sandy soil (Yuma sand) and this requires 4 B.T.U. to warm the water 1° F. A clay (Salinas clay) soil has 29 pounds of water per cubic foot of soil and requires 29 B.T.U., or two times as much heat.

Poor soil structure may slow down the penetration of rain and cause erosion. Structure of soil affects root penetration, rates of absorption, movement of water, the tilth, and the resistance of the soil to erosion by wind and water.

DESIRABLE SOIL CHARACTERISTICS

One of the best ways to summarize the material on soils is to consider some of the characteristics of a good soil. (a) The soil should furnish ample plant nutrients for good yields. (b) A soil should furnish an ample soil reservoir for available soil moisture. (c) A soil should warm early in the spring to provide early crops. The speed with which a soil warms up is largely dependent on its moisture content. (d) A soil should have a good physical condition—or be easy to work. (e) The soil reaction should be between a pH (hydrogen-ion concentration) of 6.0 and 7.5 for most plants. The pH is a measure of acidity or alkalinity, and may be defined as the common logarithm of the reciprocal of the hydrogen-ion concentration of a system.

SOIL MANAGEMENT AND PREPARATION

The desirable soil characteristics have been listed previously, but good soil-management practises are essential to maintain production on any soil.

Some aspects of good management have been included in sections dealing with fertilizers, manures, and irrigation. Farm practices should be followed that will prevent both water and wind erosion, because the topsoil is usually the richest in fertility and organic matter. Windbreaks are an efficient method of decreasing wind erosion. Soil organic matter tends to decrease erosion by wind and water. Areas which suffer severe erosion by water make use of cover crops, terracing, and strip farming as a preventive measure.

The natural tendency of a soil is to become compact through the action of rain, and also through the use of heavy farming equipment. Plant roots tend to loosen a soil. Planting, cultivating, and other soil operations are made easier by having a loose or pulverized soil. Thus, a soil is subject to several operations—plowing, harrowing, seeding, and cultivating. Land being irrigated for the first time also needs to be leveled, which may mean moving considerable soil. After the first major leveling, the land needs some leveling every two years by the use of a landplane or float.

The seedbed must be prepared carefully to provide the best possible conditions for seed germination. In order to provide a good seedbed, the soil needs to be broken down into soil particles or small clumps so the soil may be compacted. This permits the surrounding of the seed with many moist soil particles. Preparing a soil for a seedbed involves consideration of soil type, time of year, and depth of planting. In irrigated areas, there is need for a finer seedbed in the summer than in the winter. Small seed and shallow planting necessitate a carefully prepared soil. A seedbed is prepared by stirring or turning over a soil to the depth of 5 to 7 inches by a plow or disk. This procedure breaks down and mixes the soil, but cannot be done properly when the soil is too wet. Before plowing, a soil should be tested for moisture content. When a soil is grasped and squeezed in the hand, it is at proper moisture if it will retain the mold of the hand, yet can be easily crumbled. If it does not pulverize easily, the soil is too wet. Pulverizing or plowing a soil has the following advantages: (a) It permits the incorporation into the soil of organic matter, such as green and animal manures, crop residues, and weeds; (b) makes the soil loose to provide a good seedbed whose soil may be properly firmed around the seed; and (c) in cold climates improves the physical condition and kills some insects by exposing the soil to freezing weather. Among the harmful effects of plowing are (a) loss of moisture, (b) causing poor soil structure if plowed when too wet, and (c) the formation of *plow sole,* a hard, impervious layer. In plowing, the soil is turned, and the moisture from the top of the plowed soil is lost by evaporation. Plow sole may develop as the result of always plowing to the same depth, but may be lessened by variation in plowing depth and by rotating with deep-rooted crops. Since the roots of several vegetables extend to the depth of 4 to 6 feet, it is not feasible to loosen the soil to such a depth by plowing.

After plowing, the soil usually is harrowed or rolled to break up the lumps

Fig. 9. (*Top*) A type of tractor-drawn implement for leveling land. (*Bottom*) Tractor pulling disk and drag in preparing the soil for planting. This operation makes a seedbed and destroys weeds.

and clods and make a uniformly loose soil. Sometimes a large float is used after the soil has been harrowed to break clods and lumps that the harrow failed to break. This makes the soil firm. Floating also tends to help level or take down any high spots that may be caused while preparing the soil. Types of harrows include the spike-tooth, the spring-tooth, and the disk harrow; a plank or frame drag also may be used for the same purpose. Timeliness is important in these operations; sometimes plowing and harrowing are performed in one operation. Where beds are used, they are spaced from 38 to 42 inches between centers, and are formed by the use of a lister or double-moldboard plow. Sleds or bedders are used to shape the bed, and some rolling may be necessary after the bed is shaped. Clay soils require more judgment and care in handling to prevent hard clods than do sands. When crops are grown in succession, the ground rarely needs to be plowed more often than once each year.

WEED CONTROL

Crops are cultivated to kill weeds, and this practice forms a mulch of dry soil. While many weeds can be removed by the cultivator, there are sometimes weeds close to the plants that must be removed by hand. In some of these cases, selective herbicides have greatly reduced weeding costs. Weeds

Fig. 10. A pre-emergence oil spray was used to kill the weeds on the beds to the right; sprayed two days before the lettuce plants emerged from the soil. Picture was taken 34 days after spraying. (Courtesy, Shell Oil Company, Agricultural Laboratory.)

compete with the vegetables for water, nitrates, and other plant nutrients. Sometimes weeds grow faster than the vegetables and hence shade them. A weedy field is costly to harvest.

Most weeds are removed by the use of mechanical equipment. A blade type of cultivator equipped with "duck feet" or side knives is used commonly because it cuts the weeds just below the soil surface. Shovel cultivators also are used. Shallow-rooted crops should be cultivated close to the surface so the root zone is not reduced greatly. Land that is excessively weedy should not be planted to small vegetable crops without previously reducing the weed contamination. Small weeds and seedlings are much cheaper to remove than weeds which have become established. Weeds in a few vegetable crops may be controlled by spraying with selective weed killers or herbicides.

Selective herbicides are chemicals that kill certain weeds but do not injure crop plants. In contrast, *contact weed killers* destroy all plants—both weeds and vegetables. These may be used to kill weeds on a field a couple of days before the vegetable seedlings appear. Both spraying and dusting are used as a means of application. These materials should be applied with care to

Table 6*

AVERAGE DOSAGE RATES FOR USE OF SELECTIVE WEED SPRAYS

Crop	Weeds	Chemical and Dosage (Average Values Per Acre)	Volume (Gallons Per Acre)
Carrots	Foxtail, annual blue-grass, mustard, rad-ish, shepherd's purse, pigweed	Stoddard solvent (shell weed killer No. 10, Pentox No. 1)	35
Celery in beds	Same as for carrots		
Corn 12 inches high	Pigweed, lamb's quar-ters, cocklebur, morning-glory, kelp	2,4-D salt: ½ lb. acid equiv. + 10 to 100 gals. of water	Low: 10 High: 100
Onions and garlic to 6 inches high	Mustard, radish, shep-herd's purse, nettle	Sinox: 1 gal. + 3 lb. am-monium sulfate + 100 gals. of water.	100
Onions and garlic 6 to 12 inches high		Aero cyanate: 5 lbs. + 60 gals. of water Aero cyanate: 10 lbs. + 60 gals. of water	60 60
Peas 4 inches high	Mustard, pigweed smartweed, thistles, nightshade	Sinox W or Dow Selective: 13 per cent solution, ½ gal. + 15 to 75 gals. of water	Low: 15† High: 75

* Courtesy, *Calif. Agr. Ext. Cir. 157,* 1949.
† Not recommended in humid regions.

prevent injury to the grower's crops as well as those of his neighbors. The grower needs to understand the materials he is using, and be careful not to exceed the margin of selectivity by using too much chemical, too high pressure, or wrong time of application. Crop damage will result if penetrating oils reach the growing region of the plant. Some use has been made of open flames to kill weeds. By proper shielding of the plants from the flame and directing the flame, this procedure has been used with success. Our knowledge of chemical weed control is advancing rapidly, so the grower should keep informed of recent developments.

REFERENCES

1. Bouquet, A. G. B.: Garden soil management, *Ore. Agr. Ext. Bul. 612,* 24 p., 1947.
2. Crafts, A. S. and W. A. Harvey: Selective weed killers, *Calif. Agr. Ext. Ser. Cir. 157,* 16 p., 1949.
3. Hutchison, C. B.: "California Agriculture," 444 p., Berkeley, University of California Press, 1946.
4. Soils and men, *U.S.D.A. Yearbook, 1938,* 1232 p.

Chapter 5

Physiological Factors Affecting
Vegetable Production

Growth of a plant is the result of the interaction of the plant's genetic constitution, and the influence of physiological factors which make up its environment. Physiological research attempts to make environmental conditions more favorable for production or preservation of the harvested crop. Chapter 6 covers some of the genetic aspects of the subject; physiological factors and processes will be considered in this chapter.

Environment is made up of such factors as temperature, moisture, nutrient supply (fertilizers), light (duration and energy), carbon dioxide, soil reaction, oxygen, wind, and pests (insects, diseases, and weeds). The grower is interested in plant growth since that is the process by which he produces a marketable crop. A grower either selects an area with desirable factors or attempts to modify the factors for better production. In many cases both procedures are used, but the treatment differs with the factor. Some factors are modified more easily than others, but a clear understanding of them will aid the grower with his crop-production problems and in making sound decisions.

Many processes go on in plants which concern the grower very slightly except when they are called to his attention in connection with some specific field problem. The previously mentioned factors affect plant growth through their effect on various plant processes. Some of the more important processes are absorption of water and plant nutrients, photosynthesis, transpiration, respiration, translocation of food, and metabolism, which is associated with growth.

These processes may build up the plant through growth, or cause deterioration, such as respiration. The effects of both respiration and transpiration are not so noticeable on a living organism, since the plant may absorb more water and manufacture more food to replace that used by life processes. As soon as the edible part is removed from the plant, however, these processes cause pronounced effects on food value and keeping qualities. Storage conditions are selected which will reduce the losses caused by these two processes. A brief review of these processes follows.

Absorption of water and nutrients refers to the movement of these materials from the soil through the root hairs to the inside parts of the plant. *Photosynthesis* is the process by which the plant synthesizes or forms carbohydrates from carbon dioxide and water in the presence of light (energy) and chlorophyll. *Transpiration* is the giving off of water by exposed surfaces of a plant. The process of *respiration* causes the liberation of energy from organic matter and goes on in all living cells. In this process, oxygen is absorbed and there is a breaking down of carbohydrates, proteins, and fats with the liberation of heat, carbon dioxide, and water. *Growth* is an increase in size (height and volume), and in green and dry weight.

TEMPERATURE

One of the most important factors affecting vegetable production and location of production areas is temperature. Crops vary in their adaptation to different temperatures. Undesirable temperatures may be responsible for the death of plants or cause premature seeding. Temperature also affects pollination and fruit setting as well as the six processes previously mentioned.

A useful classification of vegetables is into cool and warm season crops. Such a grouping indicates that vegetables differ in their temperature requirements—affecting time of planting as well as the best temperature conditions for growth. These groups of crops have been listed in the section on classification. In greenhouse culture, the day temperatures on sunny days are maintained at 55° to 65° F. for cool season crops, and 70° to 80° F. for warm season crops.

Both high and low temperatures may result in the death of plants. Low temperatures are of greater economic importance. Plant temperatures of 1 to 3 degrees below 32° F. (the freezing point of water) will cause serious damage in many Vegetables. Since temperature affects so many processes, it would be expected to influence growth. Crops respond differently to various temperatures. Spinach will make some growth as low as 40° F. while other crops, particularly warm season crops, require higher temperatures to initiate growth. There are probably optimum ranges for the growth of crops, but these are not known with exactness at the present time. Growth usually increases with temperature, but is less rapid as plants approach or reach average temperatures of from 80° to 100° F.

Western vegetable areas vary in altitude, which of course affects temperature and growing periods of these regions. Observations made by E. H. Casseres of Turrialba, Costa Rica are helpful in illustrating the effect of altitude on temperature. In Costa Rica, vegetables may be grown near sea level and at various elevations on mountains located in the same latitude. As the elevation increases, the temperatures are cooler and a longer season is required to produce a crop. The following data illustrate the effect of altitude on the growing period of white potatoes and field corn. These data also illustrate the general rule that there is a 3.3° F. decrease in temperature for each rise of 1000 feet in altitude.

	Growing Period	
Altitude	*White Potatoes*	*Field Corn*
2000 feet	2 months	4½ months
5000 feet	3½ months	7 months
9000 feet	5 months	12 months

In recent years, it has been shown that moderately cool temperatures for several weeks may cause biennials to produce seed stalks the first year, and thus behave as annuals. This may cause serious financial loss since a crop may be planted for market and, as a result of premature seeding, be almost useless. Beets, celery, cabbage, onion sets, lettuce, and other crops exhibit this response, although conditions for seeding seem to vary with the different crops. Temperature has been shown to have an important effect on photoperiod response, as discussed later.

Pollination is usually essential for the production of fruit crops. Smith and Cochran[7] found in the case of the tomato that either high or low temperatures might be the cause of pollination failure. Plants grown at 70° and 85° F. gave a much better set of fruits than those grown at 50° and at 100° F. (See tomatoes, Fig. 88.) Peppers and sweet corn probably are affected similarly but at slightly different temperatures.

Fruit Setting with Hormones. Considerable recent research has been conducted with plant-growth regulators or hormones. As previously mentioned, these compounds are used as weed sprays, and also to root cuttings, to set fruits, and for other plant responses. Considerable work has been performed with tomatoes, since all blossoms do not set fruit particularly under high- and low-temperature conditions. Hormones have been used to increase the set of greenhouse tomatoes, but there have been some reports that the fruit does not store as well as normally set fruit. There are several chemical compounds that may be used for fruit setting. Under field conditions, 4-chlorophenoxyacetic acid (4-CPA) has been as satisfactory as any of these materials. A concentration of 50 parts per million of the salt in water is a desirable dilution. The clusters are sprayed when 3 to 5 have open flowers. Poor set of fruit due to low temperatures has been corrected by this treatment. The price of the fruit needs to be relatively high so the practise is adapted to the spring and early summer crops. Unfortunately, this material as well as others causes injury to the leaves and retards growth, so care should be used to confine the spray to the flower cluster. This necessitates hand application. There may be an increase in puffy fruits, but generally not to a significant extent. The pulp in the seed cavity of a ripe hormone-set fruit usually retains its green color. Usually very few seed are found in the fruits. Early yields have been increased from ½ to 5 pounds per plant during the period the treated plants were harvested.

WATER

Plant growth may be affected both by soil moisture and by water vapor in the air (*humidity*). There is more water in vegetables than any other constituent (see Table 10); consequently it is one of the most important needs in vegetable production. Not only is water needed for the actual production of new plant tissues, but also it acts as a solvent for minerals present in the soil. Frequently water is supplied so lavishly by rainfall or irrigation that its constant need by the plant is overlooked.

Soil moisture content may be expressed as percentage based on the dry weight of the soil. Available water also may be expressed as inches of water in a specified depth of soil. Insufficient or excessive amounts of soil moisture both are harmful to plant growth. Deficient soil moisture is indicated by a slowing down, or even cessation of growth, of the plants; reduced yields or even crop failures may result. Excessive water may decrease yields indirectly through such effects as leaching of nitrates; poor aeration; and a raised water table, which limits the depth of the root zone.

Fortunately, there is considerable range in the quantities of rainfall or irrigation water which the soil may receive and still produce maximum yield. Thus, two neighboring growers may obtain similar yields but use different amounts of water for irrigation. Water which can be absorbed by the plant roots is called *available water*. The availability of water may be expressed as *tension*. For example, moisture in a soil at the field capacity is held at a tension of about 0.1 atmosphere and at wilting or the lower level of available water about 15 atmospheres. The amount of available water in a soil is determined by obtaining both the field capacity and permanent wilting percentage of the soil. The difference between these two percentages is available water. Several days after a heavy rain or irrigation, the water moves downward. The soil is said to be at *field capacity* when this movement ceases. After the plant roots have removed all the available water the soil moisture is at the *permanent wilting percentage*. Thus, a sandy loam may have a field capacity of 16 per cent soil moisture, and a permanent wilting percentage of 9 per cent. Present evidence indicates that all vegetables can remove water from any soil to the same percentage. The amount of available water which can be stored in a soil or its root-zone reservoir, available to plants, depends upon soil type and the depth of the root system.

Atmospheric humidity—the moisture content of the air—is usually expressed as *relative humidity*. This is the percentage of moisture which the air holds at a given time compared to the maximum it could hold at the temperature existing at the time. Greenhouse vegetable growers consider

Fig. 11. Unproductive desert and a nearby cantaloupe field. Adequate soil moisture greatly affects the productivity of land.

humidity an important factor in crop production, and spray the ground and walks with water to increase it. Certain areas near the seacoast are characterized by high humidity, and are considered especially adapted to the production of certain crops even though the temperature may be cooler owing to the effects of the ocean. Patterson[6] studied the effect of humidity on the linear growth of snap beans and found that it did not affect growth unless the soil moisture was inadequate.

SOIL NUTRIENTS

Nutrient and soil relationships are complex, and only general considerations will be taken up in this section. Fertilizers and other sources of nutrients are commonly used by growers to increase yields. After the deficient nutrient or nutrients have been determined for any soil, fertilizers are selected and applied to provide these for maximum yields. The most commonly added nutrients are nitrogen (N), phosphorus (phosphoric acid, P_2O_5), and potassium (potash, K_2O). These are referred to as the major elements and there is a larger group of minor elements. Phosphorus and potassium are less likely to be leached from the soil than is nitrogen. The latter element occurs in the soil as a constituent of several compounds such as nitrates, ammonium ions, and organic nitrogen. Nitrates may be leached from a soil where there is an excess of water, and lost in the drainage water. While phosphorus and potash are primarily removed by the plant, the nitrate content of the soil is affected by farming practise as well as being removed by the plant. Commercial fertilizers are a source of soil nutrients as are animal and green manures. Green manures are grown on the soil to be turned under for organic matter and the deeper roots withdraw nutrients which are added to the surface layer after the crop is plowed under.

LIGHT

Light furnishes the necessary energy for photosynthesis, and the length of day or number of daylight hours affects the growth and flowering of plants. During the long days of summer there is probably more energy than the plant can use efficiently. Therefore, growth is limited by some other factor such as the carbon dioxide content of the air. Summer is a period when plants grow rapidly. Light is inadequate during the winter months for good growth (Fig. 12), and this factor is one of the primary handicaps of the

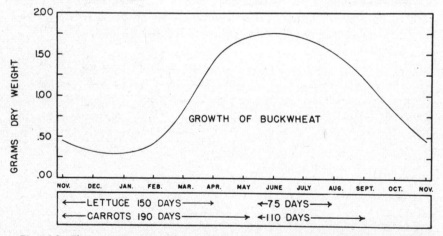

Fig. 12. The relative growth made by buckwheat plants when planted at biweekly periods throughout the year in a greenhouse. Market carrots and lettuce as well as buckwheat made slow growth from November to December because the days were of short duration and the weather was cooler for the market crops. (Courtesy, University of Maryland and University of California.)

greenhouse industry. The energy of light through the process of photosynthesis is responsible for the organic matter of a plant which makes up most of the plant's dry matter.

The seasonal variation in length of day affects the growth and blooming of certain vegetable crops. This response to day length is referred to as *photoperiodism*. This response of plants to hours of sunshine was first demonstrated in 1920 by Garner and Allard[1] while working with Maryland Mammoth variety of tobacco. They found that this variety did not blossom in the summer when grown in the latitude of Washington, D.C. Blossoms were produced by the plants when grown in a greenhouse during the short days of winter. As a result of the experiments of these and other investigators, several vegetables may be classified into three groups with respect to photoperiod response.

1. Plants not greatly affected by duration of light as to their time of blooming—or "indeterminate" plants. Crops are asparagus, cucumber, pepper, snap bean, tomato.
2. Plants that bloom during short days, usually called "short-day" plants. Crops are roselle, sweet potato.
3. Plants that bloom during the long days, usually referred to as "long-day" plants. Crops are beet, Chinese cabbage, dill, edible chrysanthemum, lettuce, radish, spinach, sorrel.

These classifications are related to a photoperiod which might be considered critical for each plant; thus the long photoperiod may differ slightly for various vegetables. In general, the critical day length for long-day plants is 12 to 14 hours. The day length for most short-day plants ranges from 8 to 10 hours. Under natural conditions, the length of day varies with the month of the year, and with latitude, except at the equator. This is illustrated in Table 7. At the equator (0° north latitude) all days are of about equal length. The March 21 and September 21 periods of sunlight are approximately the same at all latitudes. For regions north of the equator, the shortest day of the year, December 21, and the longest day, June 21, vary greatly at different latitudes. As latitudes increase, the short day is of less duration and the long day of greater duration. Day duration at Brawley, California varies from 10 hours on December 21 to 14.2 hours on June 21; similarly at Provo, Utah, the day length varies from 9.2 hours to 15.0 hours.

Continuation of vegetative growth rather than early flower formation is desirable in foliage crops, such as spinach, lettuce, Chinese cabbage, and radishes. If planted too late in the spring, these crops tend to produce flowers and seed during the long days of June before attaining sufficient vegetative growth to produce maximum yields. Although most of the effects of photoperiodism have been with respect to flower production, the vegetative growth of some plants has also been affected previous to flower production. Length of day affects the formation of onion bulbs, and varieties[3] differ as to the

Fig. 13. Radish (*top*) flowers during a 16-hour day (*left*), but not at an 8-hour day (*right*). Pepper (*bottom*) flowers and forms fruit in both day lengths and thus are indeterminate plants as to photoperiodism.

Table 7*

Day Length, or Possible Hours of Sunshine, at Different Latitudes

Degrees North Latitude	Cities or Areas Near Indicated Latitude	Hours, Sunrise to Sunset		
		Dec. 21	Mar. 21 Sept. 21	June 21
0	Quito, Ecuador	12.1	12.1	12.1
26	Miami, Florida; Brownsville, Texas	10.3	12.1	13.5
33	Brawley, California; Florence, Arizona; Alamogordo; New Mexico	10.0	12.1	14.2
35	Santa Maria, California; Winslow, Arizona; Albuquerque, New Mexico	9.5	12.1	14.3
40	Red Bluff, California; Provo, Utah; Boulder, Colorado	9.2	12.1	15.0
45	Salem, Oregon; Salmon, Idaho	8.5	12.1	15.4
50	Vancouver, British Columbia	8.0	12.1	16.2
58	Juneau, Alaska	6.3	12.2	18.1

* Courtesy, *Tide Tables—Pacific Ocean and Indian Ocean,* 1950, U.S. Dept. of Commerce, Coast and Geodetic Survey.

optimum day length for bulbing. Yellow Bermuda will produce bulbs in a shorter photoperiod than most varieties; hence it can be grown successfully in Texas as a winter crop during short days. With white potatoes, a long day seems to favor production of flowers and seed; a short to medium day favors tuber production.

Recent work[2] has shown that temperature may act as a modifying factor in the response of some vegetables to photoperiodism. The rate of flower formation may proceed more rapidly if both an optimum photoperiod and temperature are used.

CARBON DIOXIDE

Carbon dioxide is one of the raw materials used in photosynthesis for the manufacture of carbohydrates. Plants obtain this gas from the air. There are 3 parts of carbon dioxide in 10,000 parts of air (0.03 per cent). The amount of carbon dioxide in the air will vary somewhat, usually being greater near industrial centers and cities. At harvest time an acre of potato plants and tubers contains the equivalent of 7 tons of carbon dioxide and considerably more was used during the growth of the plants. Experimental data indicate that if the amount of carbon dioxide in the air is increased moderately there will result an increase in plant growth. Some research workers report increases of over 100 per cent, while others have found small differences with some crops. The logical place to use this practice would be in greenhouses where the gas may be confined to a limited space.

SOIL REACTION

There are soils in the United States that are either too acid or too alkaline for maximum production. The optimum range varies somewhat for different crops, but for many a desirable range is a pH range of 6.0 to 7.5. A pH of 7.0 is neutral; therefore this range is from slightly acid to very slightly alkaline.

OXYGEN

Oxygen is essential for growth of both the aerial and underground portions of plants. Growers are rarely concerned with this factor except in a few soils that have poor aeration. Heavy clays (Table 11) have little space remaining for air after irrigation, and such a moist soil is sometimes referred to as "waterlogged." This condition results in poor growth. Plants grown in a nutrient solution frequently become wilted if the solution is not aerated. Plants grown for several months with aeration frequently die if there is a stoppage in the aeration. Potato yields on experimental plots in Ohio have been increased by placing drain tiles under the rows, or by adding tons of sand to the soil, or by turning under large quantities of green manures. These increased yields have been attributed to the benefit from aeration. When oxygen content of a soil is low, there is usually an abnormally high concentration of carbon dioxide, which is thought to reduce the respiration of roots. There is a close correlation between the rate of absorption of water and the rate of respiration of corn roots. Oxygen is one of the factors affecting respiration.

SMOG

Crop injury to the extent of over a half million dollars has resulted to farm crops in the Los Angeles area due to smog. This term is used to describe a mixture of smoke and fog. The condition decreases visibility, causes a smarting of the eyes, and serious loss in certain crops. This type of damage has occurred in the Los Angeles area, north into the San Fernando valley, east into Riverside County, and south along the coast. Crops of Romaine lettuce, endive, and spinach are seriously affected, while beet, celery, and swiss chard are less subject to damage. Cabbage, cantaloupe, carrot, cauliflower, cucumber, pumpkin, squash, and broccoli do not appear to be affected.

The first symptom is a glazed or silver appearance on the underside of the leaf somewhat similar to freezing injury. There is usually a progressive dehydration of leaf tissue until scorched areas develop with brown necrotic spots on the top and bottom of the leaves. Air pollution is caused by gases, aerosols, and particles in the atmosphere. Some eighteen constituents have been found in the air including sulfur dioxide and trioxide, aldehydes, filterable oils, soluble chlorides, unsaturated hydrocarbons, organic peroxides, formic acid and others. It has been shown that the damage is not due to the sulfur compounds. These materials originate from various factories, automobiles and trucks, incinerators, gas furnaces, and many other sources. Normally there is a warm air stratum or layer over the South Coastal basin which is usually some 1000 to 3000 feet above sea level. Under these conditions there is no damage. When meteorological conditions cause this layer to drop to 500 feet and there is a low wind velocity for several days, smog is likely to occur. Injury to plants occurs only during periods of aggravated pollution. This condition is brought about by the impurities in the air, reduced wind velocity, and a lowered ceiling.

PESTS

Both insects and plant diseases have marked effects on reducing growth of plants. Foliage diseases reduce photosynthesis, thereby causing reduced growth as well as making them unattractive for the market. Root and stem diseases interfere with the absorption of water and minerals. Insects affect almost any part of a plant, reducing photosynthesis, cutting the stem, or making the vegetable unattractive. In processed products the presence of diseased parts of vegetables or insect injury may result in the product's being condemned under the Federal Pure Food Law. Chapter 14 deals more specifically with insects and diseases.

REFERENCES

1. Garner, W. W., and H. A. Allard. Effect of the relative length of day and night and other factors of the environment on growth and reproduction in plants. *Jour. Agr. Res. 18:*553–606, 1920.
2. Knott, J. E. The effect of temperature on the photoperiodic response of spinach. *N. Y. (Cornell) Agr. Exp. Sta. Mem. 218,* 38 p., 1939.
3. Magruder, Roy, and H. A. Allard. Bulb formation in some American and European varieties of onions as affected by length of day. *Jour. Agr. Res. 54:*719–52. 1937.
4. Mann, Louis K. and P. A. Minges. Experiments on setting fruit with growth-regulating substances on field-grown tomatoes in California. *Hilgardia 19:*309–337. 1949.
5. Middleton, John T., J. B. Kendrick, Jr., and H. W. Schwalm. Smog in the South Coastal area. *Calif. Agriculture 4:*7–10 (No. 11), 1950.
6. Patterson, C. F. Growth of seedlings of *Phaseolus vulgaris* in relation to

relative humidity and temperature. *Trans. Roy. Can. Inst. 14:*24–62, 1922.

7. Smith, Ora, and H. L. Cochran. Effect of temperature on pollen germination and the tube growth in the tomato. *N. Y. (Cornell) Agr. Exp. Sta. Mem. 175,* 11 p., 1935.

Chapter 6

Improvement of Vegetables Through Plant Breeding

Few people realize the great debt we owe to the many people who during the last 100 years have been interested in obtaining better varieties of vegetables. In the past, many desirable selections have been made by persons primarily interested in the crop, but who had little or no knowledge of the science of genetics. Many of these introductions have been failures, but the importance of the successful varieties serves to emphasize our debt to those pioneer plant breeders. Many old varieties or strains selected by them are still found in our present seed catalogues. The Chili pepper type was used about 1588. Golden Queen tomato, a yellow variety, was introduced by Livingston in 1882. Other old varieties are White Portugal onion (1810), Stowell's Evergreen corn (1856), Boston Pickling cucumber (1865), Wakefield cabbage (1866), Savoy cabbage (1870), Southport Yellow Globe onion (1888), Country Gentlemen corn (1890), and Bountiful snap beans (1898). Since 1900, the science of genetics has developed rapidly, but vegetable plants have received only recently the attention they deserve. During the last 10 or 15 years considerable emphasis has been placed on vegetable genetics, resulting in an increasing number of new varieties originated through scientific research. One example of our interest in plant breeding was the establishment by the United States Department of Agriculture of a regional experiment station at Charleston, South Carolina, for the development of better vegetable varieties for the South.

VEGETABLE VARIETIES

Bailey lists some 247 vegetables in his book, "Principles of Vegetable Gardening." From this large number of crops there are probably 40 to 50 which could be considered of major importance. There are numerous varieties, particularly of the important crops such as lettuce. In 1806 there were only 16 lettuce varieties listed in seed catalogues, but at the present time there are some 1100. Frequently a variety is listed under several names. For instance the variety Salamander lettuce may be catalogued under 50 different names. At present there are about 150 distinct varieties of which some 20 to 25 are commercially important. In many vegetable crops, plants have been found in commercial fields that have differed in type, and were propagated by growers or other people. The better varieties have been maintained and the poorer types have been abandoned because there was no specific need for them.

The above discussion raises the question of what constitutes a variety. Work[4] has divided the characters of a variety or strain into three groups: (a) Type characters, (b) performance characters, and (c) special characters. Type characters are those that are prominent and easily observed, such as the pear shape, red color, and two seed cells in the San Marzano tomato. Some performance characters are determined less easily by observation but include such characters as yield, earliness, uniformity of maturity, and resistance to disease. Special characters refer to an adaptation to special purposes such as tomatoes for canning, market, forcing, or green wraps, as well as to soil and climatic conditions. Regardless of these definite characteristics, a new variety is the result of the judgment or personal opinion of people. Since personal opinions and judgments vary, new varieties may be named which have few or no superior characters.

In a discussion of superior characters, it would seem desirable to list some actual examples. Potato breeding has expanded and advanced markedly in the last 15 years. Some of the superior characters sought in potatoes are: (a) High yield; (b) earliness; (c) wide adaptability; (d) russet skin; (e) shallow eyes; (f) hardiness; (g) good tuber shape and type; (h) quality; (i) resistance to scab, late blight, leaf roll, fusarium, mild mosaic, and immunity to latent mosaic.

CHROMOSOMES AND GENES AND THEIR FUNCTION IN INHERITANCE

Any discussion of varietal improvement through plant breeding should include some mention of the method in which characters are inherited or passed from one generation to the next. However, this subject has developed so rapidly in the last 25 or 30 years that it now constitutes a field requiring specialized training. Obviously only a few of the simpler facts can be mentioned in a limited treatment of the subject.

When a flower is pollinated by wind, insects, or any other agency, pollen from the anthers (male part of the flower) is carried to the stigma (female part of the flower). The pollen then germinates, and the pollen tube grows down the style to the egg. This pollen tube contains the male gamete which unites with the egg or female gamete to complete fertilization. The fertilized egg now develops into the embryo of the seed. By this process the potentialities of the male and female parents are combined in the offspring.

Fig. 14. Artificial pollination of flowers. The blossom at the top has been bagged to prevent cross-pollination. At the left the pollen is being placed on the stigma, and at the right the pollinated flower is protected with a capsule.

The gametes possess nuclei which contain microscopic rod-shaped bodies called *chromosomes* which are composed of chromatin. Chromosomes are the carriers of genetic characters (factors, genes) which are located at definite positions on the chromosome.

In tomato breeding, if a red-fruited tomato plant is crossed with a plant bearing yellow fruit, the seed from this cross will produce plants (hybrids) all of which will bear red tomatoes. If the hybrid flowers are self-pollinated, in the next generation there will be about three plants producing red tomatoes to every one producing yellow tomatoes. The geneticist refers to these two color genes as R and r. R is responsible for red color, and is dominant. Small r is recessive and is responsible for yellow color (Fig. 15). This example is included in order to illustrate the importance of chromosomes in plant breeding and genetic studies.

Genetic facts have been developed about vegetables as well as other plants, and animals. Corn, tomatoes, and peas have been studied more thoroughly

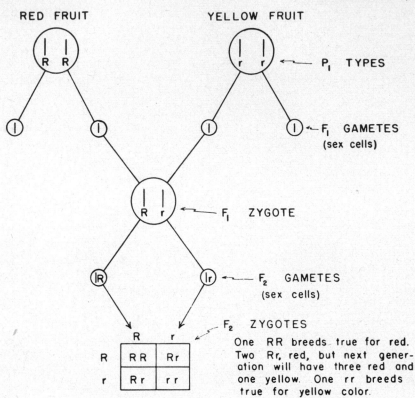

Fig. 15. The inheritance of red and yellow fruit color in tomato. Bars indicate chromosomes, though only one of the 12 pairs is shown in each zygote.

than other crops, and the location on the chromosomes of certain genes or characters has been determined. The number of chromosomes is constant for a given species but varies for different species. Chromosomes occur in even numbers—a multiple of two. For example peas have 16 or 8 pairs, and corn 20 or 10 pairs. Chromosomes are not merely masses of chromatin material but are a definitely organized series of chromatin granules whose number and order of arrangement is a persistent feature of the individual chromosome. Breeding is often difficult in plants with the higher chromosome numbers; potatoes, for example, because they exhibit complex inheritance.

RELATION BETWEEN CROP POLLINATION AND IMPROVEMENT PROCEDURE

Vegetables are propagated sexually through fertilization and asexually by using a plant part for propagation. A new variety among the plants propagated asexually is very simple to maintain without change in type—although the increase of planting stock, as for example, in potato tubers for seed, is frequently slower than in sexual propagation. In the sexually reproduced vegetables some are reproduced by self-pollination; that is, the pollen on a plant also fertilizes the egg on the same plant. In these cases the flowers are *perfect,* having both stamens and pistils in the same flower. Cross-pollinated vegetables include three types of plants with different locations of the male and female flower parts. Some vegetables have perfect flowers as previously mentioned. Some, such as corn, have the male flowers in one location on the plant and the female flowers in another and are spoken of as *monoecious* plants. Asparagus is a *dioecious* plant since the male and female flowers appear on different plants.

The actual method of pollination, whether by insects or other agents, is important also in breeding work and seed production. Plants such as tomatoes, peas, and beans are self-pollinated independently of insects or other outside agents, permitting varieties of the same crop to be grown close to each other with little or no cross-pollination. Melons, squash, and onions, on the other hand, usually are pollinated by insects traveling from flower to flower. These types of plants produce a heavy, sticky pollen which is carried on the insect's body. Still other plants such as corn and beets produce a very light, dry pollen which is carried about easily by currents of air; they are referred to generally as *wind-pollinated.* Obviously there is much cross-pollination between similar plants of the last two groups. Insect or wind-pollinated plants must be isolated or artificially protected if pure lines are to be maintained. Some of the common vegetables are listed here as to method of propagation and pollination.

Sexually propagated: Self-pollinated—Bean, lettuce, pea, tomato.

Cross-pollinated—Asparagus, beet, carrot, corn, melon, onion, pumpkin, spinach, squash.

Asexually propagated: Garlic, globe artichoke, white potato, rhubarb, sweet potato.

METHODS OF PLANT IMPROVEMENT

The technique followed in improving plants varies considerably according to the crop under consideration and the method selected by the plant breeder. In any event the basic procedure is to search out and utilize naturally occurring or artificially induced variations occurring among plants. No two individuals are exactly the same. Variation may be so slight as to be unimportant, or it may be great enough to deserve special attention. Variations among closely related plants are usually negligible. The more distant the relationship the greater is the variation to be expected. The common methods of improvement will be discussed under three main heads.

Introduction of Varieties and Species from Other Production Areas or Countries

Types Used Directly. In spite of the fact that several of our vegetables are native to the Americas, there are a considerable number of them as well as of their varieties which have been introduced from foreign countries. Areas in Europe and Asia have furnished our growers with crops such as asparagus, celery, lettuce, carrot, radish, and peas; from Europe came cabbage and beet; the onion is a native to Asia; and both cucumbers and watermelons came from Africa. Vegetable crops native to the Americas are white potato, sweet potato, snap and lima beans, tomato, pepper, summer squash, and pumpkin. The Des Moines or Table Queen squash is reported to have been brought to this country by a Dane in 1900. Big Boston, a butter-head variety of lettuce, is grown in Europe under the name Trocadero and was introduced in this country about 1890. Large-seeded lima beans were brought to this country by seamen and were named for the town of Lima in Peru. Most introductions are not suited fully to American conditions and in many cases, have been improved by selection or some similar procedure.

Use of Types for Breeding Stock. This procedure has been important, particularly in recent years, as a source of material that is resistant or immune to certain of our crop diseases. Many foreign plants are imported for plant breeding by the U.S. Department of Agriculture through the Division of Plant Exploration and Introduction. In the potato breeding program, *Solanum demissum* has been used because of its immunity to late blight. This program also includes crosses made for resistance to certain virus diseases as well as to scab—using foreign introductions as a source of resistance.

The wilt-resistant tomato variety, Marvel (developed by selection from the French variety Merveille des Marchés) has been used in developing wilt-resistant tomato varieties. In more recent years this program has been continued with the use of *Lycopersicum pimpinellifolium* (also resistant to leaf mold) and other wild types obtained from South and Central America.

Powdery mildew-resistant cantaloupe varieties No. 5, 6, and 7 owe their resistance to introductions of Indian (Asia) cantaloupes (Fig. 16). White Persian onion is an introduction from Persia and is used to incorporate thrips resistance. Lord Howe Island, an Australian variety of onion, has been used as one parent in the development of the new hybrid onion called "California Hybrid Red No. 1."

Improvement by Selection

In general, considerable plant improvement has been effected by selection. When a plant breeder desires to improve his stocks, experience has shown him that the logical procedure is to choose for breeding stock those individuals in each generation which most closely approximate his ideals. This practise if continued generation after generation almost always leads to marked improvement in the desired direction. It is this method which has led to the isolation and establishment of many varieties of plants now grown by farmers.

Many of our varieties have been developed by selection. Unfortunately in most cases no clear record is available to indicate whether mass or pure-line selection was used. It is probable that usually a combination of methods was employed. Boston Pickling (1865) and Chicago Pickling (1860) were both selections from cucumbers grown in the two respective regions. Grand Rapids variety of lettuce, used primarily for greenhouse culture but also for growing outdoors, was a selection made by Eugene Davis from Black Seeded Simpson. John Baer and Clark's Early are two examples of tomato varieties developed by selection. In peppers, Chili No. 9 was developed through selection, by Garcia in New Mexico, from the Mexican Chili variety. Pride of Muscatine is a wilt-resistant watermelon selected from the variety Kleckley Sweet, by the Iowa Agricultural Experiment Station in 1929.

Mass Selection. Mass selection simply means the selection in each generation of a number of individuals most nearly approaching the desired type for parents of the next generation. Mass selection for a few generations only often is not permanently effective but must be continued in order to keep the race or variety at its existing level. The plants selected for parents in this system usually are planted together and allowed to self- or cross-pollinate naturally.

Pure Line Selection. Although the principles involved are simple, the amount of work required by this method in producing actually superior varieties is great. In the utilization of this method the following points are of importance. (a) At the start, a large number of individual plant selections must be made and the progeny of each plant tested separately for several years. (b) Field observation should precede final selection of the individual plants to be tested. Notes taken on the original selections before harvesting will make it possible to check the first generation against the parents and thereby eliminate those which fail to give sufficient promise at the end of the first year. (c) If severe selection is exercised during the first two or three years, the future work will be reduced greatly. (d) A very thorough testing of the most promising selections in comparison with the best commercial varieties is essential. (e) Selection within pure lines is ineffective.

Clonal Selection. A variety propagated asexually from a single original individual is known as a *clone*. The place of clonal selection in agricultural practice has been a moot question for decades. It is true that a number of varieties of plants have been introduced by this means, but from a consideration of the evidence bearing on clonal selection the following generalizations may be drawn safely. (a) Selection within a clone is without effect because all the individuals composing a clone have the same genetic constitution. (b) Maintenance of valuable varieties should be safeguarded by selection of normal healthy individuals. (c) The practicability of producing new varieties of vegetatively propagated crop plants by clonal selection depends upon the frequency of occurrence of desirable bud variants. Extreme variations have been noted in the frequency with which such bud variants have been observed in different crops and varieties.

Since potatoes are reproduced from pieces of tubers, perhaps many new varieties would be expected from this source. Unfortunately many varieties were developed without any record of their method of origin. However, it is known that some 170 varieties can be traced to an early variety known as Garnet Chili. In the development of some 306 potato varieties, only about 7 per cent came from sports or mutants. Many of these varieties have been recorded, although they did not possess much usefulness. The Red Warba has been introduced and is a bud mutation from the Warba. A new strain of Cobbler has been named Pioneer Cobbler. Porto Blanco is a white-skinned mutation from Porto Rico sweet potato.

Hybridization

A *hybrid* is the progeny of a cross between two plants with different characters. The term is used frequently to indicate any type of cross. In vegetable improvement, crossing is for the purpose of incorporating good characters of both parents into one new variety.

Hybridization with Selection. After a cross is made, the characters of the two parents will appear in various combinations in the plants of the second and later generations. Plants having the desired combinations are self-pollinated for further propagation. Selection and self- or cross-pollination continues until a desirable type that breeds true is obtained.

In recent years this breeding procedure probably has been the most important consideration in most programs. One of the outstanding results of this method of breeding is the Marglobe tomato introduced in 1925 by Pritchard and Porte. The name of the variety was taken from that of the two varieties involved in crossing the Globe and Marvel. Globe has some resistance to fusarium wilt but is very susceptible to nailhead rust. Marvel is highly resistant to both. In later generations a good market type resistant to both diseases was selected. Its introduction was responsible for saving the Florida tomato industry from these two diseases.

The Pearson tomato was derived from a cross between Cal. 55 and an early-maturing variety named Fargo. Imperial F, Imperial 615, and other similarly named lettuce varieties are crosses between New York and Cos lettuce varieties. These are resistant to brown blight. Virginia Savoy spinach is a cross between an unnamed Manchurian variety and the Bloomsdale, Viroflay, and Long Standing varieties. Wisconsin Early Sweet is a variety of garden pea from a cross between the varieties Alaska and Surprise. Davis Perfect greenhouse cucumber resulted from a cross between White Spine and English Telegraph.

Backcrossing is a special way of hybridizing with selection in which selected individuals in several generations are backcrossed to one of the parent lines. This method is very effective and is often used when it is desired to incorporate one or a few desirable characters of one parent into the medium of another parent. By means of backcrossing from the very small fruited but fusarium-immune Red Currant tomato species to the Marglobe variety it was possible to transfer the disease resistance but none of the many other objectionable features of Red Currant to a large fruited horticultural variety, the final product being called Pan America. Backcrossing also was employed in some of the steps in the breeding of powdery mildew-resistant cantaloupes. (Fig. 16).

Recently in breeding programs, especially in the search for disease resistance, wild relatives of the vegetable crops are being used to a greater extent. Special techniques—beyond the scope of this text—often are required to breed

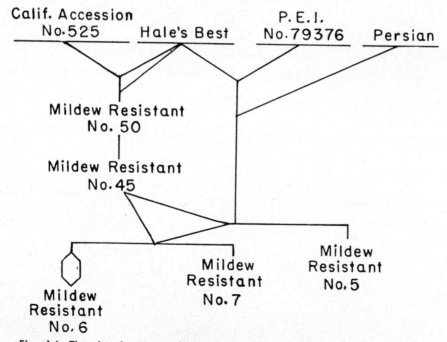

Fig. 16. The development of powdery mildew resistant cantaloupes. Controlled pollination followed by selection was used in each of the above steps in breeding.

two different species and to transfer successfully the desired characters from one to the other. In some instances the initial cross is so difficult to make or the sterility of the hybrid so great that progress, if any, is very slow; in other cases such as the one already mentioned, the cross between Red Currant and the garden tomato, characters have been transferred successfully. Other tomato species that are being used and their desired traits are as follows: *Lycopersicon peruvianum:* resistance to nematodes, spotted wilt and other diseases; *L. hirsutum:* resistance to tobacco mosaic. *Allium fistulosom* is a wild relative of the onion that is resistant to pink root, smudge, and smut, and often has been indicated as a possible source of resistance for breeding work.

Mass Production of F_1 Hybrids. As early as 1765 Kolreuter demonstrated that the first generation hybrid between two rather unrelated plants was more vigorous than either parent. This so-called *hybrid vigor* was found by East and Shull (1908–1910) in hybrids between inbred lines of corn. Such hybrids often yield more and are more uniform than either their inbred parents or the closest related varieties. In certain instances disease resistance of one line can be combined in a first generation hybrid with desirable traits of another line. Parents must be selected carefully because many hybrids have undesirable features.

The work of East and Shull stimulated work on the production of F_1 hybrid varieties of field corn—later sweet corn. At the present time hybrid varieties of corn have become so popular that more of them are grown than the old open-pollinated varieties.

Hybrid seed may be produced in quantity, and its production depends upon controlled pollination of both parents. This is simple in the case of sweet corn since the tassels may be removed from one parent and only seed saved from the detasseled plants. The method of producing corn hybrids is not applicable generally because determinate monoecious flowers are uncommon. In the case of onions it is economically possible, owing to a male-sterile variety and the use of insects, to perform the pollination; this avoids the need of emasculation or removal of stamens by hand.

The introduction of Golden Cross Bantam sweet corn in 1927 by Glen Smith[2] was one of the first successful hybrids. This corn has been very popular and in recent years additional varieties of hybrid sweet corn have appeared. Golden Cross Bantam is a hybrid produced by crossing two inbred lines of Golden Bantam known as Purdue Bantam 39 and Purdue 51 (Fig. 17). Jones and Emsweller discovered a male-sterile onion (Italian Red 13–53). This male-sterility has been incorporated into all important commercial varieties in such a manner that it can be utilized in the production of hybrid onion seed. Hybrid onions may express their superiority over standard types in a variety of ways such as increased yield, uniformity of bulb shape and maturity, color and storage characteristics. Seeds of a number of

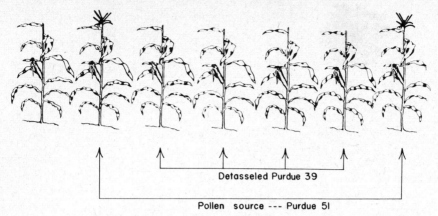

Detasseled Purdue 39

Pollen source --- Purdue 51

Fig. 17. Method of producing hybrid seed corn. The ears on the four rows of detasseled Purdue 39 are Golden Cross Bantam seed, to be planted for market production the next year.

hybrids are available from commercial seed producers. Scientists have found male-sterile plants in beets, carrots, tomatoes, peppers and squashes, but it is still essential to have some economical and convenient method of pollination.

Seed produced on a hybrid plant tends to give variable progeny. Thus it is not desirable to save seed from such plants, but essential that new F_1 seed be obtained each year for planting the commercial crop.

TESTING NEW VARIETIES

Another problem of the plant breeder is determining when a new strain or variety has enough desirable characteristics to justify introduction. Since many varieties have been introduced in the past that exhibit few worthwhile characteristics, most plant breeders are very careful about announcing a new variety without first giving it a critical test. Over a period of years the growers make the final decision as to the value of any new introduction.

The first observations and trials usually are made on the plant breeder's experimental area. This may be followed by a series of field trials to learn the variety's adaptability to various climates and soils. A grower may not wish to have replicated plots, but at least he should compare the new and old varieties side by side.

Research workers plan and conduct replicated plots in various areas so the variability in yield can be determined. This method of testing involves a mathematical procedure for determining whether differences in field yields indicate real differences in yielding ability of the varieties or differences in soil, moisture, or other factors.

Since yield per acre and crop quality are so important in determining a grower's income, he must be always on the alert to use new and better varieties. Although much of the testing can be performed by the plant breeder, the grower needs to make some trials on his own ranch.

REFERENCES

1. Davis, G. N.: A newcomer named "Red" is first hybrid onion. *Southern Seedsmen 7:*13, 52 (No. 4), 1944.
2. Smith, G. M.: Golden Cross Bantam sweet corn. *U.S.D.A. Cir. 268:*12 p., 1933.
3. Thompson, R. C.: Lettuce varieties and culture. *U.S.D.A. Farmers' Bul. 1953:* 42 p., 1951.
4. Work, Paul: Better seed for commercial vegetable growers. *Cornell Univ. Agr. Ext. Bul. 122:* 22 p., 1925.

Chapter 7

Quality and Characteristics of Seed

Most vegetable crops are propagated by the planting of seed. A seed has been defined as "a plant packed for transportation." The success of the crop is dependent largely upon the genetic characters possessed by the seed, and upon the environment under which it is grown. Therefore, the seed is really the foundation for the success of the future crop. In asexually propagated crops such as garlic and white and sweet potatoes, true seed is not used commonly for propagation.

In many crops the cost of the seed is only a small percentage of the total cost of raising the crop. The data given in Table 8 indicate that with carrots, cabbage, cantaloupe, and tomatoes, the seed cost is 1 per cent or less of the total cost. On the other hand, cauliflower is 2 per cent; sweet potatoes 14 per cent; and white potatoes 20 per cent. It is evident that the cost of seed in these latter crops is higher and so care must be exercised to prevent unnecessary cost. In tomatoes and similar crops the seed needs to be only a little better to justify a higher cost. Good seed is essential because it frequently produces higher yields per acre, produces fewer off-type plants which must be discarded during grading, and produces a higher-quality crop which may bring a higher price. Five strains of Early Santa Clara tomatoes were compared for yield at Davis in 1946. The smallest yield was 14.1 tons per acre, and the greatest was 20.5 tons per acre, with an average yield of 16.6 tons. The grower could afford to pay considerably more for the higher-yielding seed.

CHARACTERISTICS OF GOOD SEED

The important characteristics of good vegetable seed[4] may be summarized as follows: The seed should be true to name, be viable, free from seed-borne pests, free from weed seed, foreign matter, or mixtures, and be fairly priced from the standpoint of both seller and buyer.

True to Name. The purchaser wishes the seed to be exactly what he has ordered. Some vegetable seeds may be identified easily, but cabbage and cauliflower seeds are difficult to distinguish. A grower ordering cauliflower would not want cabbage seed. If he ordered early cauliflower he would not want a late strain substituted. If a tomato variety was ordered because it

Table 8

GENERAL SEED INFORMATION FOR DIFFERENT MARKET CROPS

| | Seed Per Cent Cost of Crop* | Germination Percentage | | Seeds Per Ounce‡ (approx.) | Pounds to Plant an Acre | Planting Depth, Inches | Testing Temperature, Deg. F.§ | Average Yield of Seed Per Acre Pounds‖ |
		Federal Minimum†	Merchantable					
Asparagus	..	70	..	709	80–100	1	68–86	200
Bean, lima	..	70	85	57	30–60	1–2	68–86	1,102
Bean, snap	..	75	85	113	8–15	1–2	68–86	943
Beet	0.8	65	80	1,644	¼, 2*	1	68–86	717
Cabbage	0.2	75	85	8,930	1, 4††	½	68–86	491
Cantaloupe	0.6	75	85	1,276	3¼	1	68–86	228
Carrot	1.8	55	75	23,417	¼, 2**	½	68–86	411
Cauliflower	0.4	75	90	8,930	1/16, 1**	½	68–86	421
Celery	..	55	75	71,470		⅛	68–86	555
Corn, sweet	..	75	90		15	1	68–86	1,513
Cucumber	1.6	80	85	1,077	1, 4††	1	68	256
Lettuce	2.6	80	85	25,175	1–1½	½	68	237
Onion	8.9	70	85	9,667	2, 4**	½	68	349
Pea	..	80	85	85	90–150	½	68–86	996
Pepper	14.3	55	75	4,734	⅛, 2**	½		45
Potato, sweet	20.2	..	..			4		
Potato, white	1.3	..	..		400	4	50	636
Spinach	..	60	80	2,835	8–15	1	68–86	330
Squash, summer	..	75	85	397	3–4	1–2	68–86	174
Squash, winter	0.2	75	85	397	3–4	1–2	68–86	41
Tomato	1.6	75	85	11,482	1/16, ½**	1	68–86	200
Watermelon	..	70	85	312	4	1	68–86	

* Calculations made from Adams R. L. and A. D. Reed: Farm Management Crop Manual, 185 p., Univ. Calif. Press, 1949.

† U.S.D.A. Ser. and Reg. Announcements No. 156, 1946.

‡ Assoc. Off. Seed Analysts, Proc. 1943–1944, p. 22–23, 1944.   § U.S.D.A. Cir. 480, 24 p., 1938.

‖ Acreage and production of vegetable seed 1944–1950. U.S.D.A. Bur. of Agr. Econ. 1951 and other sources (asparagus and watermelon).   ‖ Pole beans, 30 pounds; bush 60 pounds.   ** Less seed for seedbed than for direct field planting.

†† Less seed for hill planting, larger amount when drilled in the row.

was resistant to fusarium wilt, the seedsman should be sure his seed has this characteristic.

Probably one of the most unfortunate things about the seed trade is the necessity for the seedsman's so-called "nonwarranty clause." It is worded in various ways but the following is a typical example: "We give no warranty, express or implied, as to description, quality, productiveness or any other matter of any seeds, bulbs, plants or trees we send out, and will not be in any way responsible for the crop." Some seedsmen limit their liability to the cost of the seed. This clause is to prevent a seedsman from being liable for a poor crop. Thus, a grower might spend a few dollars per acre for lettuce seed and in case of a poor crop try to obtain payment from the seedsman for the marketable lettuce worth several hundred dollars. The blame for this clause falls on both the seedsmen and the growers; the relatively low cost of the seed when compared to the total cost of production is a contributing factor.

Viable. Seed must be viable in order to germinate and to produce a crop. Percentage of germination is determined usually under the conditions outlined by the United States Department of Agriculture[2]. To make an accurate test requires proper equipment and training. Germination temperatures vary for different vegetable seed and with some species there should be an alternating temperature such as 6 hours at 86° F. and 18 hours at 68° F. Some growers make preliminary tests in a greenhouse or warm room. Paper towels or other absorbent paper, cloth, or soil is used as a medium to keep the seed wet. The percentage germination obtained in the laboratory usually is higher than will be found under desirable field conditions. The minimum difference which may be expected is about 5 to 8 per cent, 10 to 15 per cent reductions are not unusual, and sometimes larger reductions are obtained. Seeds also differ as to their speed of germination in the soil. Radish germinates rapidly while parsnips are very slow and consequently radish is sometimes used to mark rows of slow germinating seed. The following classification of crops will be helpful in judging the period of time between seeding and plant appearance above the ground under favorable conditions—radish 4 to 7 days; cabbage, cauliflower, cucumber, lettuce, snap bean, sweet corn, turnip 6 to 10 days; eggplant, onion, peas, pepper, tomato 8 to 14 days; and carrot, celery, parsnip 12 to 20 days.

Viability of seeds is affected by the climatic conditions under which they are planted, their age, and storage conditions. Essentials for germination are water, oxygen, and the proper temperature; and in a few vegetables other factors may contribute, such as light treatment for newly harvested lettuce seed. Cool season crops germinate better at cool temperatures, and warm season crops at warm temperatures. Longevity of seeds refers to the number of years the seed will maintain a merchantable or commercial germination. Under ordinary storage conditions, seeds are classified as to the number of years they will retain good germination as follows:

1 year—Sweet corn, onion, parsley, parsnip.

2 years—Beet, onion, pepper.

3 years—Asparagus, bean, carrot, celery, lettuce, pea, spinach, tomato.

4 years—Cabbage, cauliflower, eggplant, okra, pumpkin, radish, squash.

5 years—Cucumber, endive, muskmelon, watermelon.

Under excellent storage conditions even seeds of poor longevity may retain good germinating power for three to five years. Seeds seem to keep well in cool northern climates, and in the dry Southwest; but poorly in the humid South and Southeast. Since a seed is a living organism, any condition which will increase life activity affects its germination and period of good germination. Either increased temperature or moisture content will speed up the seed's life activity with detrimental effects. Seeds should be kept at low temperatures, low seed moisture content, and low humidity. As the storage temperature increases the humidity should go down. Toole[8] gives the following recommendations for storing seed:

(1) For seeds exposed to a temperature of 80° F. for more than a few days the relative humidity for air should be no higher than 45 per cent.

(2) For seeds exposed to 70° F., the relative humidity of air should be no higher than 60 per cent.

(3) Very short-lived seeds (such as onion), old seed, or seed contaminated by fungi should be kept at a lower humidity than is recommended above.

(4) For seeds in cold storage at 40° to 50° F., the relative humidity of air should be no higher than 70 per cent, and preferably should not be above 50 per cent.

(5) Seeds removed from cold storage at a humidity above 50 per cent should be dried to a moisture content safe for the temperature of later exposure, unless they are to be planted within a few days.

The Federal Government has established minimum germination for certain vegetable seed, as given in Table 8. Seed moving in interstate commerce which is below these percentages for the crop must be labeled accurately as to percentage germination, and be designated as "Below Standard." Some states have a similar law which applies to seed raised and sold within the state. These laws give some protection to the grower as to seed germination.

Free from Seed-Borne Pests. The seed should be free from seed-borne diseases, such as bacterial canker (tomatoes); blackleg (crucifers); and smut (onions). In recent years several new compounds have been introduced for seed treatment. Experimental results have shown they are valuable for several species of seed. Such procedures are effective against certain seed-borne organisms as well as many soil-borne organisms that cause seed decay or infection of young seedlings. Specific recommendations regarding seed treatments are given under the discussion of each crop. While there is no advantage in treating seeds if these two types of organisms are not present, the cost is usually very small per acre. The cost of the material for treating small seed is 3 to 5 cents per acre. However, the cost is somewhat higher for large seed like pea and lima bean where large amounts of seed are planted per acre. Sometimes weevils may infest peas and beans and thereby affect their value as seed. These pests may be controlled by fumigation.

Free from Weed Seeds, Foreign Matter, and Mixtures. Mixtures of different vegetables or varieties are a detrimental factor in vegetable production, as is also the presence of weed seed or foreign matter.

Seed Fairly Priced. Seed should be priced fairly for both the seller and buyer. The first part of this chapter pointed out the importance of good seed; therefore, the seed producer should receive sufficient return to permit growing the best possible seed. Too frequently the price of seed is determined by how cheaply someone else can produce it without any safeguards. A thorough breeding program and strict field selection increases the cost of the seed produced. Much improvement can come from better seed, but the grower should both encourage the production of good seed and be willing to pay a higher price for it.

COATED OR PELLETED SEED

Some vegetable seed are coated with inert material to make a pellet which contains one seed. These coated seed can be planted individually so there is greater accuracy in distributing the seed in the row. For instance, celery seed which is very small can be coated and each seed is enclosed in a pellet which is $11/_{64}$ inch in diameter. This process is used on a very small proportion of vegetable seed and of course, is unnecessary for pea seed which is large enough to be planted accurately. Coating will be found desirable for some seeds and some farming procedures. Species of plant and farming ability will affect the economical use of coated seed.

The seeds are coated by the following procedure; the seeds are rotated in a mixer similar to a cement mixer so the individual seeds are separated. In one process the seeds are sprayed with water and then the inert material is added as a powder which sticks to the seed. This process is repeated until the seed is coated to the desired size. All of the added inert material does not stick to the seed so there needs to be repeated screening to remove the excess material. Several final screenings are necessary to ensure the desired size of coated seed. After drying, the seeds are ready to be shipped to the grower. Since seed of different species vary in size, the increase in weight from coating varies. The following data indicate the pounds of coated seed which may be obtained from one pound of vegetable seed.

Pellet size $9/_{64}$—increase one to eight, broccoli, cabbage, cauliflower, and radish; one to 10, onion; and one to 18, tomato.

Pellet size $11/_{64}$—increase one to 20, carrot; one to 50, lettuce; one to 75, celery.

The size of the pellet varies with the kind of vegetable. A pellet must be as great in diameter as the maximum length of the seed. In the case of eggplant, parsnip, pepper, and spinach the pellets are $^{13}/_{64}$ of an inch in diameter.

Planters have been developed for accurate planting of coated seed. Since coated seed costs more than uncoated seed the grower must receive some financial benefit from its use. This practise permits the use of less seed per acre, reduces thinning costs since there are few doubles which require finger thinning, and in the case of tomatoes direct seeding may reduce mosaic infection which occurs during transplanting. Some growers believe that a soil moisture near field capacity is essential for moistening the coat and insuring good germination. In some cases, coated seed has been slightly slower to germinate but this is not a critical consideration. While coated seed has permitted more accurate sowing of seed, it has also called our attention to the need for more accurate seeding. Our present equipment and new equipment can be used for more accurate seeding.

ENSURING A GOOD SEED SUPPLY

Every grower desires a supply of good seed, so some of the following safeguards will be of interest. Buy from a seedsman who through a period of years has sold good seed either to you or to other progressive vegetable producers. Never buy cheap seed without a thorough investigation; sometimes it is possible for a grower to visit the seed fields to determine which of the variety types are the most acceptable to him. Buy your seed as direct as possible—that is from a wholesaler who produces his own seed or from a retailer who is particular about the seed he purchases for resale. With a few crops of high value per acre, and seed of good longevity, a trial planting of the seed may be made a year previous to raising the crop—thus, celery seed may be purchased in 1951 for the 1953 crop, but tried out for type and other characteristics in 1952 on a small area. The use of certified seed, unless the standards of certification are known to be high, does not provide sufficient protection. There is a growing tendency for seed to be distributed in sealed packages packed by the seed producer. This practise gives the grower an assurance of the true source of his seed.

The above are some of the precautions a good producer may use but they do not take the place of grower experience in knowing where to purchase the best seed. A period of seed shortage in a vegetable is a time for utmost caution in buying.

SOME PROBLEMS OF SEED PRODUCTION

Since seed is such an important consideration in producing a crop, credit for many improvements in yield and better types of vegetables must be given to progressive seedsmen. Their business is specialized and they are not able always to offer as good seed as they would wish because of unfavorable climatic factors and other uncontrollable factors. A clear understanding of the seedsmen's problems will aid greatly the vegetable industry to make progress.

The three important types of seed are field (agronomic), vegetable, and flower seeds. Most agronomic seed has a value as livestock feed or some other useful product which has no relation to seed germination. Thus, seed low in viability may be sold as feed, and seed stocks of high germination may be planted. On the other hand, most vegetable seed of low germination must be discarded as a loss, if it cannot be used for planting.

Seed usually is grown by farmers on contract with a seed company. The company furnishes the seed grower with a special selected lot of seed, frequently designated as "stock" seed. The commercial seed to be sold to the grower is produced from such stock seed. In the case of some biennial crops, such as carrots, the seed companies grow the roots and then supply these to the farmer for seed production. The seed is threshed or freed from extraneous material on the farm and hauled to the seedsman's warehouse for cleaning. The grower is paid on the basis of the clean seed of merchantable germination. Seed companies produce the seed of items where only a small amount of seed is needed. However, some retail companies produce little seed and consequently buy it from wholesalers. Small packets of seed are put up for sale in seed, grocery, or other stores. The amount of seed per packet varies, and the quality is sometimes lower than for the commercial seed. The home and farm gardener frequently can save money by purchasing seed in ounce lots for use over a two- or three-year period.

Seedsmen vary as to methods used to ensure good-quality seed. Important features of a good seed source are trial grounds and a breeding program for the maintenance of the quality of standard varieties as well as developing new and better varieties. A seedsman's catalogue usually gives some indication as to whether his production methods meet these requirements. On trial grounds are grown seed of different varieties and strains. These can be observed for type and freedom from mixtures, although vegetables may vary slightly in different climates. Breeding programs represent crosses and selections made to produce new varieties or strains. In some companies, there is a constant effort to improve varieties, under the direction of men trained in plant breeding and methods of production, and who know the needs of the vegetable industry.

Both vegetable producers and seedsmen have problems. Table 9 indicates that the federal minimum germination varies for different crops. Carrots, celery, onions, and peppers have low percentage germination because of climatic and genetic characteristics, and not because seedsmen are less efficient in producing these crops. A seedsman spends much thought and

Fig. 18. A trial ground of a seed company, with a detailed examination of beet varieties. Note the uniformity in shape of the two varieties. (Courtesy, Ferry-Morse Seed Company.)

effort guarding against mixtures, or ensuring trueness to name. Both stock and field plantings are rogued to remove off-type or undesirable plants. Mixtures may come from foreign pollen, so different crops and varieties are

Table 9*

RELATIONSHIP BETWEEN PRICE AND FIELD PERFORMANCE OF 344 STOCKS OF RETAIL PACKETS OF CABBAGE AND RADISH SEED IN 1949

Field Rating of Crop	Average Price of Seed Per Ounce	Range in Price Per Ounce from Cheapest to Highest Priced Seeds		Average Price of Seed Per Ounce	Range in Price Per Ounce from Cheapest to Highest Priced Seeds	
	Cabbage			Radish		
Excellent	$1.26	$0.59	$1.96	$0.50	$0.39	$0.70
Good	1.18	.32	2.49	.39	.14	.75
Satisfactory	1.23	.42	2.18	.34	.14	.59
Poor	.75	.50	2.52	.45	.22	.57
Misnamed	.75	.34	1.06	.31	.22	.39

* Courtesy, *N. Y. Agr. Exp. Sta. (Geneva) Bul. 739,* 1950.

isolated to prevent contamination. Tall plants may be grown around the field as a wind barrier, such as sunflowers or corn. Isolation distance depends on kind of crop, direction of prevailing winds, the location of bee colonies or hives, the prevalence of insects, the presence of woods or other high-growing vegetation, as well as the amount and duration of fogs and cold windy weather. A few examples of isolation will be given. Cabbage seed fields should be isolated a mile from red cabbage, cauliflower, Brussels sprouts, etc. Two cabbage varieties should be isolated by one-fourth of a mile. Cross-pollination may occur at both distances of separation, but crossing results are more evident between red and white cabbage than two white types. This isolation distance is fairly typical for cross-pollinated crops. Tomato, eggplant, and pepper varieties, mostly self-pollinated crops, should be separated by 150 feet, and surrounded by a tall, dense barrier. Self-pollinated crops like lettuce, pea, and bean varieties may be grown 6 to 12 feet apart if separated by a barrier. A seedsman may make arrangements to grow a certain seed crop on a ranch not knowing that a neighbor may have a seed crop which will cause cross-pollination. Even a ranch of several hundred acres is too small to give good control of cross-pollination without the cooperation of neighboring farmers. There are many safeguards to prevent mixtures, but it hardly is possible to prevent them always. Many aspects of the seedsman's and vegetable producer's business are of mutual interest, so a clear understanding of each other's problems is helpful in producing a more efficient industry.

SEED PLANTING DEPTH

Since seeds vary in size there is also a variation in their planting depth. Large seeds are planted deeper than small seeds since they have a larger amount of stored material to use in pushing the plumule or leaf up to the surface of the ground. The seed needs to be in moist soil for good germination, and this also affects the depth of planting. On the other hand, too deep planting may be unfavorable because of low oxygen supply and lack of enough stored food for the seedling to use in reaching the surface. Seeds may be planted deeper in sandy, loose soils than in clayish soils. Different vegetables vary as to the method the plumule uses in coming through the soil. With most vegetables the stem appears first in a bowed shape and later the leaves are pulled out of the soil and the plant becomes straight. Sweet corn and asparagus plumules come straight up through the soil. The general rule for depth of planting is to plant at a depth of four times the average diameter of the seed.

FACTORS AFFECTING AMOUNT OF SEED REQUIRED
TO PLANT ONE ACRE

The seed requirements per acre of different vegetables vary greatly. White potatoes require 800 to 2000 pounds of seed per acre, and cabbage and cauliflower 4 oz., where the plants are raised in a seedbed and transplanted to the field. The amount of seed used per acre is related to the number of seed per ounce as given in Table 8. Celery has about 70,000 seeds per ounce although the weight of seed required per acre is about the same as with tomato, 11,000 seeds per ounce. This difference can be explained partially by the difference in germination and the customary waste of plants by the transplanting method.

To determine an accurate seeding rate, one must consider number of seeds per ounce, percentage of germination, and environmental conditions. A carrot grower in Monterey was interested in factors causing small carrots which reduced his yields per acre. With average seed, there are three-quarters of a million carrot plants per acre, and the planting rate is about three and one-fourth pounds. If carrot seed (a) is used which has 80 per cent germination, and 30,000 seeds per ounce, the amount of seed needed per acre is less than with seed (b) showing 62 per cent germination and 16,000 seeds per ounce. The calculations are as follows:

a. $30,000 \times 80$ per cent $= 24,000$ viable seeds per ounce

$$\frac{750,000}{24,000} = 32 \text{ ounces, or 2 pounds per acre}$$

b. $16,000 \times 62$ per cent $= 9920$ viable seeds per ounce

$$\frac{750,000}{9,920} = 75 \text{ ounces, or } 4\frac{3}{4} \text{ pounds per acre}$$

Both germination and number of seed per ounce vary between seed samples of the same crop. The seedsman usually gives the percentage of germination on the label, and this can be used to determine the correct number of viable seeds to plant per foot of row. With lettuce seed, the grower plants 24 seed per foot of row with seed germinating 90 per cent, and he would plant 36 seed per foot of row in the case of 60 per cent germination. In both cases, the grower is planting 22 viable seed per foot of row. Pounds of seed per acre is affected also by whether the crop is thinned to perfect stand or the plants are grown in a plant bed and transplanted to the field. More seed is needed with the direct seeding of lettuce, cabbage, cauliflower, and tomatoes than when they are transplanted. When cabbage is started in a seedbed for field setting, growers plant 4 oz. of seed for each acre to be transplanted. When the crop is direct-seeded in the field, 2 pounds of seed are used per acre and the plants are thinned to obtain the desired stand.

FACTORS AFFECTING SPACING OF PLANTS

Plants should be spaced to obtain maximum yield and quality. The basic consideration is area per plant. Small plants like radishes are spaced so there is about two-tenths square foot per plant; medium-sized plants like white potatoes, two and one-half square feet; large canning tomatoes, about 16 to 24 square feet; and watermelons 54 to 81 square feet. Area per plant may be affected by variety or method of culture. Pearson canning tomatoes are spaced 12 to 24 square feet per plant, while the Early Santa Clara is given 36 square feet. Stake tomatoes are planted 9 to 15 inches apart in the row, thus using 2.7 to 5 square feet per plant.

Distance between rows usually is selected for convenience in farm operations or because farm machinery is adjusted for use on rows spaced a standard distance. Close spacing in the row may be used for cabbage if a small head is desired for market. Lettuce tends to produce a large head in summer and a small head in winter. Growers attempt to regulate size of head by thinning summer lettuce to 12 inches apart and winter lettuce to 14 inches apart. In land where nutrients (fertilizers) or water are likely to be a limiting factor in growth, the plants will be spaced with large area per plant.

Calculation of number of plants per acre may be made by dividing the square feet per acre (43,560) by the square feet per plant. Thus tomatoes spaced 6 to 4 feet would have 1815 plants per acre, while those spaced 3½ by 4 would require 3111 plants per acre.

REFERENCES

1. Leach, L. D. and B. R. Houston: Seed treatments for field and vegetable crops. *Calif. Agr. Exper. Sta. Lithoprint,* 6 p., 1944.
2. Rules and recommendations for testing seeds. *U.S.D.A. Cir. 480:* 24 p., 1938.
3. Toole, E. H.: Storage of vegetable seeds. *U.S.D.A. Leaflet 220:* 8 p., 1942.
4. Work, Paul: Better seed for commercial vegetable growers. *Cornell Agr. Ext. Bul. 122:* 22 p., 1925.

Chapter 8

Plant Growing

In most vegetable areas, it is customary to produce plants of some crops for transplanting to the field. Such plants are produced in artificially heated structures or naturally warmer areas. This procedure is more essential in areas of severe winter and short growing season than in certain sections of the Southwest which have mild winters. The advantages and disadvantages of the transplanting method versus direct seeding in the field vary as to climatic area and the skill used by the grower in either case. Likewise, these considerations vary somewhat for different crops. Some items which should be considered in these two practises are given below for areas where there may be a choice as to the procedure followed.

	Transplanting	*Field seeding*
Cost of seed	Low	High
Transplanting cost	High	None
Thinning cost	None	High
Set-back from transplanting ..	Some	None which permits later seeding
Germination conditions	Usually good	Variable to poor
Adaptability to different species	A few crops	Almost all crops
Disease	May increase contact diseases such as mosaic	———

If the grower decides to produce plants for transplanting to the field, there are the considerations of plant-growing structures as well as plant-growing methods. These will be considered in following paragraphs.

PLANT-GROWING STRUCTURES

Plant-growing structures are varied, both as to cost and possible control over temperature in adverse weather. These might be listed in the following order with the most expensive structures given first: (a) Greenhouses; (b) hotbeds; (c) coldframes and plant protectors such as hotcaps, brush and paper; and (d) special outdoor areas which give the plants some protection or make them easier to care for. Both of the first two structures have artificial heat. The greenhouse has sufficient head space so men may work inside. Hotbeds are wooden frames covered with glass sash or other material which conserves heat and admits light. In addition, it provides artificial heat. The general construction will be considered later. A coldframe is similar to a hotbed but lacks artificial heat. Hotcaps are made of transparent paper, and are set over the individual plants or hills, and receive heat only from the sun. Brush and paper sometimes are stretched on the north side of the row to give some protection; this method is used in Imperial Valley for cantaloupes and other crops. The use of brush protection is shown in Fig. 19. Seed sometimes is planted in protected areas to obtain better germination or for the convenience of caring for the plants as to irrigation, fertilization, or pest control. These protected areas may be located close to the field to be planted or they may be distant, as in the East, where tomato plants are grown in Georgia for the Indiana and Maryland canning crops. The Moapa Valley in southern Nevada is used for this same purpose. These are cases of going to a much warmer climate to grow plants with the additional cost of transporting for several hundred miles.

A period of 8 to 12 weeks usually is required to produce plants large enough for transplanting to the field. Length of this period is affected by climatic conditions.

Fig. 19. Imperial Valley cantaloupes planted under hotcaps with brush and paper for further protection.

Construction of a Hotbed. These structures are used to produce plants for field setting where a crop is planted in weather that requires artificial heat to obtain germination and early growth. The beds are located (a) close to a building or a windbreak to give protection against cold winds, (b) near a supply of water, (c) at a convenient place from the standpoint of the other farm work, and (d) the beds usually are extended east and west and slope toward the south, to obtain maximum heat from the sun. The frame may be made of wood, cement, or other materials. Wood is a common material, and 1-inch boards are used. The south side of the bed should be 4 to 6 inches lower than the north side. Thus, boards 12 inches in width may be used for the south side and a 16-inch board for the north side. The sides are held in place by posts made of 2 by 4 inch lumber, and the ends are enclosed with boards. Glass sash, 3 by 6 feet commonly are used. They are similar to window sash with 3 or 4 vertical rows of glass. The glass is in short panes, which overlap. The rain will flow toward the low side and fall on the ground. This hotbed is of the single-sash type. The double-sash type may be used on a bed of double width, or 12 feet. In this case, the two sashes slope in opposite directions like the two sides of a roof. Such a bed usually extends north and south.

There are several sources of heat for hotbeds among which are electricity, hot water, steam, hot air, or fermenting organic matter such as animal manure. Special lead-covered electric cables may be used and should be placed within 2 inches of the soil surface to ensure rapid germination. Steam or hot water usually is passed through pipes in the soil. Steam may be discharged into a tile line under the soil and in this case, also may be used for steam sterilization of the soil, if the boiler has sufficient capacity. A manure hotbed requires considerably more care in preparation. Manure from grain-fed horses is preferred, and fermentation should be started before placing it into the bed. Hot water sometimes is applied to aid in starting the process of heating. The manure heats when in a pile, and should be turned once so the cold outer part is placed in the middle of the pile for uniform heating. A week to 10 days may be required for preparation of the manure. The depth of manure used depends on the temperature needed in the hotbed. Thus, 12 inches may be sufficient in a mild climate whereas 24 inches will be required in a cold climate. The manure may be placed on the surface of the ground or in the bottom of a pit according to what type of bed is to be prepared. From 4 to 6 inches of manure should be put in place and then well tamped. This process is continued until the requisite amount has been used. Tamping is essential to obtain uniform heating. The manure generates heat slowly, rises to a peak, and then subsides. This peak usually is sufficient to kill seedlings, and seed should not be planted until the peak has been passed, as shown by a thermometer placed in the bed. Heat from a manure bed gradually decreases as spring approaches, so the only procedure for maintaining the heat is by its conservation. Beds may be covered with grass mats, straw, or strawy manure to keep the beds from losing too much heat at night.

Glass sashes frequently are used in hotbeds. In mild climates, cloth coverings of muslin or light canvas may be used, particularly for coldframes. There are methods of treating muslin to preserve it, but with good care it will last 2 or 3 years. Transparent cellulose films over a screen wire base are available for covers. These are cheaper than glass and allow more light through than muslin; but this type of material lasts only a few years. Single pieces of muslin frequently are sewed together to cover a bed 10 to 12 feet wide and 80 to 100 feet long. Construction of a hotbed is shown in Fig. 20.

Care of Hotbed or Coldframe

Starting plants in a hotbed is an intensive culture; thus conditions for plant growth usually are made as nearly ideal as possible. The plants are grown in 4 to 6 inches of soil—rich loam or sandy loam—free from plant pests. Composted soils frequently are used. Loam and sod and/or manure are composted together. Two or three parts of this soil plus one part rotted manure and one part clean sand may be mixed together and used for the hotbed soil. Fertilizer sometimes is used to increase growth, but nitrogenous fertilizers particularly should be avoided near the time of transplanting. Nitrogen tends to increase succulent growth and thus, may make plants difficult to harden.

The seed is planted at the usual depth—with rows about 4 to 6 inches apart—and thinned if necessary. The soil needs to be kept moist by careful watering. There is usually a tendency to overwater, but the most common limiting factor in growth is low temperature, particularly in a coldframe which has no artificial source of heat. The plants should be watered during the middle of the day so they will dry before night, as a precaution against the spread of disease.

Ideal temperatures for warm season crops are 70° to 75° F. during the day and slightly lower (55° to 60°) at night. Cool season crops should be 60° to 65° F. during the day, and also lower (50° to 55°) at night. The plants need to have ventilation, and this usually is taken care of during the warmer part of the day. The sash may be lifted and a block placed under it; or, later in the spring, removed entirely.

EFFECT OF TRANSPLANTING ON GROWTH

Transplanting has a retarding effect on growth, though this rarely is observed in a field where all of the plants are transplanted. This retardation is one reason why direct-seeded tomatoes may be planted later in the field than in the hotbed and produce as high yields. The retarding effect of transplant-

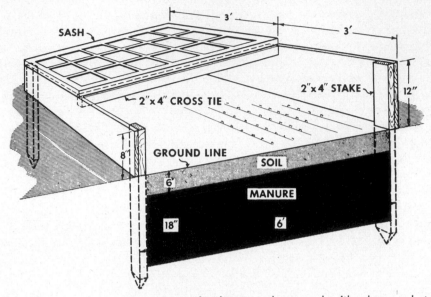

Fig. 20. A hotbed using manure for heat, and covered with glass sash to permit the entrance of light.

Fig. 21. Watering a tomato plant cold frame just before the seed germinates; this type of frame uses muslin for a cover.

ing may be observed if one plant is transplanted and another left undisturbed. Loomis[10] has made a study of the effect of transplanting on different vegetable crops. The following two groups separate plants as to their ease of transplanting.

A. Commonly and successfully transplanted: Cabbage, cauliflower, celery, onions, peppers, and tomatoes.

B. Difficult to transplant: Sweet corn, beans, cucumbers, melons, squash, and pumpkins.

In general the retardation of growth is dependent upon the species of plant, age, and the conditions of transplanting. The difference due to species of plants is related to the rate of new root formation after transplanting. Plants in group B form new roots slowly, and there is a tendency for the roots to be suberized or cutinized which makes them less effective in absorbing water. Young seedling plants are transplanted with less retardation than older plants of same species. Germinating seedlings usually may be transplanted regardless of species of plant. Conditions of transplanting refer to

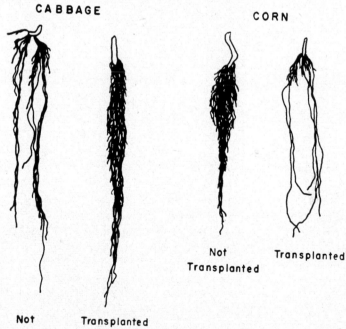

CABBAGE **CORN**

Not Transplanted Transplanted

Not Transplanted Transplanted

Fig. 22. Root replacement on eight week old cabbage (*left*) and two week old corn (*right*) plants. In each pair the plant on the left was not transplanted and the other was transplanted. Corn transplants poorly because of insufficient root replacement. (Courtesy, Cornell University.)

whether the plants have roots free of soil or have a ball of dirt around the roots. The above classification is more applicable for bare-rooted plants than for those that have soil on the roots or are grown in pots.

HARDENING OF PLANTS

Vegetable plants usually are prepared for transplanting to the field by reducing their rate of growth or *"hardening"* them. Such plants will withstand better the unfavorable conditions of transplanting, such as less intake of water, hot drying winds, and low temperatures. A hardened plant tends to be hard and stiff rather than succulent (Fig. 23, p. 86). The foliage is dark green and may exhibit purple pigment, as in tomatoes; or waxy purple, in the case of cabbage. Rapid growth results in a medium- to light-green foliage. These external changes, due to hardening, are accompanied by certain changes in chemical composition. Carbohydrates such as sugars, starches, and pentosans, tend to accumulate. The purple pigment in the leaves is an indication of high sugar content. High sugar content also results in a more rapid formation of new roots after transplanting. A warm season crop when hardened will withstand temperatures one or two degrees below 32° F., but cool season crops will withstand much lower temperatures—even 20° F. for cabbage. Part of the success in growing well-hardened stocky plants is to give them adequate space in which to grow. Cabbage needs about 4 square inches per plant, and tomatoes slightly more.

A hardened plant may be produced by subjecting it to cool weather or insufficient water, since both prevent rapid growth. Where the nights are cool, the sash may be left off during the day, and later, at night to reduce growth; but care should be used to prevent any frost injury. As the plants become large enough for field setting, the soil moisture should be reduced carefully so the plants may be finished under rather dry conditions, even with the exhibiting of slight wilting. There is evidence that hardening may cause decreased early yields, but with a possible increased season yield. This indicates that there is danger in hardening plants too much where an early crop is desired. With canning tomatoes, the early fruits are likely to be wasted, so this would not be a disadvantage.

FIELD SETTING

Plants are dug from the plant beds with as little injury as possible. Digging should be preceded by ample watering. After the plants are dug, they should be covered with moist sacks and kept in the shade so there will be little loss of water from the plants. Sometimes leaves or portions of leaves are removed from plants to reduce the area transpiring water at transplanting time. This is for the purpose of establishing a better balance between the intake of water by roots and its loss from leaves. Experimental evidence[9] has shown with some representative vegetables that pruning does not aid survival. Heavy pruning results in a reduction of early yields and also of total yield. Light pruning does not give beneficial effects. Usually, transplanting machines are used for field setting. This equipment opens a trench 4 to 6 inches deep; the plant is placed at the proper place, one quart of water is added by the machine, and the soil is pressed about the plant by wheels set at an angle. One of the most important operations in transplanting is pressing the soil firmly around the roots of the plant so there is good contact with the soil. Pressure should be exerted toward the plant, and downward, so the soil is pressed around the entire root system, to prevent air pockets near the roots. Watering settles the soil around the roots. Hot and windy weather greatly increases water loss from plants. If difficulty is experienced from wilting, the plants may be set in the afternoon and evening on a still day, with better success.

REFERENCES

1. Beattie, J. H.: Greenhouse construction and heating, *U.S.D.A. Farmers Bul. 1318,* 38 p., 1937.
2. Beattie, J. H.: Sash greenhouses, *U.S.D.A. Leaflet 124,* 8 p., 1946.
3. Binkley, A. M.: Starting vegetable plants. *Colo. Agr. Exper. Sta. Bull. 475,* 24 p., 1943.
4. Bouquet, A. G. B.: Construction and operation of the coldframe in vegetable growing, *Ore. Agr. Ext. Cir. 258,* 5 p., (Mimeo.) 1937.
5. Bouquet, A. G. B.: Growing early vegetable plants under glass, *Ore. Agr. Ext. Cir. 342,* 8 p., (Mimeo.) 1940.
6. Bouquet, A. G. B.: Growing greenhouse vegetables—cucumbers, *Ore. Agr. Ext. Cir. 433,* 3 p., (Mimeo.) 1944.
7. Clark, R. Ralph: Booster and starter solutions for vegetable transplants, *Ore. Agr. Ext. Ser. Bull. 703,* 4 p., 1950.
8. Schneider, G. W. and A. B. Fite: Hotbeds and coldframes, *N. M. Agr. Ext. Cir. 164,* 15 p., 1944.
9. Kraus, James E.: Effects of partial defoliation at transplanting time on subsequent growth and yield of lettuce, cauliflower, celery, peppers, and onions, *U.S.D.A. Tech. Bull. 829,* 35 p., 1942.
10. Loomis, W. E.: Studies in the transplanting of vegetable plants, *Cornell Univ. Agr. Exp. Sta. Mem. 87,* 63 p., 1925.
11. Menke, M. W.: Coldframes—hotbeds—flats in Nevada, *Nev. Agr. Ext. Ser. Bull. 93,* 14 p., 1944.

Chapter 9

Irrigation of Vegetables

In common with other succulent plants, vegetables are composed very largely of water. In addition, a considerable proportion of the plant's dry matter has been manufactured from water, since this compound is one of the raw materials of photosynthesis. One botanist, to indicate the importance of water in a plant's composition, defined a "plant as a supported column of water." Table 10 illustrates the predominance of water as compared with certain other substances contained in two representative vegetable plants—spinach (a foliage crop) and the tomato (a plant grown for its fruit). This table indicates that the vegetables' content of water is many times that of constituents so frequently purchased in commercial fertilizers, and indicates the importance of giving special attention to the ingredient which makes up so large a proportion of the plant, and which is so essential to its life processes.

In addition to being important in a plant's composition, water is a solvent for transferring essential nutrients and foods to various parts of the plant. Much of the water which is absorbed by the roots passes through the plant and is given off as vapor in the process called *transpiration*. This large amount of water lost by transpiration is not included in the representative figures given in Table 10. Transpiration rates are affected by various environmental factors. Rate of water loss increases progressively as temperatures and winds increase and as humidity decreases. In fact, individual large plants will use several gallons of water per day. On an acre basis, this amounts to many tons of water per season. Santa Clara canning tomatoes, for example, will use 2000 or more tons of water per acre to produce an average crop at Davis, California.

The amount of water used by a plant to produce a pound of dry matter is called the *water requirement*. The water requirements of different plants vary; there are also differences between the water requirement of the same kind of plant grown in different climatic areas. Many plants use 350 to 600 pounds of water to produce a pound of dry matter. Since these large amounts of water are supplied to the plant by the soil, it is convenient to consider the soil as a reservoir of water, which needs to be replenished periodically by rainfall or irrigation.

Table 10

AMOUNT OF WATER AND SOME OTHER CONSTITUENTS IN CROPS
OF SPINACH AND CANNING TOMATOES; POUNDS PER ACRE

Ingredient in Crop Portion of Plant	Spinach, Leaves	Tomato		
		Leaves and Stem	Fruit, Ripe and Green	Total
Total crop	10,000	50,000	26,000	76,000
Water	8,750	42,700	24,310	64,010
Dry matter	1,250	7,300	1,690	8,990
Nitrogen	70	138	49	187
Phosphoric acid	20	35	14	49
Potash	90	305	76	381

SOIL MOISTURE RESERVOIR

Most growers pay rather close attention to the growth and appearance of that portion of the plant which is aboveground. An important part of the plant is located in the soil and thus deserves serious consideration. The soil provides water, nutrients or fertilizers, anchorage, and should possess both a desirable soil reaction and oxygen content for favorable growth. Particularly in the case of irrigation does the grower need to examine the soil for moisture content by means of a soil tube or auger; if these are not available, a shovel may be used.

The soil holds water which can be used by plants (available water), and usually a smaller amount which is unavailable. The amount of water that a soil can hold is a soil characteristic and varies with the soil. In connection with plant growth, the range and amount of available water may be measured by two limits of soil moisture. After a rain or irrigation when the water has ceased moving downward, there occurs the upper limit in amount of available water termed *field capacity*. This moisture content is almost identical with "moisture equivalent," which is determined by a laboratory method. In this method the wet soil is centrifuged with a force equal to 1000 times gravity, and the soil moisture determined after treatment. The lower limit of available water is called the *permanent wilting percentage*. The *wilting coefficient* sometimes is given the same meaning but unfortunately this is not always true when the latter has been determined by a formula based on moisture equivalent measurements. The *permanent wilting percentage* or P.W.P. is determined by growing a plant, usually a sunflower, (Figure 23) in a moist soil and then determining the moisture content of the soil (P.W.P.) at the time of permanent wilting[6]. Soil type affects the amount of available water which a soil will hold. Table 11 gives data on the upper and lower limit of available water for several soil types. Thus, in

Fig. 23. (*Top*) Bare-rooted plants used for setting fields of "green wrap" or canning tomatoes. The two stocky plants are preferred and are due to better care, wider spacing, and more light.

(*Bottom*) A graded series of sunflower plants used to determine the permanent wilting percentage of a soil. Plant 102 at the right is turgid (4.1 per cent soil moisture), plant 105 is permanently wilted (3.6 per cent), and plant 97 has passed this stage (3.3 per cent).

general, sandy soils may store about three-quarters inch of available water per foot of depth; loams similarly will store about one and one-half inches; and clays about two and one-half inches. This has been illustrated in Fig. 24, where three inches of water were applied to a sandy loam, a loam, and a clay. Since the sandy loam holds less water per foot of depth, the water penetrates to a depth of six feet, while in the clay the water penetrates only one and two-tenths feet.

Table 11*

RELATION BETWEEN SOIL TYPE AND AVAILABLE WATER IN THE SOIL

Soil Type	Location	Moisture Equivalent or Field Capacity	Permanent Wilting Percentage	Inches Available Water Per Foot of Depth	Pore Space, Percent at M.E.†
Yuma sand	Arizona	4.79	3.17	0.26	42
Delano sandy loam	California	9.09	4.17	0.80	37
Yolo fine sandy loam	California	16.80	8.93	1.26	28
Wooster silt loam	Ohio	23.36	6.12	2.89	15
Salinas clay	California	34.50	16.80	2.83	4

* Courtesy, *Amer. Soc. Hort. Sci.* 40:483–92, 1942.
† M.E. is moisture equivalent

Another factor affecting the amount of moisture available to the plant is the depth of rooting. In Table 12 vegetable crops have been classified as shallow-rooted (2 feet deep), moderately deep-rooted (4 feet), and deep-rooted (6 feet). A crop which removes the water to a depth of 6 feet will be able to obtain several times as much water as a crop growing on the same soil, whose roots are primarily in the top 2 feet. Figure 25 illustrates the combined effects of moisture-holding capacity of soil type and the effect of depth of rooting on the water in the soil reservoir. Tomatoes, a deep-rooted crop, can obtain a greater amount of available water than sweet corn, a shallow-rooted crop. In both cases the sandy soil furnishes less available water than the clay. Both of these factors are important in affecting the size of the water reservoir for plants as well as frequency and amount of water needed per irrigation. A good irrigation implies filling the soil to field capacity throughout the root zone. Poor irrigation refers to incomplete filling of the soil as to depth, or leaving dry vertical areas due to poor lateral movement.

In all the above cases the soil has free drainage, but some soils have hardpan or an impervious layer of soil which may limit the root growth and free drainage. When hardpan is within a few feet of the surface, the volume of soil used for water storage is reduced and a water table may build up unless careful irrigation practices are used.

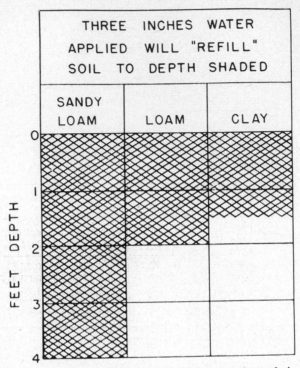

THREE INCHES WATER APPLIED WILL "REFILL" SOIL TO DEPTH SHADED		
SANDY LOAM	LOAM	CLAY

Fig. 24. Effect of soil type on the depth of penetration of three inches of water. (Courtesy, University of Arizona.)

Another important factor is whether the permanent wilting percentage of a soil is affected by the vegetable crop. Our present data indicate that the roots of different species of plants remove the soil moisture from a soil to the same percentage. This fact is important and greatly simplifies our irrigation practices.

Fig. 24 illustrates another important moisture-soil relationship. When a soil is irrigated, the water fills the first few inches of soil above field capacity, and drainage removes the excess water so the soil is at field capacity. The depth of soil, wet to field capacity, depends upon the amount of irrigation water or rain. It is impossible to wet a soil half full of available water under field conditions; the soil is always wet to field capacity.

DETERMINING THE NEED FOR IRRIGATION

In areas where crops must be irrigated for maximum production, it is essential to be able to determine the proper time for irrigation. Two criteria are available for this purpose: (a) The soil becomes depleted of soil moisture, which must be replenished; and (b) when the soil is unable to supply

Table 12*

DEPTH OF ROOTING† OF TRUCK CROPS AND TOTAL AMOUNTS OF IRRIGATION WATER SUGGESTED FOR COMMERCIAL PRODUCTION IN CALIFORNIA‡

Shallow-rooted (down to 2 feet)	Water Applied, Inches	Moderately deep-rooted (down to 4 feet)	Water Applied, Inches	Deep-rooted (down to 6 feet)	Water Applied, Inches
Cabbage	12	Bean, pole	15	Artichoke	12
Cauliflower	12	Bean, snap (spring)	12	Asparagus	20
Celery	30	Bean, snap (fall)	18	Muskmelon, inland valleys	18
Lettuce, winter	6	Beet	18	Muskmelon, Imperial Valley	24
Lettuce, summer and fall	18	Carrot, coastal area	18	Lima bean	12
Lettuce, Imperial Valley	18	Carrot, Imperial Valley	24	Squash, winter	18
Onion, intermediate	15	Cucumber	15	Sweet potato	18
Onion, late	24	Eggplant	24	Tomato, inland valleys	24
Potato, early	30	Pea, winter	6	Tomato, coastal areas	12
Potato, late	20	Pea, fall	18	Watermelon	15
Spinach	9	Pea, Imperial Valley	18		
Sweet corn	18	Pepper	18		
		Squash, summer			

* Courtesy, Calif. Agr. Exper. Sta. Lithoprint Leaflet, 1943.
† Onions are very shallow-rooted. With this crop it is necessary to maintain available water in the surface 6 to 10 inches for maximum yields.

Potatoes, lettuce, and corn develop poor root systems. A few roots penetrate deeply, but they are not numerous enough to permeate the soil thoroughly at greater depths. It is necessary to keep available soil moisture in the surface foot of soil, especially for the first part of the growing period.

Growers believe that frequent irrigations give best yields with celery.

Tomatoes will root 6 feet or more in deep soils before irrigation is necessary. Apply heavy irrigations before harvesting, and wet the soil to 6 feet. With canning tomatoes, in most soils no irrigation will be necessary during the harvesting period if the soil has been thoroughly wetted just before harvest.

Muskmelon will root to nearly 6 feet by maturity. There may be reduction in set of late fruit when moisture is almost depleted in the surface 3 feet.

‡ The amounts of water are for soils wet to field capacity to the different depths by rain or a preirrigation.

sufficient water for maximum growth there is a cessation of plant growth followed by other indications of insufficient water—a change in the color of the foliage, and perhaps wilting. Figure 25 shows the removal of soil moisture by a tomato plant in which the clear areas represent the water that has been used by the plant, and the shaded areas the unused water. On July 9 more than half the available water has been removed from the top 5 feet, which indicates the need for an irrigation. Fig. 26 illustrates the effect of ample irrigation, compared with no irrigation, on the growth of a shallow-rooted crop (sweet corn) and a deep-rooted crop (watermelons). Sweet corn yield is increased greatly by irrigation, while yields of watermelons are affected only slightly. The sweet corn graph shows the height of corn was less on the nonirrigated plot (A) as early as May 27. At the end of the season, the greatest growth of corn had been made by the heavy irrigation treatment B, and the least by A. In the latter case there has been insufficient water—with reduced growth. The graph (Fig. 26) giving the growth of watermelon fruits, shows little or no effect from irrigation on growth of melons, and yields indicate the same condition. This illustrates the same point; but in this case fruit measurements show that soil moisture was ample for growth.

The most accurate but time-consuming method of determining the need for irrigation is to determine the field capacity and permanent wilting percentage of the soil, followed by calculating the soil moisture at different depths in the field at periodic intervals. The depth of sampling should be the root zone or deeper. The frequency of sampling would be greater for shallow-rooted crops on sandy soils than for deep-rooted crops on clay soils. A simpler but less accurate method is to sample the soil with a soil tube or auger and determine the approximate wetness by color or feel. Most soils change color between the field capacity and the permanent wilting percentage; usually the soil is darker at field capacity and becomes lighter colored as the moisture content approaches the permanent wilting percentage. An inferior tool to use for soil sampling is a shovel, but may be used on the top foot or two of soil.

The second method for determining the need for irrigation depends upon the effect of insufficient water on plant growth. Growers will find it helpful to be able to recognize these effects. First, there is a slowing down of the rate of growth, which may be noticeable through growth measurements or by the lack of light green young growth. The color of the foliage becomes a darker green, often almost bluish or grayish, as the supply of water becomes insufficient. A few plants wilt, such as radishes, peppers, and spinach; sweet-corn leaves tend to roll; but many plants can obtain enough water from the subsoil to prevent wilting, though they may be unable to make any growth.

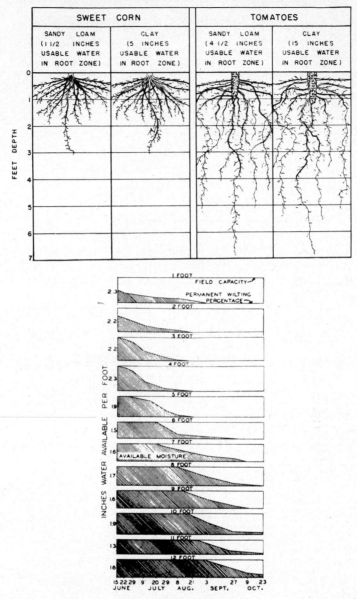

Fig. 25. (*Top*) Effect of soil type and depth of rooting on the size of the soil moisture reservoir.

(*Bottom*) Water removed by tomato plants on a nonirrigated plot. Clear areas, indicate water removed; hatched areas, amount of available water still in the soil.

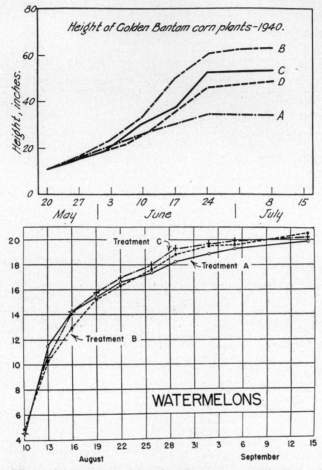

Fig. 26. Effect of irrigation on height of sweet corn (shallow rooted), and on diameter of watermelon fruits (deep rooted). Treatment A received no irrigation; B, ample water; C, medium amount of water; and D, light irrigation. As shown by the spread of the curves, the corn growth was greatly affected by irrigation, while little effect was evident on watermelons, since it is a deep rooted crop. Watermelons possess a larger soil moisture reservoir.

METHODS OF APPLYING WATER TO THE SOIL

Irrigation water may be applied to the soil by (a) surface irrigation, (b) sprinkling, or (c) subirrigation. By far the largest area in the West practises the use of surface irrigation; and the water may be applied in furrows between beds, or in furrows between widely spaced rows, and occasionally by flooding over the surface. The older sprinkling method was through stationary pipes and nozzles, but more recently there has been

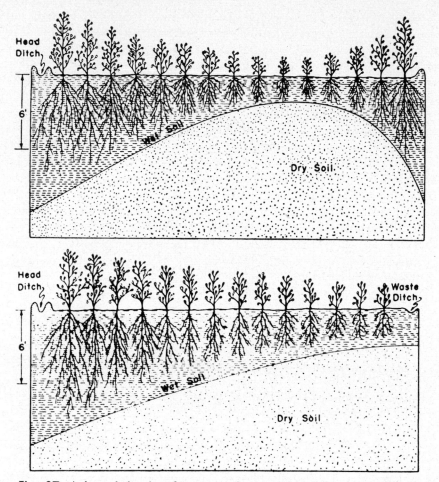

Fig. 27. A long irrigation furrow results in penetration to greater depth where the water enters (*top*); also at the end of the furrow unless there is a waste ditch (*bottom*). (Courtesy, University of Arizona.)

developed a system of portable pipes. The pipes are laid on the ground and may be moved to another location after the sprinkler heads have applied sufficient water. Not all soils permit moving of pipe because of stickiness when wet. Subirrigation is limited to areas of organic soils, mineral soils with an impervious clay subsoil, or with subsurface drain tile. In organic soils, parallel ditches are made about 800 feet apart, and the soil irrigated by filling the ditches with water and draining the ditches (after wetting the soil) from one ditch to another. In California these ditches are called "buckeyes." Where the soil is not wet uniformly, smaller ditches are used in addition; these are called "spud" ditches, and are 18 inches deep.

Surface irrigation is successful where the land is properly graded, and permits the use of large amount, or "head" of water; it is also usually lower in cost of equipment and labor. Sprinkling may be used successfully on hilly areas which cannot be leveled. Sprinkling wets the soil over the entire surface, eliminates field ditches, and permits the even application of small amounts of water.

The cost of bringing water to a field is about the same for surface and sprinkler irrigation. Johnston[4] indicates some of the costs of putting the water under pressure and sprinkling of fields. The cost of putting water under pressure is $3.00 per acre foot, moving of sprinkler lines will cost from $10.00 to $25.00 per acre foot, and depreciation on sprinkler system will be from $4.80 to $24.00 per acre. In sprinkling there may be a loss of 10 to 25 per cent of the water by evaporation to the air but there is also some loss of water through seepage from dirt ditches. On the other hand surface application of water will cost from $2.00 to $8.00 for labor per acre foot. Uneven land, small areas with crops of high value, or special problems may justify the use of sprinkler irrigation.

SLOPE OF SOIL AND LENGTH OF IRRIGATION FURROWS

Land improperly leveled, leaving low spots, will make the soil difficult to irrigate and may cause the "drowning out" or killing of the plants in the low spots. Drowning out is due to a lack of oxygen which is essential for the absorption of water. A cubic foot of soil is filled mostly by the soil, some of the remainder by water, and there should be some space left for air. The last column of Table 11 gives the amount of air space at moisture equivalent for various soils. The sands have more air space than clays. An irrigation fills the soil temporarily above field capacity until drainage has an opportunity to remove excess water. Some clays at field capacity or above, have little or no air space.

The following general rules will be helpful in determining slope for more uniform water penetration:

	Slope per 100 feet	*Approximate length of run*
Sandy loam	3 to 12 inches	200 to 300 feet
Loam	2 to 7 inches	400 to 600 feet
Clay	1 to 3 inches	800 to 1200 feet

MOVEMENT OF WATER FOLLOWING IRRIGATION

The object of irrigation is to wet all the soil in the root zone to field capacity so the roots may obtain water and plant nutrients from the entire volume of soil. Unsatisfactory yields are caused by the failure to wet all the soil, particularly near harvest when the plant's need is greatest. Fig. 24 indicates the effect of soil type and the depth of penetration of a given amount of water. A similar situation is shown in Fig. 28, where the water was applied to a furrow between two beds (C). Water tends to move downward, but there is also a lateral movement of water that is termed *subbing*. In a successful irrigation, the water moves laterally a sufficient distance to wet all the soil. The lateral and downward movement is due to both gravity

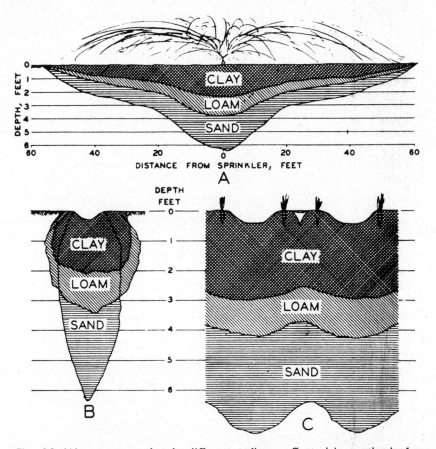

Fig. 28. Water penetration in different soils as affected by method of application. If the same amount of water is applied, a sandy loam will be wet deeper than a loam or a clay. (A) Sprinkler application wets the soil unevenly; therefore a 50 per cent overlap is needed. (B) Single furrows between flat planted crops, like tomatoes (rows 6 feet apart). Since water moves primarily downward, only about one-half of the soil is wet by single, narrow furrows. (C) Bed irrigation as used for carrots.

and capillarity; there is also some upward movement by capillarity—greatest for the first hour, then at a slower rate. A clay or fine-textured soil has a greater capillary pull than a coarse soil like sand. Therefore, in a clay, the moisture will move farther even though the rate is slower than in a sand. Capillary movement accounts for only a small amount of the water that "subs." When water fails to wet all the soil, the usual suggested practice is wider furrows, longer irrigation periods, keeping water at greater height in ditches, or closer furrows where this is possible. The deciduous fruit growers frequently resort to flooding to ensure filling all the soil with water. This might be used on some vegetables if weeds can be controlled as the crop matures. Diagram B in Fig. 28, illustrates a possible condition in widely-spaced crops such as tomatoes. When the vines are small several furrows may be used; as the crop grows larger, a broad, central furrow will permit wetting the largest possible area of soil.

In areas where there is hardpan the water moves down to this impervious layer and then spreads out. Capillary water from this free water surface will then wet the soil uniformly above it, according to the distance water will move in the soil by capillary action.

Diagram A, Fig. 28 indicates the penetration from a sprinkler application; it illustrates the need for a 50 per cent overlap of sprinkler heads, as the amount of water applied is much greater close to the head than at the circumference of the circle.

AMOUNT AND FREQUENCY OF IRRIGATION

Frequent irrigations are expensive because of the higher cost for labor and a waste of water. Labor is frequently more expensive than water; thus, a few applications are more economical than many. If the soil is over-

Table 13*

RELATIVE FREQUENCY AND AMOUNT OF IRRIGATION WATER AS AFFECTED BY
TYPE OF SOIL AND DEPTH OF ROOTING

Depth of Rooting	Sandy Soil		Loam Soil		Clay Soil	
	Days between Irrigations	Application, Acre-inches	Days between Irrigations	Application, Acre-inches	Days between Irrigations	Application, Acre-inches
Shallow, 0–2 feet	4–6	1–2	7–10	2–3	10–12	3–4
Moderately deep, 0–4 feet	7–10	2–3	10–15	3–4	15–20	4–5
Deep, 0–6 feet	10–12	3–4	20–30	4–5	30 or more	5–6

* Courtesy, *Calif. Agr. Ext. Ser. Emer. Food Pro. Leaflet,* 1943.

irrigated there is a loss of water to soil depths below the roots. In many soils the water applied to the top 3 to 6 inches is lost to the air by surface evaporation. Since roots will not be found in air-dry soil this water is of no use for plant growth. This loss of irrigation water is in proportion to the number of irrigations. In a Delano sandy loam, this amounts to about 0.23 inch for the upper 4 inches of soil, while in Salinas clay it is about one inch per irrigation. On a Salinas clay the use of 3 unnecessary irrigations would mean the waste of 3 inches of water lost through surface evaporation.

Frequency of irrigation is related to soil type, depth of rooting, and available water in the soil. The relationship between the first two are shown in Table 13. In general, the grower should irrigate at as wide an interval as crop, soil, and farm operations will permit. For shallow-rooted crops this would be when one-third to one-half of the available water has been used, and for deep-rooted crops when one-half to two-thirds of the available water has been extracted. The frequency of irrigation is related to the amount of water in the soil reservoir.

YIELD AND QUALITY

Often people in an irrigated area assume that irrigation is necessary for all crops, or they may irrigate all vegetables with about the same amount of water. Irrigation does increase yield for many crops; but in areas where the winter rainfall is 16 to 18 inches, the increase in yield is much greater for shallow-rooted crops. In areas with little or no winter rainfall it is customary to preirrigate; this makes conditions similar to those in areas having winter rains mentioned above. Crops making part of their growth during the winter rainy period will also require less irrigation for good production. Winter rains add considerable water, and loss by transpiration is less.

As shown by irrigation experiments at Davis, California, the yields of shallow-rooted crops may be increased several hundred per cent while deep-rooted crops may be increased from a few per cent up to 50 per cent. The effect of irrigation on yield is directly related to the amount of water held in the soil reservoir until maximum yield is produced. Additional water will not increase yield.

Tests in irrigating tree fruits have indicated that little effect on quality may be expected as long as plant growth does not slow down or cease entirely because of insufficient soil moisture. When soil moisture is close to the permanent wilting percentage for a majority of the roots, growth will cease even if the plant remains turgid. Under such conditions composition of the plant is affected. Frequently melons may be slightly sweeter, and stem and leafy tissue may become tougher under these conditions. There is insufficient evidence on this point to permit definite conclusions as to the effect on quality of all vegetables.

SOIL MOISTURE AND SEED GERMINATION

Moisture is one of the essential conditions for the germination of seed. The effect of a relative amount of available soil water on the germination of vegetable seed is given below[3]. The seed was planted in soil having a permanent wilting percentage of 8.6 per cent, and a field capacity of 15.7 per cent.

Group I. Good germination when the soil is half or more filled with water.

Cool season crops: Cabbage, onion, radish, spinach, turnip.

Warm season crops: Cantaloupe, cucumber, pepper, summer squash, sweet corn, tomato, watermelon, winter squash.

Group II. Good germination when the soil is more than half filled with water.

Cool season crops: Beet, carrot, lettuce, pea.

Warm season crops: New Zealand spinach, snap bean, lima bean.

Group III. Good germination when the soil is at or above field capacity.

Cool season crop: Celery.

The above grouping indicates that in the case of one type of seed, namely celery (Group III), a special effort should be made to keep the soil moisture close to or above field capacity.

Group I and II seeds seem to germinate to some extent below field capacity, but even with these plants the rate of germination will be more rapid if the soil moisture is near field capacity.

QUALITY OF WATER

Water usually contains dissolved salts and in some cases sediment soil. Cations of calcium (Ca), magnesium (Mg), sodium (Na), potassium (K), and anions of carbonate (CO_3), bicarbonate (HCO_3), sulfate (SO_4), chloride (Cl), nitrate (NO_3), as well as boron (B), frequently occur in water to varying degrees. Some are beneficial, others like the sodium salts of carbonates, sulfates, and chlorides are harmful; and some such as boron may be either, according to the concentration.

Some growers, by keeping the soil relatively wet are able to use waters rather high in salt content where other growers fail. Boron content of water is not objectionable if at, or below, one-half part per million. Crops differ in their sensitivity to boron.

Wilcox has classified plants as to their tolerance for salinity. Vegetables which may be grown on soils of strong salinity are kale and garden beets; those on soils of medium salinity are onions, squash, carrots, asparagus, tomatoes, rape, and garden beets.

REFERENCES

1. Brown, J. B., L. D. Doneen, and P. A. Minges: Irrigation of home gardens, *Calif. Agr. Ext. Ser. Emer. Food Pro. Leaflet,* 4 p., 1943.
2. Doneen, L. D., and John H. MacGillivray: Suggestions on irrigating commercial truck crops, *California Agr. Exp. Sta. lithoprint leaflet,* 5 p., 1946.
3. Doneen, L. D., and John H. MacGillivray: Germination (emergence) of vegetable seed as affected by different soil moisture conditions, *Plant Phys. 18:* 524–29, 1943.
4. Johnston, C. N.: Irrigation by sprinkler system, *California Agriculture 2:* 3, 14 (No. 11), 1948.
5. Lewis, M. R.: Practical Irrigation, *U.S.D.A. Farmers' Bul. 1922:* 69 p., 1943.
6. MacGillivray, John H., and L. D. Doneen: Soil moisture conditions as related to the irrigation of truck crops on mineral soils, *Proc. Am. Soc. Hort. Sci. 40:* 483–92, 1942.
7. Turville, E. S. and Donald L. Hitch: Irrigating in Arizona, *Ariz. Agr. Ext. Ser. Cir. 123,* 60 p., 1944.

Chapter 10

Fertilizers, Manure, and Organic Matter

The use of fertilizers and manures is one of the common methods of increasing yields. Farmers place considerable emphasis on high yields because the cost of production per package is usually lower, though high yields in themselves do not ensure a lower cost. Table 14 shows that the cost of production per package may be either higher or lower with increased yields. Growers make every effort to supply fertilizer or any other deficiency since an increased expense in one item does not increase greatly the cost per package. The fixed costs such as taxes, interest, depreciation, land preparation, irrigation, and cultivation are about the same regardless of yield.

A fertility program for vegetable production involves the consideration of commercial fertilizers, animal manures, green manures, and crop residues. Fertilizers supply primarily plant nutrients such as nitrogen, phosphoric acid, and potash. The other materials supply limited amounts of plant nutrients and, in addition, organic matter which is recognized generally as an essential component of soils. Each of these materials has particular advantages, as discussed in the succeeding pages.

COMMERCIAL FERTILIZERS

The fertilizer industry has developed greatly in the last quarter century through the greater use of commercial fertilizers. Although there are other means of supplying plant nutrients, this one is of primary importance. Through the years there have been many advances in the fertilizer industry, as new synthetic compounds, cheaper cost, more efficient application, better conditions for application, and accuracy in composition. Fertilizers have several advantages which may be summarized as follows. (a) Through increased yields the use of fertilizer usually decreases the cost of production per package; (b) requires less equipment and labor per pound of nutrient applied than animal manure; (c) larger amounts of available plant food per pound of fertilizer; (d) fertilizer available in any amount; (e) available in a great variety of analyses suitable for various crops and soils; (f) may improve quality of the crop, and (g) sold on the basis of guaranteed analysis.

The importance of the different nutrients and their sources will be discussed next.

Nitrogen (N). This is one of the elements most commonly used to increase crop yields. It is a constituent of all proteins and chlorophyll. Plant tissue usually contains more nitrogen than any other fertilizer element. For many years the natural deposits of sodium nitrate in South America was the chief source of nitrogen for fertilizers. In recent years, several processes have been developed for fixing this element from the air as well as salvaging waste nitrogen from steel manufacture and other industries. This has made available several new compounds at lower cost. Nitrogen is still the most expensive fertilizing nutrient and the inorganic sources are cheaper than the organic. Nitrogen is absorbed by the plant both as nitrates and ammonium forms of nitrogen, and at present are considered equally available to plants. Leaching of soluble nitrates below the root zone and changes occurring in the soil make an adequate nitrogen fertilization program more difficult than with the other elements.

Nitrogen applications are used to produce a rapid leafy growth of vegetables. Most leafy vegetables are grown under cool, wet conditions, and are classified as cool season crops. In cool, wet weather vegetables frequently need an application of nitrate nitrogen because of loss through leaching and because low temperatures depress nitrification. Nitrification refers to the formation of nitrates in soil from organic matter by bacterial action. Nitrogen fertilizer materials may be classified as to their form of nitrogen as follows:

Nitrate nitrogen (NO_3)
  Nitrate of soda, 15 to 16½ per cent N
  Calcium nitrate 15½ to 17 per cent N

Ammonium nitrogen (NH_4)
  Ammonium sulfate, 19½ to 21 per cent N
  Ammoniated phosphates, 10 to 16 per cent N
  Anhydrous liquid ammonia, 82 per cent N

Organic nitrogen
  Animal tankage, 5 to 10 per cent N
  Dried blood, 6 to 14 per cent N
  Fish meal, 6½ to 10 per cent N

Synthetic organic nitrogen
  Calcium cyanamid, 21 to 23 per cent N
  Uramon, 42 per cent N

Ammonium and nitrate nitrogen
  Ammonium nitrate, 17 per cent N (NH_4) plus 17 per cent N (NO_3)

Anhydrous liquid ammonia is added to irrigation water forming ammonium hydroxide (nitrogation) or this gas may be injected directly into the soil (nitrojection). Both of these procedures are used extensively and are reasonable in cost. Ammonium hydroxide may be purchased also as a liquid for adding to irrigation water and in some states urea is dissolved in water

Table 14*

RELATION OF YIELD OF SWEET POTATOES TO COST PER PACKAGE,
FROM RECORDS OF FOUR REPRESENTATIVE GROWERS

Cost Items	Costs Per Acre			
Cultural labor and materials	$26.10	$43.19	$31.07	$28.04
Harvesting costs	18.49	26.70	24.17	13.68
Other costs	11.96	25.91	15.54	24.48
Total costs per acre	$56.55	$95.80	$70.78	$66.20
Yield, pounds per acre	5,438	7,852	17,262	3,600
Cost per package	$1.04	$1.22	$0.41	$1.70

* Courtesy, *California Extension Service Mimeograph.*

for similar use. In California the use of liquid fertilizers has increased from 422 tons in 1944 to 13,461 tons in 1949. Complete fertilizers also are available in liquid form.

Most of these forms of nitrogen become available to plants at different rates. The organic forms such as tankage are available slowly. Through bacterial action the organic matter is changed to ammonia nitrogen and then to nitrate form. Their price is high because of their value for livestock feed. There should be a few weeks' delay between the application of cyanamid, and the planting of the crop, since toxic materials are formed during the decomposition stages.

Phosphorus (P). In fertilizers, phosphorus is referred to as phosphoric acid (P_2O_5). This element is a vital constituent of some proteins (nucleo proteins) and phosphatides. While both soils and plants contain only rather small amounts of this element, it is still important in crop production. In many cases western soils are supplied more amply with this element than is true of the East. However, in general, it is necessary to use some phosphorus containing fertilizer for high yields. The phosphorus compounds found in the soil are principally combinations of calcium or magnesium with phosphorus and oxygen. Phosphorus also is found in organic matter of the soil.

Most phosphate fertilizers are derived from ground phosphate rock. The phosphorus is made water-soluble through treatment with sulfuric acid, forming mono- and dicalcium phosphate. In 16 per cent superphosphate about half the weight is phosphorus salts and the other half gypsum. "Treble" superphosphate is made by the use of phosphoric acid and thus, no gypsum is formed. The principal phosphatic fertilizers are superphosphate, with 14 to 22 per cent available phosphoric acid; double superphosphate (treble), 40 to 50 per cent; and ammoniated phosphate, 20 to 52 per cent. Organic sources of phosphorus are bonemeal, containing 17 to 30 per cent total phosphoric acid; animal tankage, 5 to 18 per cent; and fish meal 5 to 8 per cent.

Potassium (K). Potassium is referred to in the fertilizer industry as potash (K_2O). Potassium, next to nitrogen, is the most abundant in plants. Even though present in plants in fairly large amounts, the exact role in plant nutrition is not understood fully. There is evidence that its presence is desirable for carbohydrate manufacture, particularly for translocation and storage of these compounds. In the case of sweet potatoes, it has been found that potassium is essential for cambium growth. With insufficient quantities, sweet potatoes are long and narrow rather than "chunky."

The chief inorganic sources of potash with their respective percentages of available potash, are muriate of potash (KCl), 47 to 61; sulfate of potash (K_2SO_4), 47 to 52; manure salts, 19 to 32; kainite, 14 to 22; and hardwood ashes, 2 to 8.

Minor Elements. Besides the major elements discussed previously there are other elements that have increased yields on certain limited soil areas. These are boron, copper, iron, magnesium, manganese, sulfur, and calcium. Still other elements like aluminum, bromine, chlorine, iodine, silicon, sodium, and zinc are found also in plant tissue. Boron deficiency or overabundance may reduce yields. An overabundance of boron causes toxicity and is found in the West where irrigation water is sometimes high in this element. Boron deficiency has been found in several areas of the West. Amounts which should be applied will vary from five to 25 pounds of borax to the acre; the amount will depend upon both the crop and the soil conditions.

Mixed Fertilizers. In mixed fertilizers, two or more simple sources of nutrients such as ammonium sulfate, acid phosphate, and muriate of potash are mixed together to make a fertilizer of the desired analysis. Some filler is added usually to bring the weight up to a ton, and also to act as a conditioner. The composition is expressed customarily in a combination of numbers, such as 10-10-5. A fertilizer thus denoted contains 10 per cent nitrogen, 10 per cent phosphoric acid, and 5 per cent potash. A fertilizer *ratio* expresses the relationship between the nutrients in the smallest possible numbers, or a 10-10-5 is a 2-2-1 ratio. The term *grade* refers to the percentage composition of nitrogen, phosphoric acid, or potash, such as a 10-10-5 fertilizer. *Analysis* refers not only to these major constituents, but also to other minor constituents such as borax, magnesium sulfate, et cetera. Fertilizer analyses are made by approved methods, and their correctness is checked by the state control agencies. The method of calculating the amount of fertilizer materials and filler needed for a ton of fertilizer is given in Table 15. Some fertilizer materials are deliquescent; that is, they take up moisture from the air. With those materials an absorbent filler should be used such as dried blood, tankage, cottonseed meal, and cyanamid to prevent caking. A sack of basic materials contains few impurities. A 100-pound sack of ammonium

Table 15

Method of Calculating the Simple Fertilizers Needed to Mix One Ton of 10-10-5 Fertilizer

Simple Fertilizer	Nutrient in Fertilizer	Per cent of Nutrient		Computations of Simple Fertilizers and Filler Needed for One Ton of 10-10-5
		Simple Fertilizer	Mixed Fertilizer	
Ammonium sulfate	Nitrogen	20	10	$\frac{10}{20} \times 2{,}000 = 1000$ pounds
Treble super-phosphate	Phosphoric acid	44	10	$\frac{10}{44} \times 2{,}000 = 455$ pounds
Muriate of potash	Potash	50	5	$\frac{5}{50} \times 2{,}000 = 200$ pounds
Filler	—	—	—	345 pounds
Total				2000 pounds

sulfate contains 97.7 pounds of the ammonium sulfate salt; 1.9 pounds of moisture; and 0.4 pound of impurities[7].

In recent years growers have used fertilizers which contain more units of plant food per 100 pounds. One unit is 1 per cent, or 20 pounds per ton of plant nutrients. "High-analysis" fertilizer contains 20 to 30 units; and a "concentrated" fertilizer contains over 30 units. A 10-10-5 fertilizer contains 25 units and would be a "high-analysis" fertilizer. Usually, one ton of 10-10-5 may be purchased for less money than 2500 pounds of 8-8-4 even though they both contain the same amount of plant nutrients. In the 10-10-5, there is less bulk to handle, with a saving in labor, as well as freight, sacks, etc.

Similar yields may be obtained by applying the simple fertilizers, but where more than one fertilizer must be added there is a saving in the use of mixed fertilizers. The mixtures cost less to apply, are drilled more easily, are balanced more easily and effectively from the standpoint of acidity or basicity, and require less care on the grower's part to apply the correct amount.

Most fertilizers are either acid or alkaline in their reaction according to the basic elements of potassium, sodium, calcium, and magnesium; or the acidic elements of nitrogen, phosphorus, sulfur, and chlorine. Ammonium sulfate or Ammo-phos ($16\frac{1}{2}$ per cent N)—(an acid fertilizer)—requires about 108 pounds of calcium carbonate per unit of nitrogen to neutralize the acidity of the fertilizer. Sodium nitrate (an alkaline fertilizer) furnishes the equivalent 36 pounds of calcium carbonate per unit of nitrogen to neutralize acidity of the soil. Calcium nitrate furnishes similarly 28 pounds of calcium carbonate basicity, and cyanamid 54 pounds. On acid soils, it may be a disadvantage to use a fertilizer which will increase the acidity; likewise a fertilizer which will decrease the acidity may have some advantage.

Comparing Fertilizer Costs. Calculations as to the cost of nitrogen, phosphoric acid, and potash in fertilizers are desirable in order to make accurate comparisons. If ammonium sulfate costs $56.00 per ton and contains 21 per cent or units of the nitrogen, the cost per unit is $2.67 (Table 16). This procedure is applicable to simple fertilizers with one nutrient. With Ammophos or a complete fertilizer it is necessary to use the cost of one or more nutrients from a simple fertilizer and assign the remaining cost to the other nutrient. In Table 16 for Ammo-phos this procedure has been followed. The cost of nitrogen was obtained from ammonium sulfate and when the remainder is charged to phosphoric acid it is somewhat higher than treble phosphate. Other cost procedures can be used for complete fertilizers. Cost per unit is only one consideration in selecting a fertilizer. The price of fertilizer is subject to change so the data in Table 16 are used only to illustrate the method of calculation.

Table 16

THE RELATIVE COST OF A FERTILIZER UNIT OBTAINED FROM DIFFERENT FERTILIZERS

Name of Fertilizer	Composition Per cent	Cost Dollars Per Ton	Cost per unit or 20 pounds		
			Nitrogen	Phosphoric Acid	Potash
Sodium nitrate	16	$62.00	$3.88	. .	. .
Ammonium sulfate	21	56.00	2.67	. .	. .
Uramon	44	135.00	3.07	. .	. .
Treble phosphate	42	70.00	. .	$1.67	. .
Sulfate of potash	52	63.00	. .	. .	$1.22
Ammo-phos	16–20	84.00	2.67	2.06	. .

Methods of Applying Fertilizers. As land is farmed for a greater number of years the need of commercial fertilizers tends to increase in amount per acre. Fertilizers must be used efficiently, particularly when cost of production needs to be kept low. Formerly, fertilizer was applied broadcast and either plowed or disked into the soil. When the phosphoric acid and potash are mixed in this way they may become fixed by the soil and much of it is not available to the plant roots. In recent years the application of plant nutrients in bands (Figs. 29 and 30) near the seed and plant has been practiced generally. Band applications may result in the fixing of the fertilizer particles in direct contact with the soil, but the particles near the center of fertilizer core are available to the plant. Applying in bands permits a smaller application, with production of the same yield as may be obtained with a larger amount applied broadcast.

Fertilizer attachments may be had for applying the material in continuous bands so the plants will use the fertilizer effectively without injury. With seeds, it is desirable to place the band three inches on either side, and three

Fig. 29. Method of applying phosphoric acid and potash is important on soils where these materials are fixed. Band application on the left has greatly affected the growth of beans. (Courtesy, Western Washington Experiment Station.)

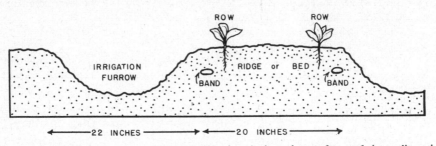

Fig. 30. Fertilizer bands are placed 3 inches below the surface of the soil and 2 inches from the plant.

inches below the seed. With onions grown by transplanting the best response is obtained by placing the fertilizer four inches under the row (Fig. 31). Fertilizer should be applied early, that is, near the time of seeding or transplanting. Beans, peas, and cucurbits seem to be more susceptible than other vegetables to fertilizer injury. Changes taking place between the soil and the chemical fertilizers are important in determining the method of application. Nitrate and other nitrogen materials which are changed to nitrates in the soil, are water-soluble and may be applied broadcast. Care should be used to prevent burning by their falling on plant leaves or stems, and only limited amounts should be applied at a time to prevent wasteful leaching. Ammonium sulfate is changed sometimes to nitrate before being absorbed by plants, and may be fixed temporarily to a limited extent. Organic nitrogen fertilizers undergo more extensive changes as a result of bacterial action before the nitrates are formed, and are not therefore, as readily available as chemical fertilizers.

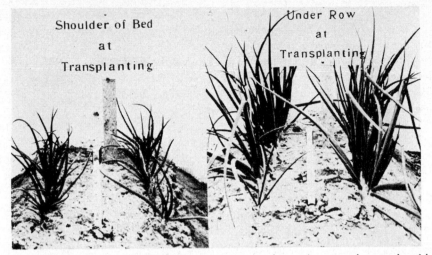

Fig. 31. Fertilizer placed close to the row shows increased growth with onions. Fertilizer placed under the row (or in the shoulder of the bed) was within 3 or 4 inches of the seed.

Fertilizer Use in the West. Western farm lands have been cultivated for a relatively short time as compared to those of the Atlantic Coast, which were settled in Colonial times. This may explain partially why Western soils are richer in plant nutrients. Also, the moderate rainfall in the West has resulted in less leaching of soil nutrients. While nitrogen is the predominant fertilizer need of Western soils, recent reports indicate that phosphate and potash are becoming more important in crop production. Over a period of years both nitrogen and phosphate have been essential fertilizer constituents in the Southwest, namely Coachella and Imperial Valleys of California, and in the Yuma and Salt River areas of Arizona. Tomatoes in the Walla Walla district need both nitrogen and phosphate while other vegetables tested need only nitrogen. Western Washington fields for peas should receive both phosphate and potash. In Oregon and Montana the pea crop needs phosphate and frequently nitrogen. Various mixed fertilizer analyses have been recommended in Western Oregon for vegetables. On the intensively used muck soils of this area fertilizer high in phosphate and potash are used successfully. This applies to Western Washington as well. Boron is lacking sometimes for a few crops in limited areas. There is considerable influence for the use of complete fertilizers; but, unfortunately, there is an insufficient amount of fertilizer tests in some areas for specific recommendations. Growers tend to be more generous in their use of fertilizer on high-priced crops both as to amount and analysis since this one factor does not increase greatly their cost of production. More detailed discussion for the different crops will be given under each vegetable.

The use of fertilizers in the West is small compared to some of the areas in the East such as the South Atlantic states (Table 17). At the present time the use of commercial fertilizers is increasing much more rapidly in the West than for the rest of the United States. During the period given in Table 17, fertilizer tonnage increased 130 per cent in United States but 220 per cent for the 11 Western states. Both Idaho and Colorado farmers increased their use of fertilizer to a much greater degree.

Table 17*

FERTILIZER CONSUMPTION IN WESTERN, SOUTH ATLANTIC, AND THE UNITED STATES

State or Area	Tons—2000 Pounds		
	5 Year Average 1935–1939	1945	1950
Montana	4,154	8,000	16,000
Idaho	5,186	30,000	65,050
Wyoming	1,522	3,000	6,500
Colorado	2,694	15,379	37,974
New Mexico	2,112	8,000	13,494
Arizona	6,279	29,453	76,000
Utah	1,990	6,026	28,554
Nevada	500	750	1,940
Washington	24,630	56,504	81,147
Oregon	16,260	37,434	107,931
California	209,123	483,591	640,646
Western—Total	274,450	678,137	1,075,236
South Atlantic†	3,687,374	5,266,329	6,354,364
United States	7,270,802	12,299,390	18,346,132

* Courtesy, *Fertilizer Review 14:* No. 3, 1949; *16:* No. 2, 1951.
† Delaware, Maryland, District of Columbia, Virginia, West Virginia, North Carolina, South Carolina, Georgia and Florida.

DETERMINING FERTILIZER REQUIREMENTS

Each grower has the problem of deciding what fertilizer is best for his crops to obtain economical yields. The answer to this problem will be affected by the nature of the soil and its parent material; the type of crop being grown; past crop history of the soil; the fertilizer program; and the climate. The program should be planned to prevent any major or minor element deficiency, rather than striving for mathematically correct ratios and amount of fertilizer.

Many different methods have been used to determine the correct fertilizer for a given piece of land and crop. The grower may obtain valuable information from experience in his area, and from neighbors' experiences; but he should make some simple tests on his own land. It is not too costly to fertilize a trial strip through a field to observe the effect on plant growth and yield. Fertilizer experiments can be classified into two groups: (A) Those performed on the crop soil in place; and (B) those where the soil is removed to some other location for testing or measuring plant growth. The methods thus classified are as follows:

A. *Soil in place*
    1. Fertilizer trials on the soil
    2. Plant tissue tests on the crop
    3. Deficiency symptoms of the crop
B. *Soil removed for testing*
    1. Pot test in greenhouse on soil and crop
    2. Neubauer and Cunninghamella tests on soil
    3. Quick chemical tests on soil

The procedures listed above will be discussed only briefly. Fertilizer tests are used commonly and Table 18 is a good example of this type of research

Table 18*

AVERAGE POTATO YIELDS FROM A FERTILIZER EXPERIMENT IN
KERN COUNTY, WHITE ROSE VARIETY

Plot Treatment†			100-Pound Sacks Per Acre			
Nitrogen	Phosphoric Acid	Potash	U. S. No. 1's	U. S. No. 2's	Eggs and Peewees	Total
0	0	0	36	20	34	90
100	0	0	213	28	21	262
150	0	0	247	38	16	301
100	86	0	230	40	34	304
100	0	150	199	31	22	252
100	86	150	231	36	33	300
Least Significant Difference			27	5	6	25

* Courtesy, *California Extension Service Mimeograph.*
† Fertilizers used 500 and 750 pounds of ammonium sulfate, 200 pounds of treble superphosphate, and 300 pounds of potassium sulfate.

work. Such a fertilizer experiment is conducted by laying out a series of equal-sized plots in a field. Several fertilizer treatments are selected to bring out the desired information and these fertilizers applied. Four or five reapplications of the same treatment are desirable. In Table 18 the soil evidently needed nitrogen as shown by previous work, and the amount of nitrogen needed was the primary goal. Phosphoric acid and potash also were included to see if these might be deficient. The response to fertilizer is determined by recording yields. In plant tissue tests, a portion of the plant— usually petioles of active growing leaves—are tested chemically for the relative amount of nitrogen, phosphorus, and potassium. Previously developed standards are needed to interpret the readings. Plant tissue tests require skill in diagnosing the fertilizer needs. A starved plant first shows a slowing of growth followed by almost cessation. The appearance of the plant is changed and, in the case of nitrogen deficiency, the plant is a light or yellowish green. Phosphorus starvation is indicated by a dark-green color because the nitrates are not used in growth. Both of these deficiencies cause an accumulation of sugars with the possible development of purple anthocyanin pigments. Potassium deficiency is shown by dead spots in the leaf and sometimes marginal burning.

Pot tests for fertilizer needs are performed in glazed pots of one- or two-gallon capacity, in the greenhouse. The field soil is placed in the pots and the desired fertilizers are added. The deficiency is determined by measuring the growth of the plant. Many times these tests are preliminary to field fertilizer experiments. Biological soil tests, like the Neubauer, as well as chemical tests on the soil are used to determine nutrient deficiencies. The chemical tests were used first in the East on acid soils and probably need to be modified before being used on the alkaline or near alkaline soils of the West.

SOIL REACTION AND ITS IMPORTANCE

Soils may be classified as to their reaction as being either acid or alkaline. Extremes of either of these conditions may result in low yields; but crops vary as to the optimum soil reaction for best growth. Areas of high rainfall —in the East, Middle West, and South—usually have acid soils. Soils of the arid, and semiarid West, as well as some mucks, are slightly acid or alkaline in reaction. The reaction of a soil is the result of the kind of rock materials from which it was formed. Reaction is influenced by type of irrigation water, leaching, or lack of drainage, as well as by degree of removal of salts by plant growth.

Hydrogen Ion Concentration[3]. The reaction of a soil may be expressed with regard to its hydrogen ion concentration—designated as pH. In order to express this concentration without the use of large fractions, it is given as the logarithm of the reciprocal of the hydrogen ion concentration. Thus, neutral reaction—or the hydrogen ion concentration of pure water—is a pH of 7.0. Smaller numbers indicate increasingly greater acidity, and larger numbers than 7.0 increasingly greater alkalinity. A soil having a pH of 6.0 is weakly acid, but is 10 times more acid than a pH of 7.0. A pH of 5.0 is 100 times more acid than a pH of 7.0. A pH of 6.0 is 1.2 times as acid as a pH of 6.1. Agricultural soils occur with a pH as low as 4.0, and as high as 9.0, though most cultivated soils are in the range of pH 5.0 to 7.5.

Another common method of expressing the acidity of a soil is the pounds of lime required per acre to change an acid soil to a favorable plant reaction. One ton of limestone will change the cultivated layer of soil from a pH of

5.0 to one of 6.0, in the case of sandy loams, while 2½ tons frequently are required for a clay loam. Just as lime is used to decrease acidity, sulfur may be used to increase acidity or decrease alkalinity.

Soil reaction affects the plant growth largely through its action[9] on the soil: By modifying its physical condition; making nutrients available to roots; influencing growth of microörganisms; affecting the growth of some disease organisms; and hydrogen (acid) or hydroxyl (alkaline) ions may have a toxic or destructive effect on root tissues. Physical conditions of clays, and some loams, is affected unfavorably by an insufficient supply of calcium. Lime acts as a binding agent which flocculates the soil, and may directly affect aeration, moisture, and nutrient supply. Either strong acidity or alkalinity deflocculates the soil and causes poor physical condition. Phosphorus becomes less available as the soil solution increases in acidity below pH 5.5. Potassium may be affected above a pH of 7.5. With increasing acidity, calcium and magnesium are less available for plants because of decreased supply as well as greater competition for them by acids. Iron, manganese, copper, zinc, and possibly boron are less available above the neutral point. The soil solution is thought to be in the best range for availability of all nutrients between a pH of 6.0 to 7.5.

Alkali soils usually occur in arid regions or in wet, poorly drained areas. There are two types called "white" and "black" alkali—from the appearance of the surface incrustations. White alkali refers to a soil which contains an excess of neutral salts, such as chlorides and sulfates. A soil which contains injurious amounts of soluble carbonate, either with or without chlorides and sulfates, is referred to as black alkali. The latter type always contains some absorbed sodium. The formation of alkali soil is due usually to a high water table and the movement of salts to the surface where they remain after the evaporation of the water. Kelly[5] states that the rate of accumulation of the salts is dependent upon three factors: "(a) the rate of capillary movement of water through the soil, (b) the rate of evaporation, and (c) the salt content of the ground water."

FARM MANURE AND COMPOST

The use of animal manures is one of the oldest methods of fertilizing vegetables, particularly in the market-garden and greenhouse industries. Manure benefits vegetable growth through the addition of nitrogen, phosphoric acid, and potash, as well as by the addition of organic matter. It also may improve the physical condition of the soil, reduce erosion, and increase the number of beneficial microörganisms, and perhaps add growth-promoting substances. The importance of plant nutrients has been discussed under fertilizers; the importance and value of organic matter will be considered in the section on green manures. The animal manure produced on general farms usually is not for sale, but in areas specializing in poultry and dairy production there is still considerable manure for sale to the vegetable grower.

Manure is made up of the solid and liquid excretions of farm animals, together with some straw or other bedding material. About 73 per cent of the nitrogen, 79 per cent of the phosphoric acid, and 87 per cent of the potash of an animal's food is recoverable in fresh manure[6]. Manure usually is sold by weight or volume without much regard for its water or plant food content. Among the several factors affecting its composition are feed, bedding, age and species of animal, stage of decomposition, and care used in storing the manure. The composition of bedding—and its absorptive capacity—are important in obtaining manures of highest fertilizer value. The urine contains about 65 per cent of the total potash, 45 per cent of the total nitrogen, and less than 10 per cent of the phosphoric acid found in both the solid and liquid portions of manure.

Decomposed manure is less likely to injure plants, has few viable weed seeds, and is easier to work into the soil. Decomposition results in serious losses of organic matter and plant food. A ton of mixed cow and horse manure was allowed to rot for three months in a tightly-floored shed. This manure suffered the losses and gains found in Table 19. There are serious losses of organic matter, total and available nitrogen. Through the destruction of organic matter there has been a gain in pounds of available phosphoric acid in the decomposed material. It requires 5400 pounds of fresh excrement and bedding to produce a ton of rotten manure. Due to the great loss of organic matter and the retention of certain nutrients (that did not leach out) there was an increase in the percentage of nutrients per ton of the rotted manure. One ton of rotted manure is worth more than one ton of fresh manure. Conditions recommended to reduce losses during storage are: keeping the manure under a shelter, thoroughly compact, slightly moistened, and not disturbing it until it may be spread on the field where it is to be used.

Composition of Manure. Manure varies as to composition, so analyses can be used only in a general way. Moisture content, original nutrient composition, amount of bedding, and storage losses all vary. Moisture content greatly affects the amount of nutrients per ton. The data found in Table 20 give some general analyses of manure. In general, nitrogen is the most plentiful in manure, and phosphorus the least abundant. This has led to the recommendation that a sack of 18 per cent superphosphate be added to each load of manure. Manure is of rather low nutrient content when compared to commercial fertilizers. Cow manure with 82 per cent moisture contains one and two-tenths units of plant nutrients per 100 pounds while most commercial fertilizers contain 20 units or more for the same weight. Under summer conditions in the West, manure may have as little as 20 to 30 per cent moisture, which will increase appreciably nutrient percentage.

Availability of Plant Nutrients in Manure. The recovery by the plant of

Table 19*

EFFECT OF ROTTING ON THE COMPOSITION OF FRESH MIXED HORSE AND COW MANURE, STORED THREE MONTHS IN A TIGHTLY FLOORED SHED

	Total Weight	Organic Matter	Nitrogen		Phosphoric Acid		Total Potash
			Total	Available	Total	Available	
	Pounds	Pounds	Pounds	Pounds	Pounds	Pounds	Pounds
Fresh manure	2,000	485	12.3	1.65	6.2	3.8	15.3
Fresh manure (after rotting)	745	220	9.9	0.40	6.2	5.0	16.3
Percentage change from rotting							
Per cent loss	63	55	20	76	0	..	..
Per cent gain	..	..	..	..	0	32	7
Composition of 5400 pounds fresh manure after rotting	2,000	590	26.6	1.08	16.6	13.5	43.8

* Courtesy, Ohio Agr. Exp. Sta. Bull. 605, 1939.

Table 20

GENERAL COMPOSITION VALUES OF MANURE*

Kind of Animal	Daily Production Per Animal, Pounds			Dry Matter Per Ton, Pounds	Composition of Manure, Per Cent			Nutrient Units Per 100 Pounds
	Solid	Liquid	Water, Per Cent		Nitrogen N	Phosphoric Acid, P_2O_5	Potash K_2O	
Horse	35.5	8.0	70	600	0.67	0.25	0.60	1.5
Cow	52.0	20.0	82	360	0.54	0.20	0.47	1.2
Hog	6.0	3.5	82	360	0.50	0.35	0.45	1.3
Sheep	2.5	1.5	65	700	1.09	0.40	1.00	2.5
Chicken	0.1	..	60	800	1.10	0.80	0.60	2.5
Average	..	..	72	560	0.8	0.4	0.6	1.8

* Manures vary in composition from 3.0 to 0.7 nutrient units per 100 pounds. Nutrient content varies also with moisture content. These values are based on averages from several sources.

nutrients applied in manure varies with soil conditions and climate. About one-half of the nitrogen is recovered the first year; this is primarily from the urine portion of the manure. A larger proportion of the phosphoric acid and potash are used by the plants during the same period. Subsequent bacterial action will make more of the nutrients available from the undecomposed organic matter. This is of value in feeding plants in the latter part of the growing season. In warm climates most of the value of manure is obtained during the season of application, while in the cooler areas the effects may last for two or three seasons.

Soil bacteria are largely responsible for decomposing organic matter from manure and other sources, thus, liberating nutrients for plant roots. Since this action has been going on for years, most soils have the needed bacteria. In reclaimed mucks or peats, manure is applied sometimes at the rate of three to four tons per acre to supply bacteria. The growth of bacteria—with liberation of nutrients from the organic matter—is affected by factors such as oxygen, moisture, temperature, and reaction of the soil. The organic matter must supply sufficient energy for the bacteria. Optimum oxygen, moisture, and soil reaction for bacteria are similar to conditions for good plant growth. Maximum bacterial activity occurs between 80° to 100° F., and decreases at higher or lower temperatures.

Nitrification refers to the action of bacteria changing organic matter or ammonium compounds to nitrates. There may be other bacterial changes preceding the forming of nitrates. Many organisms can produce ammonia, others change ammonia to nitrates, or to nitrites and then nitrates. Large applications of organic matter, particularly strawy manure, greatly increase the number of bacteria because of the large amount of energy available.

Bacteria need not only energy, but nitrates, phosphates, etc. as well, for their growth. Therefore, when the bacteria are present in large numbers, they compete with the crop plants for nitrogen and may cause nitrogen starvation of the cash crop. This may be prevented by turning under manure without excessive straw, using succulent rather than mature green manures. The amount of green material should be kept in the range of 6 to 10 tons per acre. If 10 tons or more of green manure is added to the soil there should be an application of 150 pounds of ammonium sulfate or similar fertilizer. When the bacteria die and decompose these nutrients are liberated for plant growth.

Composted manures are looked upon with favor by market gardeners and others because of the plant food which readily is available and because the material is easy to apply. Little consideration is given to the great destruction of organic matter in composting the manures. In the production of early plants, it is customary to prepare soil-organic matter composts to use in soil mixtures for seeding and potting.

GREEN MANURES

In order to maintain the organic matter of the soil it is essential to follow a farm practice of plowing under animal manures, plant residues, or crops grown especially for incorporating in the soil, called *green manures. Cover-crops* are grown primarily to prevent erosion, and green manures are grown to add organic matter to the soil. Frequently, however, the same crops may fulfill both of these functions. This agricultural practice has been considered desirable by farmers in many countries over a long period of time. Like other agricultural practices it does not always give immediate beneficial results in proportion to the expense involved. Successful use depends upon its adaptation to agricultural practices, and to climatic and economic factors.

Organic Matter in the Soil. Organic matter is derived from plant growth and may be incorporated in the soil directly or through the application of manure. Table 21 calls attention to the relative amount of nutrients and organic matter in commercial fertilizers, manure, green manures, and crop residues. All add plant nutrients and all except commercial fertilizers add organic matter. The analyses of commercial fertilizers are given in percentage of water-soluble nutrients, while the analyses of the organic materials are on the basis of total analysis.

Advantages and Disadvantages of Green Manures. The advantages of green manure are: (a) Through decomposition of the organic matter the nutrients are made available for plant growth; (b) the organic matter added improves the soil as a home for the plant's roots; and (c) when legumes are inoculated properly, they may fix the nitrogen of the air. This latter process may add 30 to 100 pounds of nitrogen per acre to the soil. The nutrients

Table 21

RELATIVE COMPOSITION OF DIFFERENT SOURCES OF NUTRIENTS
AND ORGANIC MATTER

	Pro-duction Per Acre, Tons	Organic Matter Per Ton, Pounds	Nutrients Per Ton, Pounds			
			Nitrogen	Phosphoric Acid	Potash	Total
Commercial fertilizer, 8-8-4	..	little	160.0	160.0	80.0	400.0
Manure*	..	560	16.0	8.0	12.0	36.0
Green manure, vetch†	3.3	300	9.0	3.0	8.0	20.0
Crop residue, carrot	4.9	229	3.8	1.4	8.8	14.2

* When availability of nutrients is considered, manure is only slightly more valuable than green manure.

† Cost per acre: disking and planting, $5.00; 40 pounds of vetch seed $5.00; or about $3.00 per ton of growth.

come from surface and subsoil as well as from the fixed nitrogen of the air. Green manures recover and save nutrients which might otherwise be lost by leaching. All these nutrients are added to the surface foot of soil where there are numerous crop roots. Organic matter makes a soil friable or easy to crumble and improves aeration. This means that the physical condition has been improved which, in turn, aids irrigation through better water penetration. Decomposition of organic matter results in the formation of carbon dioxide gas which may cause the liberation of plant nutrients in the soil or an increase in the rate of photosynthesis. Soil organic matter reduces or prevents erosion. Most of these advantages are interrelated in improving crop production.

The more important disadvantages of green manures are: (a) The cost of seed and land preparation; (b) the loss of the land for production of a cash crop; and (c) the possibility of improper handling of green manure crops, resulting in nitrogen starvation of the succeeding crop, as discussed earlier. If plants are too mature, or if too large quantities of organic matter are turned under it accelerates greatly the growth of bacteria; these bacteria need nutrients such as nitrogen for their growth, and compete with crop plants for the nutrients.

Organic matter in the soil is primarily of value when it is being decomposed, and this suggests the need for renewing the supply. Cultivation causes a steady decrease in the nitrogen content of the soil—an indication that the organic matter content has decreased. Records in the Midwest indicate a decline of 40 per cent in nitrogen content over a period of 40 years. It is difficult to increase the organic content of the soil, and most programs are for the purpose of preventing its decrease. Data obtained with several Mississippi Valley soils show that their nitrogen content decreases more rapidly in the southern than northern climates. Thus, northern soils in cooler areas frequently have a higher nitrogen content. Their nitrogen composition is highest with a mean annual temperature of 32° F. and the least at 70° F. In the warmer climates where the organic matter decomposes more rapidly there is, however, the advantage of obtaining a quicker return from their use. Many agriculturists believe that the productivity of soils is correlated with its organic matter content.

Legumes and Nitrogen Fixation. Most rotations contain a legume primarily because of its ability to fix nitrogen from the air. Roots of legumes have swellings or nodules (Fig. 32)—when naturally or artificially inoculated. The size and shape of nodules varies with crops and strains of bacteria. These nodules are caused by bacteria which obtain their nourishment from

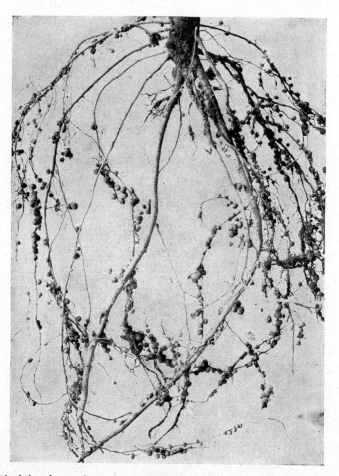

Fig. 32. Nodules formed on the root of a legume by nitrogen-fixing bacteria.
(Courtesy, U. S. Department of Agriculture.)

the legume, and in turn supply the plant with nitrogen fixed from the air. The greatest amount of nitrogen is fixed on poor soils which have little organic matter. Each strain of nodule bacteria will cause its own specific nodules on certain legume crops. Care must be used to make sure the proper strain is present in the soil or is provided otherwise for the green manure crop. If the proper bacteria are not present in the soil, nodules will not be formed. Bacteria may be supplied in a soil known to have the proper organism in a previous crop, or through the use of artificial cultures. These cultures are shaken up with the required amount of water and sprinkled on the seed. The soil containing the bacteria is dried, pulverized, and screened. The legume seed are slightly moistened, the soil is mixed with seed, and then dried before planting. The three legume vegetables require the following types of bacteria for nitrogen fixation: Pea, Vetch Group IV; snap bean, Bean Group VI; and lima bean, Cowpea Group III.

Azotobacter. This is a form of free-living bacteria that also occurs in the soil and does not live in plant roots. Fixation of nitrogen by this organism occurs in a neutral or alkaline soil in the presence of carbohydrates for energy. Fixation of up to 25 pounds of nitrogen per year has been attributed to azotobacter by some workers.

Kinds of Plants for Green Manures. Many types of plants are used for green manures. Their selection for a given situation depends upon the climate, the soil type, acidity, and the time of the year when grown. Legumes are preferred because of their ability to fix nitrogen from the air, and their higher nitrogen content. Table 22 enumerates some crops that may be grown in different seasonal and climatic areas. Green-manuring crops are grown, as far as possible, in those months of the year when land is not occupied by vegetables. In most areas, it is possible to produce a green manure crop sometime in the year; in the cooler areas this is during early fall or winter. Crops not injured by frost and preferably those which will survive the winter and resume growth in the early spring are most desirable. In warmer areas where vegetables may be grown during winter and early spring, the summer and fall periods are then available for green manures, and crops that will thrive in hot and even dry weather are used.

Economics of Green Manuring. This practise is more important in permanent agriculture or in maintaining fertility over a period of years than where land is leased for a year or two. If only plant nutrients are needed, fertilizers would seem to be the logical choice. The main reason for growing green manures seems to be organic matter, since that from animal manures is not so quickly available. Green manures provide fair quantities of both organic matter and nutrients. They may be produced frequently with less cost than manure. There are certain advantages to green manures which cannot be evaluated accurately as given in Table 21. Such items as better physical conditions and prevention of erosion are difficult to express in monetary terms.

Table 22

SUGGESTED GREEN MANURE CROPS FOR DIFFERENT CLIMATIC AREAS*

Cool-season Crops		Warm-season Crops	
Nonlegumes	Legumes	Nonlegumes	Legumes
Adapted to areas where soil freezes at least 1 inch deep			
Rye (75) Oats (65)	Vetch, hairy (30) IV, or with rye Red clover (15) II Sweet-clover (20) I Hubam clover (20) I	Millet (30) Sudan grass (25)	Cowpeas (120, 25) III Red clover (15) II
Adapted to areas of killing frost, but little frozen ground			
Rye (75) Barley (90)	Vetch, purple (45) IV, or with rye Austrian peas (35) VII Fenugreek (40) I Sweet-clover (20) I	Millet (30) Sudan grass (25)	Cowpeas (120, 25) III Calcarata vetch (45) IV Mung beans (12) III
Adapted to areas of no, or rare, killing frosts			
Rarely used	Bur-clover (15) I Bard (vetch) (45) IV Austrian peas (35) VII Fenugreek (40) I	Rarely used	Sesbania (25) III Cowpeas (120, 25) III Crotalaria (20, 8) III

* Numbers in parentheses indicate pounds of seed per acre; where two amounts are given, the first is broadcast and the second is for planting in rows. Roman numerals indicate the group of bacteria used for inoculation; with nonlegumes it is desirable to use more nitrogen in cash-crop fertilizer.

Yields of green manure crops vary with the length of growing season. In Table 21, the vetch was plowed under in March, and if grown until May or June the tonnage probably would have been double that given in the table. High yields of green manure crops would be considered in the range of 15 to 20 tons. If the soil is deficient in any nutrient, fertilization should be practised to produce maximum yield of green manure crops. Care should be used in plowing under the growth while still succulent; if permitted to become hard or stiff it is difficult to cover, and is low in nitrogen content; this may result in a nitrate deficiency of the soil. If plowed under in a succulent stage, decomposition will proceed rapidly in a moist soil and a crop may be planted after two or three weeks. Frequently, it is necessary to turn under the green manure before maximum growth is obtained in order to have the ground ready in time for seeding of the succeeding crop. Seeds containing food reserves of fats are more likely to give poor germination in decaying green manure than are starchy seeds.

REFERENCES

1. Anderson, M. S., and W. M. Noble: Comparison of various chemical quick tests on different soils, *U.S.D.A. Misc. Pub. 259,* 23 p., 1937.

2. Baur, Karl, F. T. Tremblay, G. A. Cummings, and D. B. Eldredge: Fertilizer placement for canning and freezing peas in Western Washington, *Wash. Agr. Exp. Sta. Bull. 504,* 20 p., 1948.

3. Byers, H. G., W. S. Anderson, and R. Bradfield: General chemistry of the soil, *U.S.D.A. Yearbook. Soils and men,* p. 911–29, 1938.

4. Clore, W. J. and C. L. Vincent: Vegetable fertilizer studies in the Walla Walla area, *Wash. Agr. Exp. Sta. Bull. 508,* 12 p., 1949.

5. Kelley, W. P.: The reclamation of alkali soils, *Cal. Agr. Exp. Sta. Bul. 617,* 40 p., 1937.

6. Salter, R. M., and C. J. Schollenberger: Farm manure, *Ohio Agr. Exp. Sta. Bul. 605,* 69 p., 1939.

7. Sauchelli, V.: What's in a fertilizer bag? *Better Crops With Plant Food. 27:* 17–22; 40–48, 1943.

8. Thomas, R. P.: The use of rapid soils tests in the United States. *Jour. Amer. Soc. Agron. 28:* 411–19, 1936.

9. Truog, E.: Soil acidity and liming, *U.S.D.A. Yearbook. Soils and men,* p. 563–81, 1938.

10. Ulrich, A.: Summary of field fertilizer experiments with potatoes at Shafter on Hesperia sandy loam, *Cal. Ext. Serv. Mimeo.* 3 p., 1939.

11. Volz, A. G. and B. B. Burlingame: Sweet potato cost production study for the 1938 crop year with five-year summary, *Cal. Ext. Serv. Mimeo.* 14 p., 1939.

12. Whittaker, C. W.: Mixing fertilizers on the farm, *U.S.D.A. Farmers' Bull. 2007,* 13 p., 1949.

13. Fertilizers for Eastern Washington, *Wash. Agr. Ext. Bull. 385* (Revised), 1950.

14. Fertilizers for Western Washington, *Wash. Agr. Ext. Bull. 386* (Revised), 1950.

Chapter 11

Preservation of Vegetables

Harvesting of vegetables is followed by a period of time before they are consumed or processed. During this period changes take place in their food value and quality, which makes them less desirable for food. Most consumers give little consideration to the best conditions for storing vegetables, but the requirements of storage have been studied carefully and the results applied to commercial operations. About 89 per cent of our vegetables are consumed fresh, and the balance preserved by such techniques as canning, dehydration, freezing, and pickling. Storage methods should be used which will keep losses to a minimum and preserve the quality to the best advantage for marketing. In the case of fresh vegetables these changes continue until consumed or cooked, but in the case of processed vegetables the change occurs only up till the time of heating or killing of the vegetable. After processing there is little change in the vegetable.

PHYSIOLOGICAL PROCESSES

After harvest there is a continuation of life processes in the vegetable. In the case of fruits and a few other crops the harvested portion can no longer obtain water or organic foods from the plant, hence, the vegetable can only maintain or suffer a decrease in food materials or undergo possible changes in texture and flavor. Much of the decrease in weight is due to loss of water and consequently a leafy crop like lettuce will suffer as much loss in one week as potatoes will in a month or two because the skin of the potato tends to prevent water loss. Humidity and temperature are important factors. Greatest weight loss occurs at low humidities and high temperatures. The destructive life processes that occur during storage are transpiration, respiration, chemical changes, growth, and sometimes the development of rots. Seed production from carrot roots and other biennials may be affected by storage temperature and treatment. Asexually propagated crops like white potatoes may be affected in a similar manner. Storage of vegetable seed has been considered in Chapter 7.

During respiration, organic substances of the cells are broken down, with liberation of energy or heat, carbon dioxide, water, and an absorption of oxygen. This process is increased by high temperatures. The rate of respiration and hence, deterioration, doubles or triples for each increase in temperature of 10° C. or 18° F. (Fig. 33). Respiration also is affected by the amount of injury or bruising, kind and age of the crop, as well as the oxygen and carbon dioxide content of the atmosphere. Aerobic oxidation process can be illustrated by the following equation:

$$C_6H_{12}O_6 + 6\ O_2 \longrightarrow 6\ CO_2 + 6\ H_2O + (673\ \text{kilogram calories})$$

sugar   oxygen   carbon dioxide   water   heat

In the cooling of a car of vegetables there are two sources of heat which must be removed. These are called vital and sensible (or field) heat. Heat of respiration is designated as vital heat and must be dissipated by cooling since it is free energy. Unless this heat is removed the temperature surrounding the vegetable will increase, resulting in an increased rate of respiration. Sensible heat refers to the field heat of the vegetable as well as similar heat found in packages and other materials put in the car. After the car has been reduced to the desired temperature there is a small amount of additional ice used to remove the vital heat. However, refrigerator cars have considerable conduction of heat and leakage, which is a source of ice meltage as the car moves to market.

Transpiration is the loss of water from the plant in the form of vapor or gas. In the case of leaves much of the water loss is through the stomata, and in the case of stems and other structures the water is lost directly through the

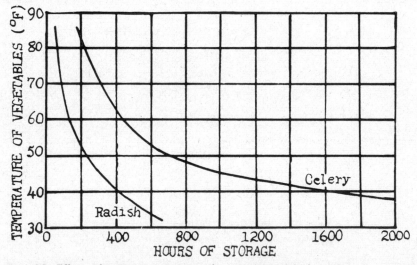

Fig. 33. Effect of temperature upon the storage period and keeping quality of two cool season crops. Both celery and radish store much longer near 32° F. than at 85° F. (Courtesy, *Journal of Agricultural Research*.)

surface cells. With certain vegetables such as tomato and peppers most of the water is lost through the stem scar. Transpiration is important in storage since such losses cause wilting or shrinking of the vegetable, with impairment of quality. Both temperature and humidity are important factors affecting water loss.

Chemical changes refer to the transformation of chemical compounds in the plant, which affect quality. The development of lignin in stored asparagus causes toughness. After harvest in some vegetables, there is a change from starch to sugar which may improve their taste. Crops in this group are winter squash, sweet potatoes, parsnips, and tomatoes. In sweet corn and peas there is a change from sugar to starch—the latter indicating poor quality and over-maturity.

Poor storage conditions or prolonged periods of storage may result in losses due to soft rot and other parasitic organisms. Inasmuch as bruised or immature specimens are more subject to attack from these organisms, it is important to prevent bruising while harvesting vegetables. Crops should have reached their proper stage of maturity before harvesting. Diseases in storage can be controlled partially by the use of proper sanitary measures as well as by providing the correct temperature, humidity, and ventilation.

In fresh storage, the physiological processes are retarded by controlling the environmental conditions, such as temperature and humidity. Preservation through canning, freezing, and dehydration may result in further detrimental changes for a very short time during preparation and processing. Respiration does not occur after processing, and the food is preserved for a considerable period, for marketing, without further change.

FRESH STORAGE

Several workers have developed tables listing the most desirable temperature and conditions for storing vegetables. The material in Table 23 was adapted from Rose, Wright, and Whiteman[6]. Since temperature is an important storage factor, for ease of classification the crops have been arranged according to storage temperature. Cool season crops, with the exception of white potatoes, should be stored at or near 32° F. Warm season crops are stored higher than 32°, with the exception of sweet corn. Those warm season crops which may be picked slightly immature should be stored at 10 to 15 degrees higher than the ripe fruits. Potatoes are stored at about 40° since lower temperatures will cause the starch to change to sugar and cause the potatoes to be undesirable for food. Recommendations regarding humidity and storage period also are given without classification. In many vegetables, the storage period will vary with variety. Thus, early varieties of onions may be stored 10 to 12 weeks, and late varieties up to 32 weeks. Approximate freezing temperatures also are given.

Several of the warm season fruits fail to ripen normally when subjected to chilling temperatures of lower than 50° F., with actual chilling at 40° or lower. Such temperatures may occur in early spring or late fall before the crop is harvested and may express their effects through several symptoms. Unfortunately, these do not appear at harvest time, but are noticeable after a storage period. Surface pitting or shallow surface depressions of varying extent appear on the vegetable. This condition has been observed on summer squash (Fig. 34), cucumber, and green bean. Chilling frequently increases susceptibility to decay by mold and bacteria. Melons and tomatoes exhibit a delay or failure to ripen after exposure to low temperatures. Chilling also may cause darkening of internal tissues. Many symptoms cause reduced storage life. Crops known to be subject to chilling effect are cucumber, eggplant, melon, okra, pepper, snap bean, summer squash, sweet potato, tomato,

Table 23*

COMMERCIAL STORAGE CONDITIONS FOR VEGETABLES

	Cool Season Crops			
Crop	*Temperature, °F.*	*Relative Humidity Per Cent*	*Storage Period,† Weeks*	*Average Freezing Point °F.*
Artichoke, globe	32	95	3–4	..
Asparagus	32	90	3–4	29.8
Beet:				
Topped	32	98	4–12	26.9
Bunch	32	90	1–2	
Broccoli, sprouting	32	95	2–3	29.2
Brussels sprout	32	95	3–4	..
Cabbage	32	95	12–16	31.2
Carrot:				
Topped	32	98	16–20	29.6
Bunch	32	90	1½–2	
Cauliflower	32	90	2–3	30.1
Celeriac	32	98	12–16	..
Celery	32	95	8–16	29.7
Endive	32	95	2–3	30.9
Garlic (dry)	32	75	24–32	25.4
Kohlrabi	32	98	2–4	30.0
Leek	32	90	4–12	29.2
Lettuce	32	95	2–3	31.2
Onion	32	75	12–32	30.1
Onion sets	32	75	24–32	29.5
Parsnip	32	95	8–16	28.9
Pea (green)	32	90	1–2	30.0
Radish (winter)	32	98	8–16	..
Rhubarb	32	95	2–3	28.4
Rutabaga	32	98	8–16	29.5
Spinach	32	95	1½–2	30.3
Turnip	32	98	16–20	30.5
Potato, white	38–50	90	12–20	28.9

Table 23—(Continued)

Warm Season Crops

Crop	Tempera-ture, °F.	Relative Humidity, Per Cent	Storage Period,† Weeks	Average Freezing Point °F.
Corn, sweet	31–32	90	½–1	28.9
Muskmelon (cantaloupe)‡	34–40	78	1–1½	29.0
Bean:				
Snap	34–40	90	1–2	29.7
Lima (unshelled)	34–40	90	1–3	30.1
Melon:				
Honeydew and honeyball	36–38	85	2–4	29.0
Casaba and Persian	36–40	85	4–6	. .
Watermelon	36–40	85	2–3	29.2
Pepper, sweet	40–45	90	3–4	30.1
Tomato, ripe	40–50	85	1–1½	30.4
Cucumber	45–50	95	1½–2	30.5
Eggplant	45–50	90	1½	30.4
Okra	50	95	2	30.1
Pumpkin	50–55	75	8–24	30.1
Squash, summer	50	95	2–3	. .
Squash, winter	50–55	75	16–24	29.3
Sweet potato	55	85	8–24	28.5
Tomato, green	55–70	90	3–5	30.4

* Courtesy, *U.S.D.A. Cir. 278* with some changes in data.

† Approximate storage period to indicate period from harvest until consumed or discarded. Examine crop discussion for further information.

‡ For ripe melons; unripe fruits slightly higher temperatures.

and watermelon. Probably all warm season crops are subject to chilling injury except sweet corn.

The greatest cooling action of ice occurs when it changes from a solid to a liquid. The cooling capacity of ice is expressed in British thermal units (B.T.U.); this unit is the quantity of heat required to raise the temperature of one pound of water 1° F. at or near its point of maximum density. When ice melts, 144 B.T.U. of heat are required. There is also some cooling when either ice or water becomes warmer in temperature. The specific heat of ice is one-half and of water is one. When ice changes one degree in temperature, as from 29° to 30° F., it has the cooling power of one-half B.T.U. per pound; similarly water requires one B.T.U. of heat per pound to increase temperature one degree F.

Fig. 34. Chilling or low temperature damage to summer squash fruit. The surface exhibits pitting after 16 days at 32° F., followed by 2 days at 70° F.

Since ice is stored below freezing it may be delivered to a vegetable shipper at a temperature of 28° F. for example. When this ice changes from 28° F. to a liquid at 40° F. it has a cooling power of 154 B.T.U. per pound.

The quality of a vegetable may be preserved better if the temperature can be lowered rapidly soon after harvest or packing. This procedure has been called *precooling* and is for the purpose of reducing the rate of respiration and transpiration. At the present time there are four different procedures or mediums used to precool vegetables as follows: ice, air, water, and vacuum. Crushed ice is used both in the package and over the top (Fig. 35) of the load to cool vegetables rapidly. The most frequent use has been with cool season crops which are harvested under cool temperature conditions. More recently top ice has been found advantageous in the shipment of cantaloupes and sweet corn. In the second method electric fans are used to circulate the air more rapidly in the refrigerator car and hasten ice meltage. The fans are placed in the uppermost opening from the ice bunkers of a loaded car. A continuous stream of air from the ice is blown through the load and back to the ice bunker. In 8 to 12 hours a car may be cooled to the desired temperature as compared to four to six days in transit without fans (Fig. 36). Cars on a siding may be cooled by the use of refrigerator equipment on a truck

Fig. 35. Top-icing a car of peas. The blocks of ice are pulverized in the machine and blown over the top of the load. (Courtesy, Preco, Inc.)

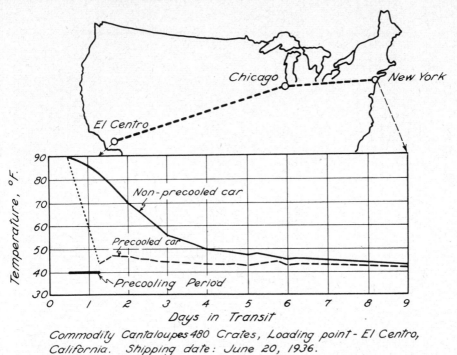

Fig. 36. Transit temperatures of cantaloupes during a 9-day period. Note the lower temperature of the fruits in the precooled car. (Courtesy, Preco, Inc.)

or by placing cars adjacent to brine towers. In both cases cool air is blown into the car and packages of vegetables. A recent innovation is small fans below the floor rack which precool the car in transit (Fig. 36). The fans may be powered by electric motors at the packing house, but use power from the axle of the car when in transit. Some vegetables like asparagus, may be passed through a bath of ice water (35° to 40° F.) and cooled to the desired temperature in 15 to 30 minutes after which they are loaded into an iced car for shipment. Vacuum cooling is dependent upon the fact that vacuum causes water to evaporate thus cooling the vegetable, but water loss is not sufficient to cause wilting. When the water changes from a liquid to a gas, heat is extracted from the vegetable. Each pound of water evaporated requires 1000 B.T.U. for evaporation. This procedure seems better adapted to leafy vegetables like lettuce that have a large thin leaf surface. Vacuum cooling has been used for cooling this crop. The packed crates without ice are run into an air tight container on small cars. The door is sealed and a vacuum drawn on the container. This procedure in precooling is of recent origin. Precooling is desirable for many crops shipped during the warmer part of the year.

The loss of water from vegetables is very important. Since refrigerator cars are dependent upon ice for refrigerant, the humidity of the cars is fairly high. This is an advantage for most crops. In the case of onions and garlic humidities are desired as low as 75 per cent. In recent years some crops have been waxed to reduce water loss. In cold storage, sprinkling may be used to raise the humidity and prevent the shriveling of the crops.

Mechanical harvesting equipment has produced considerable saving in the amount of harvest labor, but there is frequently some mechanical injury to the crop. Injuries disfigure the product, increase transpiration and respiration losses, and favor infection by rot organisms. Some vegetables may be bruised without breaking the skin, which is also detrimental; sweet potatoes may suffer severe losses from such injury. If a crop is to be stored, every possible effort should be made to prevent bruises or cut places.

STRUCTURES FOR FRESH STORAGE

The different methods of storage need to be considered in more detail. Fresh vegetables are stored under various conditions which may be grouped as follows: (a) Little or no temperature and humidity control; (b) use of ventilation with cooler outside air, in naturally cool areas or during the cool season of the year; (c) use of artificial refrigeration either in cold storages or by means of ice to cool refrigerator cars. Both temperature and humidity are important in the preservation of vegetables for fresh consumption.

Many vegetables are stored temporarily with little regard for the conditions employed. Crops vary as to their rate of change in storage: peas, sweet corn, and asparagus deteriorate rapidly, but such crops as white potatoes, onions, and rutabagas change slowly and sometimes are referred to as hardware items. Among the nonrefrigerated storage places may be listed outdoor pits, outdoor storage cellars, and basements of buildings. Winter storage of some vegetables is possible by digging a pit and lining it with straw or similar material. After placing the vegetables in the pit in a pointed pile they are covered with 6 to 8 inches of straw and then several inches of soil. An opening is left at the top for ventilation. The air surrounding the vegetables is moist and cool. In the more permanent types of storage, the structures should be insulated adequately. This adds little to the cost and is of great assistance in the regulation of temperature, particularly in fall and spring. Ventilation may be provided by placing outlet ducts at the ceiling, extending to the outside through the walls or roof. Inlet ducts for cold air should enter through the floor. Dampers should be installed in these ducts so the flow of air may be regulated. During the cooler months the storage temperature may be lowered by opening the dampers at night and closing them in the morning. Air circulation in the cellar is important, and may be increased by the use of slatted floor racks or by keeping the produce in slatted containers arranged to provide sufficient space so air flow will occur. In addition suction fans may be installed to draw the air in from the outside and force it under the floor racks. Crops requiring temperatures of 32° to 40° F., and having a maximum possible storage period of a month or longer, may be stored successfully in this type of a building in cool climates. Crops such as sweet potatoes, pumpkins, and winter squash, requiring temperatures of between 50° and 55° should be placed in above ground storages, with ventilation. Sometimes artificial heat is needed to maintain these temperatures. Humidity may be increased by sprinkling water on the floor and walls; or reduced by the use of calcium chloride. An accurate thermometer should be provided so temperatures may be checked.

With cold storage the temperature may be regulated accurately by the use of mechanical refrigeration and thermostatic controls. Control of humidity also is desirable. This type of storage may be owned by a grower if he is operating on a large scale, or may be rented from commercial concerns in nearby cities. Rates usually are based on the storage conditions requested and the period of storage.

Refrigerator cars are in reality storage units, built so they may be moved on the railroads. These cars have well-insulated floors, ceilings, and walls, with floor racks to facilitate ventilation (Fig. 37). An ice bunker is located

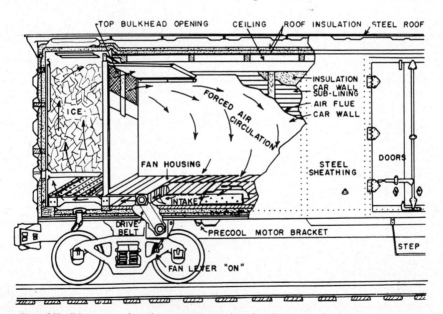

Fig. 37. Diagram showing structure, ice bunkers, and air movement in a fan-equipped refrigerator car. Packaged vegetables are placed on floor racks to the right of the ice bunker. Fans reverse the direction of air flow from that obtained without fans. (Courtesy, Preco, Inc., and University of California.)

at each end of the car, with openings into the body of the car at top and bottom for air circulation. The bunkers have a total ice capacity of about five tons—the source of cooling. Salt may be added to the ice to cause more rapid melting, hence, a more rapid cooling of the produce. Precooling may be employed for the same purpose.

The temperature of a refrigerator car may be regulated by icing, ventilating, and sometimes heating in winter to prevent freezing. Under refrigeration the desired temperatures are obtained by the amount and frequency of adding ice, use of fans, use of salt, and location of the ice in the package or car. In the shipping of some crops such as early potatoes, and asparagus, the ice usually is placed only in the bunkers. Lettuce, peas, and carrots are shipped with crushed ice in the package and also blown over the top of the load. Certain other crops are shipped with only top ice; some with top ice and small blocks between the packages (pigeon-hole ice). Fall tomatoes, onions, watermelons, sweet potatoes, and some early potatoes move in refrigerator cars without ice. In this case the ventilators are opened or closed to regulate the temperature.

In recent years there has been a growing use of consumer packages for several vegetables. Such units are more attractive in appearance, the vegetables have been washed and are not handled by the store customers, and these units tend to limit the minimum amount which can be purchased at one time. The vegetables are packaged usually at the wholesale level but also are packaged by growers' organizations and retail stores. Packaging increases the cost of the vegetable in many cases, but reduces the housewife's work of washing and discarding of stems and unusable parts of crops such as spinach. Consumer packages are used commonly for potatoes, spinach, tomatoes, celery, and salad and soup mixes. Potatoes are packed in 5, 10, and 25 pound sacks sometimes with a transparent window on the smaller sacks. Small plants of celery are packed in transparent wrapper with an excess of leaves removed. Four or five tomatoes are packed in a cardboard box with a transparent window or a boat with an overwrap. With some vegetables ventilation of the package is essential. Storage life varies in the store so some packages may need reconditioning.

PROCESSED VEGETABLES

Processing procedures have been classified as canning, dehydrating, freezing, and pickling. The data regarding the amount of processed food must be obtained from several sources, consequently the following figures should be used only to compare their general importance. In 1950, the following approximate amounts of vegetables were processed: canned, 4,500,000 tons (7); cucumber pickles and kraut, 400,000 tons (7); frozen, 250,000 tons (8); and dehydrated, 30,000 dried tons (8). Processing factories tend to be located in or near areas of low cost of production having a long period for harvesting a quality crop.

The convenience and ease of transportation of canned foods have made them an essential source of food. About 11 per cent of our per capita consumption of vegetables consists of processed products and canned vegetables are the most important item. The most important canned vegetables are tomatoes, sweet corn, and peas; others in their order of importance are snap beans, beets, and asparagus. The first canning was done in France in 1809 and by 1820 Underwood in Boston and Kensett in New York were producing canned foods in the United States. Commercial canning did not make rapid growth until the introduction of labor-saving machinery. Machine shelling of peas with a "viner", machine husking and cutting of corn from the cob, and mechanical shellers for lima beans have affected the industry greatly, as well as the machine manufacture of tin cans.

Various vegetables are handled differently as to certain canning details, but in general many of the procedures are similar. The following operations are performed on most vegetables: Inspecting the crop as received from the grower; removing imperfect or low-quality vegetables from the cannery inspection belts; preparing for canning by removal of nonedible parts— as tomato skins and core, corn husks, etc; filling of vegetables into cans; adding salt or salt and sugar brines; exhausting; capping the can with a lid; processing or sterilizing; cooling; labeling; and placing in cases. Most vegetables are blanched by heating in steam or hot water to stop life processes and deterioration. Processing or sterilizing refers to heating the closed can so the minimum temperature is high enough to prevent the development of spoilage organisms. For storage, cans may be placed in a warehouse and need only to be protected against freezing.

Canning factories represent considerable investment in buildings and equipment so the owners frequently process more than one crop to reduce overhead per case. Canning procedures are somewhat similar for both fruits and vegetables so these may be handled in the same factory. An individual crop may require some equipment which is not of general use on all crops, but the retorts (sterilization), can closing machines, fillers and some other equipment may be used for all vegetables. A corn husker and pea viner are examples of equipment having limited use. Table 24 lists the canning periods for several vegetables processed in western states. Spinach, asparagus, tomatoes, and pumpkin are examples of crops that are harvested at different seasons in California and may be processed in one factory. Also some factories are large enough to handle more than one crop at a time. Table 24 lists some 17 vegetables and other minor crops which are canned. Some vegetables like tomatoes are the basis for several canned products such as canned tomatoes, juice, catsup, chili sauce, soup, paste, and purée. The last product is added to many other foods in small amounts.

Table 24*

CANNING PERIODS FOR DIFFERENT VEGETABLES† IN THE WESTERN STATES

Crop	California	Colorado	Idaho	Montana	New Mexico	Oregon	Utah	Washington	Wyoming
Asparagus	Apr. 1 June 30					May 1 July 1	May 20 June 5	May 1 July 1	
Beans Lima	Sept. 1 Oct. 31						Aug. 5 Oct. 1		Aug. 15 Sept. 15
Beans Snap	Aug. 1 Oct. 15	July 15 Oct. 1		July 15 Sept. 20	July 15 Sept. 25	Aug. 1 Sept. 5	July 10 Oct. 15	Aug. 1 Sept. 5	July 15 Sept. 20
Beets	May 5 Dec. 20					July 1 Oct. 15	June 1 Oct. 15	July 1 Oct. 15	July 1 Sept. 25
Corn			Aug. 1 Sept. 15	Aug. 12 Sept. 20		Aug. 15 Sept. 30	Aug. 15 Sept. 25	Aug. 15 Sept. 30	Aug. 20 Sept. 25
Carrots						Aug. 20 Oct. 15	Aug. 15 Oct. 15	Aug. 20 Oct. 15	Sept. 1 Sept. 30

Kraut		All year		All year		All year	All year	All year	All year
Peas	Apr. 10 June 30	June 15 Aug. 1	June 1 July 20	July 1 Aug. 20		June 10 Aug. 20	June 10 Aug. 10	June 10 Aug. 20	July 1 Aug. 25
Pickles	All year					All year		All year	
Pumpkin and squash	Oct. 1 Nov. 15	Oct. 5 Nov. 15		Sept. 25 Oct. 10		Oct. 1 Nov. 30	Oct. 1 Nov. 15	Oct. 1 Nov. 30	Oct. 1 Oct. 15
Rhubarb						May 1 June 10		May 1 June 10	
Spinach	Feb. 20–Apr. 20 Oct. 1–Dec. 15				Aug. 15 Oct. 15	Sept. 1 Oct. 15		Sept. 1 Oct. 15	
Tomatoes	July 10 Nov. 10	Aug. 15 Oct. 15	Aug. 20 Oct. 15		Aug. 15 Oct. 15	Aug. 15 Oct. 1	Aug. 15 Oct. 15	Aug. 15 Oct. 1	Sept. 10 Sept. 25

* Courtesy, American Can Company.

† Other vegetables canned in California: Artichokes—Feb. 1 to April 30; pimientos—Sept. 15 to Dec. 15; Brussels sprout—Nov. 15 to Jan. 8; sweet potato—Sept. 15 to Nov. 30.

The cost of the canned product is made up of many separate items including, the cost of raw product or vegetable, labor, cans and other supplies, depreciation, and factory overhead. Table 25 shows the relative cost of the raw product in comparison to the other canning costs for representative canners in the United States. The cost of the vegetable ranges from 22 to 35 per cent of the total cost. In the case of green asparagus, the raw product may represent 50 per cent of the total costs. The canner's profits vary from year to year and evidently 1938 was an unprofitable year for many canners. A canner's margin of profit usually is very small per case, but with a large volume the total profit may be considerable. Industries operating on a small margin of profit may be affected greatly by a small change in price of the finished product.

Table 25*

RELATIVE COST OF CANNING SEVERAL VEGETABLES FOR THE UNITED STATES

Expense Item	Per Cent of Canner's Selling Price							
	Corn		Peas		Snap Beans		Tomatoes	
	1938	1948	1938	1948	1938	1948	1938	1948
Raw product (paid to grower)	22	27	35	33	29	35	26	28
Other costs	95	68	85	65	89	62	97	67
Profit	17†	5	20†	2	18†	3	23†	5

* Courtesy, Supplement to Information Letter of National Canners Association No. 1265, December 17, 1949.
† Loss.

Dehydration as a method of food preservation has been practiced for centuries with a limited number of crops. Dried foods are concentrated because most of the water has been removed and thus, are used when transportation facilities are inadequate for the fresh product. Thus, 1000 pounds of tomatoes canned and packed would weigh 1500 pounds, but only 85 pounds when dried and packed (Table 2). In this case the drying ratio is 15 to 1; or 15 pounds of fresh product will give 1 pound of the dried product. The drying procedure varies, but frequently the vegetables are washed and peeled mechanically. After trimming, they are diced, blanched, and loaded on trays for the drying tunnel. The vegetables usually are stored or shipped in metal containers. Most vegetables are dried until they contain 5 per cent or less of water.

The freezing of fruits and vegetables has developed rapidly in recent years. But in spite of their reputation for high quality, less than 1 per cent of our vegetables are consumed in this manner. In the preparation of frozen vegetables, heat is used first to stop the action of enzymes and life processes, through the use of steam or hot water. The product is then quick-frozen at temperatures from 0° to — 20° F. on a continuous belt, in a salt brine solution, or in packages. It is important to have the product well packaged to prevent desiccation and toughening. After freezing, the product should be held at about 0° F. in order to retain the quality. Most vegetables eaten raw, such as lettuce, tomatoes, and watermelons, with the exception of cantaloupes, do not make pleasing frozen products. Vegetables which usually are cooked have been found to be more desirable.

Pickling is the process whereby conditions are made unfavorable for the growth of damaging microörganisms. The salt and vinegar used in pickling, and the lactic acid formed by fermentation, act as preservatives of the food. Sufficient salt or vinegar must be added to prevent the growth of the injurious microörganisms. Lactic acid bacteria produce this acid from the sugars present in the vegetables. When salt or solutions of salt are added to vegetables, the plant juices are extracted, and lactic bacteria will act on these, provided air is excluded. Cucumbers for pickles, and cabbage for sauerkraut are the two vegetables most commonly preserved by the pickling process.

REFERENCES

1. Beattie, J. H., and D. H. Rose: Home storage of vegetables and fruits, *U.S.D.A. Farmers' Bull. 1939,* 29 p., 1943.
2. Bouquet, A. G. B.: Vegetable storage, *Ore. Agr. Ext. Bull. 601,* 4 p., 1943.
3. Case, W. M.; Exina Davenport, and Inez M. Eckblad: Home Storage of Fruits and Vegetables, *Colo. Agr. Ext. Ser. D-12,* 7 p., 1942.
4. Cruess, W. V., and G. MacKinney: The dehydration of vegetables, *Calif. Agr. Exp. Sta. Bull. 680,* 76 p., 1943.
5. Joslyn, M. A., and W. V. Cruess: Home and farm preparation of pickles, *Calif. Agr. Ext. Cir. 37,* 24 p., (revised) 1943.
6. Rose, D. H., R. C. Wright, and T. M. Whiteman: Commercial storage of fruits, vegetables, and florists stocks, *U.S.D.A. Cir. 278,* 60 p., 1949.
7. U. S. Department of Agriculture, Commercial truck crops for market and processing, 1951.
8. *Western Canner and Packer, 43;* No. 6. 1951.

Chapter 12

Vegetable Grades and Grading

Grading refers to the classification of vegetables into groups based on factors of quality, condition, and size. The factors upon which a grade or standard usually is based are dependent on variety, maturity, color, shape, freshness, firmness, and complete freedom from certain defects such as decay, breakdown, wet sunscald, or such other conditions that may cause the individual specimen to be almost a complete loss. For the less serious defects such as scars or other blemishes which injure the appearance of the specimen, certain degrees of injury may be permitted. The area or seriousness may be indicated by the terms as "free from injury," "free from damage," or "free from serious damage" in their grades, with further specific definitions for each defect. U. S. Standards for vegetables are used throughout the United States. In most states the use of these grades is optional. Some states base their standardization program on U.S. grades and in such instances, they provide for the required standards to be enforced by the state. This is particularly true of potatoes. In at least one state, California, there is also a separate and distinct set of enforcement standards which affect the vegetable industry. California state enforcement standards include requirements for standard packs, markings, and containers, in addition to quality standards. Vegetables which fail to meet these standards cannot be sold or marketed through fresh market channels, but sometimes are sold for processing or livestock feed. Any violators are subject to court action which may result in a fine or a prison term or both.

During the first World War, the Food Administration requested the U.S. Department of Agriculture to develop standard grades for potatoes[3]. All potato handlers were ordered to use these grades for buying or selling this commodity during the war period. Research work for the purpose of developing effective grades for potatoes and other horticultural crops had been conducted for several years previous to 1917. This was the first use of Federal grades. By 1922, Federal grades were used to inspect 100,635 cars; and 862,111 cars of fruits and vegetables in the 1950–51 fiscal year. Although potatoes were the first crop to be inspected, this service now covers a wide range of commodities, such as: grains, alfalfa hay, meat, many fruits and vegetables, canned vegetables, frozen vegetables, and even tomato plants. Grading of fruits and vegetables was a common practice previous to 1917, but all of these cases lacked so-called "third party inspection" by trained personnel. The buyer and seller are both interested parties so it is logical to ask an unbiased third party to determine the grade with fairness and accuracy. Inspections according to grades may be made by Federal, Federal-State, State, railroad, and private inspectors.

In the early days of vegetable production the growers or associations would strive to market a standard pack which was designated by brand names or other means. Competition between brands became so acute that state legislatures attempted to develop grades or standards for produce. Many of these standards were suggested by enthusiastic horticulturists who often tended to suggest impossible standards which could not be used in commercial practice. These grades could be changed by whomever passed them. In some cases this was a state legislature and in other cases growers' organizations. On some city markets policemen were assigned the duty of enforcing local grades. The development and enforcement of local grades led naturally to a request for supervision by Federal and State agencies with the use of trained personnel.

There were several inventions previous to the first World War which caused increased transportation and consumption of fruits and vegetables. An industrial expansion began previous to the twentieth century which greatly increased the population of cities. This, in turn, greatly increased the demand for vegetables. Refrigerator cars were developed during and after the Civil War. The first refrigerator car was patented in 1868. At that time ice was available primarily from that frozen on bodies of water during winter and stored for summer use in ice houses. The present type of ammonia compressor was developed about 1875 and this made ice available in all areas of the United States regardless of winter climate. Cold storage facilities have increased greatly in recent years and have been an important means of encouraging the orderly marketing of vegetables. When a market is overloaded with some vegetables a portion may be put in cold storage for sale a few days or weeks later. The transportation period from production areas to market also has been shortened; this permits many vegetables to be placed on the market in better condition. In recent years the railroads have made ninth morning delivery in New York City from El Centro, California; while in 1917, it was twelfth morning delivery. In the last 10 years there has been considerable interest in transporting vegetables from the west coast to the east in refrigerated trucks. A small volume is being moved in this way and trucks deliver vegetables into Chicago on the fifth morning from the West.

As the market volume of vegetables increased there was demand for more uniformly graded crops and the use of the same grades each year. Factory workers wished to buy quality produce and were willing to pay a fair premium for the better vegetables. In order to meet this need the Federal government developed a grading system which is the primary system in use at the present time. It is supervised by unbiased Federal employees, usually with the cooperation of state governmental agencies. This type of grade may be referred to as voluntary, since it is used only when either the buyer, seller, or some interested party requests an official certificate of grade. A grower may mark his goods according to U.S. grades without going to the expense of Federal inspection. However, in such a case, the grower is held responsible for the accuracy of the grade. California also has state enforcement standards for fruits and vegetables. These state standards include several features, such as minimum quality standards, packing, and marking requirements, and they also set up dimensions for standard containers. Some of the quality standards require only minimum quality, and some standards are relatively high, depending upon the decision of the industry and their agreement at the time when the legislation was enacted. The packing, marking, and standard container requirements are to provide a standardization of these factors in the packing and labeling of vegetables, but more important they are designed to prevent fraud, deception, and false labeling. These state standards are compulsory for all producers within the state of California, and for each crop that the state legislature has established a grade.

FIXED VERSUS FLEXIBLE GRADE STANDARDS

Our present grades are of the fixed type or they are the same regardless of whether a farmer has a good or poor crop. If the total yield of a given crop is low, there is usually a higher price and poorer quality produce frequently can be marketed at a profit. Some people have suggested that a fixed grade reduces farm income and have suggested that a flexible grade be used[1]. A flexible grade would be more severe when there were large yields and good quality, and less severe in periods of under production.

Some growers of vegetables might be favorable to flexible standards, but buyers and receivers would be opposed to them because they would have no assurance that cars would be of uniform quality. The present Federal grades permit the grower to sort his potatoes according to five grades varying in quality. These grades are called "U.S. Fancy, U.S. Extra No. 1, U.S. No. 1, U.S. Commercial, and U.S. No. 2." Some vegetables however, do not have a grade higher than U.S. No. 1. Another method may be used to accomplish the same goal and that is to obtain a certificate giving the percentage of the specimens meeting the U.S. No. 1 grade except for the decay defect. A car of potatoes may be sold as 85 per cent of the tubers meeting the U.S. No. 1 grade or other percentages chosen by the shipper. If the grade defects are within 3 per cent the certificate may read "defects well within grade tolerance." Better results will be secured through the use of U.S. standards with varying percentages of U.S. No. 1 quality rather than flexible grades which may deteriorate into an absence of standards.

ADVANTAGES OF GRADING

With such a rapid growth in the use of grades, particularly the optional types, it is desirable to consider some of their advantages:

1. They furnish a common language for the buyer and seller to use in their financial transactions.

2. Permit f.o.b. ("fob") selling of vegetables. A buyer in New York City may purchase a car of U.S. No. 1 potatoes in Idaho without personally inspecting them.

3. There is fairness to both buyer and seller through third-party inspection.

4. Makes for orderly marketing of crops; this frequently results in a higher price to the producer since most of the poorer grades are not marketed.

5. Gives the grower a definite goal to attain in his farming operations.

6. A grade certificate may be used as legal evidence to establish the value of a commodity. The crop may be warehoused properly and money borrowed on the evidence of quality given by the certificate.

7. Enables the shipper to pool various growers' lots in uniformly graded cars.

8. Furnishes a uniform basis of grading of products under marketing agreements.

9. Establishes a basis of settlement of claims against carriers, particularly if the shipper also has a destination certificate.

10. State enforcement standards form a base below which no vegetable can move either intrastate or interstate, and both the producer and consumer are benefited.

11. State enforcement standards prevent fraud, deception, and mislabeling.

DISADVANTAGES OF GRADING

While the advantages of grading are numerous there is still need for discussing the disadvantages from the standpoint of developing our knowledge of this subject. Some of the disadvantages listed below do not apply to all grading situations, but are of general importance.

1. U.S. grades are not used in some crops because the shipper does not receive a premium over private brands.

2. U.S. No. 1 grade may be too wide a range of quality to indicate the true superior quality of a shipper's pack. A shipper may pack two or three standards within U.S. No. 1 quality.

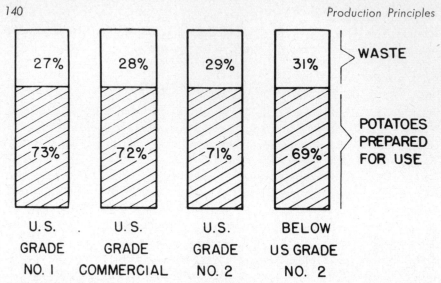

Fig. 38. The amount of waste increases slightly with the use of poorer grades of potatoes; some additional time is required to remove the increased waste from the poorer grades. (Courtesy, Cornell University.)

3. There is little difference in the food value of different grades of a crop. Lower grades exhibit greater defects which increase amount of waste and cost of removal (Fig. 38).

. 4. Change in condition from shipping point to market is an important consideration to the buyer even though caused by conditions beyond his control. Grades describe condition accurately only when there has been a recent inspection.

TYPES OF GRADES

When both Federal and State enforcement standards are considered there are really three general types of grades. (a) Fresh vegetables usually are selected so they meet the requirements of one grade in a package such as U.S. No. 1 or U.S. No. 2. From a marketing standpoint, fresh vegetables need a uniform grade in each package and usually in volume production; each car contains only one grade of produce. (b) In canning crops there is no need for sorting into No. 1's and No. 2's; therefore the vegetables of acceptable grades are mixed in the package. An inspector samples the load and determines the percentage of U.S. No. 1's, U.S. No. 2's, and culls. With canning tomatoes, a grower might be paid $20.00 per ton for U.S. No. 1's, $10.00 for U.S. No. 2's, and nothing for culls. The grower would receive $15.00 per ton for a load of tomatoes averaging 50 per cent U.S. No. 1's, and 50 per cent U.S. No. 2's. (c) The California enforcement standards usually give one minimum grade for each crop. Both state and Federal grades describe a minimum quality that the package must meet or exceed.

HOW GRADES ARE ESTABLISHED

U.S. standards are worked out on an industry wide basis. If a certain industry believes that it would be advantageous to develop U.S. standards, individual shippers or trade organizations may forward their request to the Fresh Products Standardization and Inspection Division of the Production and Marketing Administration, U.S. Department of Agriculture, at Washington, D.C. This organization, which has a small staff of technical employees, will then conduct investigation and research work on the product in the different parts of the country where the particular product is handled commercially, and grading and packing operations are observed in each locality. Meetings of representatives of the industry are held in the various producing sections. The market receivers also are consulted and frequently it is necessary to consult vegetable specialists and pathologists of the College of Agriculture to obtain further necessary information. When sufficient information is secured, the standards are drafted. These are reviewed in Washington and then submitted to the trade for further review. When final agreement is reached it is necessary that such standards be published in the Federal Register previous to the time that they can be issued officially by the Department of Agriculture as official standards.

The California state enforcement standard usually is initiated by some group of producers, packers or other interested persons. These standards generally are based on research made either by the industry group proposing them, in some cases by the Bureau of Fruit and Vegetable Standardization, or the University of California. A grade or standard is written generally by conference between all the parties concerned, including the legislator who will introduce the bill into the legislature and sponsor it, and the Legislative Counsel Bureau, who provides advice so that when it becomes a part of the Agricultural Code it will be entirely legal. After approval by the state legislature, this standard then becomes a part of the California Agricultural Code after being signed by the Governor. Generally, standards which have been worked out and prepared for introduction to the legislature seldom have any controversial features.

COST OF INSPECTION

The Federal grades are optional with producers and buyers; therefore if some interested party asks for inspection, he is charged for the service. The usual charge is $7.20 per car. In some cases where a small amount of a large number of products is inspected such as for delivery to institutions or army camps the charges are made on an hourly basis. Fresh products inspected for delivery to processors usually are made on a tonnage basis, but the inspections sometimes are paid for on a weekly basis.

The California enforcement standards are compulsory for fresh vegetables grown or sold within the state. Inspectors are paid from the State budget without specific charges to local producers. In the case of the state tomato grade, it is agreed mutually that the cost will be paid equally by grower and canner on a tonnage basis.

FEDERAL INSPECTION TERMS

Shipping Point Inspection Service is maintained in practically all states by cooperative agreements between the Production and Marketing Administration and some state agency. Usually the state agency is the State Department of Agriculture. In some states where there is no well recognized Department the cooperating agency may be a College of Agriculture or some industry agency that is interested in the welfare of the fruit and vegetable shippers. The Shipping Point Inspection Service is available to all financially interested parties, whether growers, shippers, packers, or transportation agencies. The general plan of operation under a cooperative agreement is that the state will collect the fees, provide for the salaries and expense of the inspectors, and generally handle all matters that particularly pertain to the financial end of the organization. The Federal Department will control the licensing of the inspectors and be responsible for the interpretation of Standards, method of making inspections, and certificate writing. This is necessary in order to maintain uniform operation throughout the entire country.

The inspection of products in the receiving markets is handled under the direction of a Federal Supervisor and is done largely by inspectors directly in the employ of the U.S. Department of Agriculture. Considerable training and experience is required to qualify for this position since inspectors must familiarize themselves with products from all parts of the United States. It is further necessary to have detailed knowledge of diseases of vegetables since it is necessary frequently in cases of controversy to place responsibility on receivers, transportation companies, or shippers in order to settle claims properly. Occasionally receivers may be dissatisfied with cars of products inspected and certified as of a certain grade at shipping point. In such cases the receiver, or complainant, is privileged to request an appeal inspection. In such cases two inspectors usually are assigned to make the appeal inspection which generally requires more detailed sampling and a very careful analysis. If the car lot is found to be up to grade the original inspection is sustained and a double charge is levied against the applicant. However, if it is found that the Shipping Point Inspector was in error, the certificate is reversed and there is no charge against the applicant. Many inspections on the receiving markets are made for condition only, that is to determine the percentage of decay or some other factor which might have changed during transit.

The inspection certificates issued by either the Federal or Federal-State Inspection Services are accepted as prima facie evidence of the facts stated in the certificate by all Federal courts and also by those state courts which have passed legislation recognizing the certificate as prima facie evidence.

INTERPRETATION OF GRADES

Field experience in grading cannot be replaced by either classroom or laboratory work. However, it is possible to consider some aspects of interpreting grades to advantage. Most fresh produce grades use similar terminology in describing defects and tolerances. The complete U.S. standards for potatoes are too extensive to be included, but a description is given of the U.S. No. 1 grade. The California enforcement standard for potatoes is somewhat briefer and should be considered first for this reason. The reader should remember this is a minimum grade and potatoes failing to comply are either reconditioned for market or sold for potato chips, flour, or other uses.

CALIFORNIA ENFORCEMENT STANDARD FOR POTATOES
(Effective May 9, 1951)

"Potatoes shall be free from mold, decay, soft and wet rots, black heart, and hollow heart; and free from serious damage due to insect injury, freezing, sunscald, dry rots, scab, growth cracks, sunburn, second growth, cuts, bruises, grass roots, nematodes, or other causes. Damage to any one potato is not serious unless it causes a waste of 10 per cent, by weight, of the individual potato.

"Damage by cuts shall also be considered serious when both ends are clipped or when more than an estimated one-fourth of the potato is cut away, or in the case of long varieties when the remaining portion of the clipped potato weighs less than six ounces.

"Not more than 5 per cent, by weight, of potatoes in any one container or bulk lot may be below these requirements.

"Containers of potatoes shall not bear any marking, brand, or designation of quality such as 'extra selected', 'selected', 'select', 'extra fancy', 'fancy', 'choice', 'No. 1', or other similar superlative designations which imply a reasonable high quality, unless the contents of the container conform at least to the requirements of the U.S. No. 1 grade established for potatoes by the U.S. Department of Agriculture."

U.S. STANDARDS FOR U.S. NO. 1 POTATOES
(Effective June 1, 1949)
General

"Numbers and letters in parentheses following grade terms indicate where such terms are defined under definitions. All percentages shall be calculated on the basis of weight. The tolerances for the standards are on a container basis. However, individual packages in any lot may vary from the specified tolerances as stated below, provided the averages for the entire lot, based on sample inspection, are within the tolerances specified. When the tolerance specified is less than 10 per cent, individual packages in any lot may contain not more than double the tolerance specified except that for frozen potatoes, or those affected by soft rot or wet breakdown, not more than one-tenth of the packages may contain more than double the tolerance but not more than four times the tolerance specified, and except that at least one defective and one off-sized specimen shall be permitted in a package.

"**U.S. No. 1.** shall consist of potatoes of one variety or similar varietal characteristics which are fairly well shaped (1), not frozen, which are free from freezing injury, blackheart, late blight, southern bacterial wilt, ring rot, and soft rot or wet breakdown (2), and from damage (3) caused by dirt (3j) or other foreign matter (3j), sunburn, second growth (3a), growth cracks (3a), air cracks (3b), hollow heart, internal discoloration (3 and 4), external discoloration (3c), cuts, shriveling (3d), sprouting (3e), scab (3f and g), dry rot, rhizoctonia (3h), other disease (3), wireworm (3i), other insects or mechanical or other means (3).

"Unless otherwise specified the diameter (5) of each potato shall be not less than 1⅞ inches.

"**Tolerance for defects.** In order to allow for variations other than size, hollow heart, and internal discoloration, incident to proper grading and handling, not more than a total of 6 per cent of the potatoes in any lot may fail to meet the requirements of the grade, but not more than 3 per cent shall be allowed for potatoes affected by southern bacterial wilt, ring rot, or late blight, and including not more than 1 per cent for potatoes which are frozen, or affected by soft rot or wet breakdown. In addition, not more than 5 per cent may be damaged by hollow heart and internal discoloration."

DEFINITIONS

"(1) Fairly well shaped means that the appearance of the individual potato or the general appearance of the potatoes in the container is not materially injured by pointed, dumbbell-shaped or otherwise ill-formed potatoes.

"(2) Soft rot or wet breakdown means any soft, mushy, or leaky condition of the tissue such as slimy soft rot, leak, or wet breakdown following freezing injury or sunscald.

"(3) Damage means any injury or defect which materially injures the edible or shipping quality or the appearance of the individual potato or the general appearance of the potatoes in the container, or which cannot be removed without a loss of more than 5 per cent of the total weight of the potato including peel covering defective area. Any one of the following defects or any combination of defects the seriousness of which exceeds the maximum allowed for any one defect shall be considered as damage.

"(a) Second growth or growth cracks which have developed to such an extent as to materially injure the appearance of the individual potato or the general appearance of the potatoes in the container.

"(b) Air cracks which are deep, or shallow air cracks which materially injure the appearance of the individual potato or the general appearance of the potatoes in the container.

"(c) External discoloration, when skinned areas on individual potatoes are materially affected by dark discoloration, or when the general appearance of the lot is materially affected by discoloration.

"(d) Shriveling when the potato is more than moderately shriveled, spongy, or flabby.

"(e) Sprouting when more than 10 per cent of the potatoes have sprouts over three-fourths of an inch long.

"(f) Surface scab which covers an area of more than 5 per cent of the surface of the potato in the aggregate.

"(g) Pitted scab which affects the appearance of the potato to a greater extent than the amount of surface scab permitted or causes a loss of more than 5 per cent of the total weight of the potato including peel covering defective area.

"(h) Rhizoctonia when the general appearance of the potatoes in the container is materially injured or when individual potatoes are badly infected.

"(i) Wireworm, grass root or similar injury when any hole, on potatoes ranging in size from 6 to 8 ounces, is longer than 3/4 inch or when the aggregate length of all holes is more than 1 1/4 inches. Smaller potatoes shall have lesser amounts and larger potatoes may have greater amounts, provided that the removal of the injury by proper trimming does not cause the appearance of such potatoes to be injured to a greater extent than that caused by the proper trimming of such injury permitted on a 6 to 8 ounce potato.

"(j) Dirt when the general appearance of the potatoes in the container is more than slightly dirty or stained, or when individual potatoes are badly caked with dirt or badly stained; or other foreign matter which materially affects the appearance of the potatoes.

"(4) Internal discoloration means discoloration such as is caused by net necrosis or any other type of necrosis, stem-end browning, internal brown spot, or other similar types of discoloration not visible externally, except blackheart.

"(5) Diameter means the greatest dimension at right angles to the longitudinal axis. The long axis shall be used without regard to the position of the stem (rhizome)."

INSPECTION PROCEDURE

The general procedure for grading potatoes is similar for both the state and Federal grades. Let us examine the state potato standard and consider the essential items in grading a sack of potatoes. There are three important considerations: (a) To be able to select the tubers with imperfections or defects and be able to identify the defect; (b) to be familiar with the tuber tolerance or the waste permitted on each tuber; and (c) to be familiar with the package tolerance or the amount of tubers permitted to exceed the tuber tolerance in the package. The state grade lists the various defects a grader should be able to identify. Some of these defects are given after the words *"free from"* which means if the tuber has this defect the tuber tolerance is exceeded. Defects like insect injury and sunscald must be free from *"serious damage"* which is defined as "a waste of 10 per cent, by weight, of the individual potato." The weight of potatoes which exceed their tuber tolerance is used to determine whether the package tolerance is exceeded and if so, the sample does not comply with the grade. The state standard sets forth the package tolerance as "not more than 5 per cent, by weight, of potatoes in any container or bulk lot may be below these requirements."

If we examine each tuber in a 100 pound sack of potatoes and find two pounds of tubers slightly affected by soft rot, we must set them aside to be considered in the package tolerance. Soft rot is a defect listed under *"free from."* In addition we find three pounds of potatoes affected by sunburn but in cutting away the affected portion of the tuber only 9 per cent of the tuber is affected. These potatoes are not considered in the package tolerance because the waste is less than 10 per cent. There are also three pounds affected by sunscald and the defect causes a loss to each tuber of 10 per cent or more. The sunscald potatoes exceed the tuber tolerance and must be added to the two pounds of soft rot so there is a total of five pounds. Since the package tolerance is five pounds this sack of potatoes complies with the state standard. Other defects could be used as examples, but this discussion points out the meaning of the two tuber tolerances and the application of the package tolerance.

The same type of procedure is used to grade potatoes under the Federal grades such as U.S. No. 1 potatoes. The Federal grade needs to be examined to familiarize one's self with the different defects and their tolerances. In the

U.S. No. 1 grade, the potatoes must have "similar variety characteristics" and also be "fairly well shaped." These defects are judged on appearance which is described in the grade as well as by experience obtained by grading under supervision. The defects under *"free from"* for U.S. No. 1's are not identical with those of the state grade. The tuber tolerance for "damage" is different as is the package tolerance. Since grades may be changed, the above grades are given to illustrate the grading technique.

White Rose potatoes from Kern County, California, usually are inspected to obtain a U.S. No. 1 certificate. The potatoes are brought from the field, washed, small potatoes removed and the remainder are sorted into the U.S. No. 1 and U.S. No. 2 grades. The potatoes are sacked and 360 (100-lb.) sacks usually are loaded into each car. As the sacks are trucked into the car the inspector takes a sack and proceeds to inspect each tuber in the sack. Perfect potatoes and those that comply with the tuber tolerance are returned to the sack. Potatoes exceeding the tuber tolerance are segregated for further consideration. Next the segregated tubers are compared to the item listed under the "tolerance for defects" (package tolerance). If these are not exceeded the sack of potatoes complies with the U.S. No. 1 potato standard. Six or more sacks are selected and similarly graded. This usually can be done as the car is loaded; thus, a good random sample is obtained. The car tolerance is more liberal than that listed for one sack. Most shipping point inspection is performed as the car is loaded. In the case of bunch carrots the detailed inspection is performed in the field where the carrots are bunched, with a secondary check made at the packing house.

MEANING TO THE CONSUMER OF A U.S. NO. 1 GRADE

Is the use of the U.S. No. 1 grade only of value in the wholesale markets or is it of some value to the consumer? When the shipper labels a sack of potatoes with U.S. No. 1, he has indicated a desire of complying with the standards of this specific grade. Usually, the shipper has had the potatoes inspected by a Federal employee, but this is not necessarily true. Whoever packed and labeled these potatoes is responsible for the accuracy of this grade. There is no enforcement of the accuracy of this grade by the Federal government unless the grade is challenged by some interested party. Unfortunately, change in condition after packing does not alter grade according to Federal procedure, but in some states local inspection enforces accurate labeling. The potatoes under these circumstances must meet the U.S. No. 1 standard at the time of sale or be reconditioned or relabeled. In order to answer this question accurately a person needs to know local regulations about misbranding and the extent of enforcement. The consumer is able to buy better quality of fruit and vegetables when there is a proper grading program. Even though a product may lose its grade designation before it reaches him, the consumer is benefited indirectly just by the fact that grades serve as the basis of the original purchase and sale. During the past two or three years, there has been considerable interest in definite consumer standards particularly among prepackagers and consumers. Consumer standards have been issued for husked corn on the cob, carrots, tomatoes, potatoes, and spinach. Consumer grades usually permit a smaller tolerance for off-grade specimens than the other type of grades.

REFERENCES

1. Black, J. S.: "Agricultural Reform in the United States," 511 p., New York, McGraw-Hill Book Co., 1929. (Flexible standards for grades p. 411–12).
2. Extracts from the *Agricultural Code of California* pertaining to general provisions and fruit, nut, and vegetable standardization, 339 p., 1950.
3. Sherman, W. A.: "Merchandising Fruits and Vegetables," 494 p., New York, McGraw-Hill Book Co., 1928.
4. Spangler, Raymond L.: Standardization and inspection of fresh fruits and vegetables, *U.S.D.A. Misc. Pub. No. 604,* 28 p., 1946.

Chapter 13

Food Value of Vegetables

Agriculture is our primary source of food. Vegetables are important especially in our food, because of their mineral and vitamin content. In studying the proper vegetable production methods, it is desirable to know something of the food value of vegetables and their essential contribution to the people of the world. Furthermore, there is need for developing a knowledge in peace time so we will be prepared in periods of scarcity. Food supplies may be increased by enlarging the acreage, by increasing the yield per acre, or by growing crops which are high in food nutrients per pound.

WHAT IS FOOD?

Vegetables are regarded as food. What is meant by this statement? Considerable thought has been given this subject and a perfect or complete food is considered as any material which supplies sufficient nutrients to maintain a man in good health while at active work. The requirements as to nutrients and amounts were considered by the food committee of the League of Nations in 1935. This study was continued by the National Research Council (U.S.), and in 1943 the so-called "Recommended Dietary Allowances" were published. These were given separately for persons of different ages and sexes. Not all the essential nutrients were listed since in a mixed diet sufficient quantities of the minor nutrients usually are furnished. The 1943 Allowance listed 12 milligrams of iron as an essential item, but the 1945 recommendations do not include iron, and also changed some vitamin values. There is evidence at the present time that an adult male needs little iron. The present values[8] for a moderately active man weighing 70 kilograms (155 pounds) are listed below:

Energy	3,000 calories	Ascorbic acid	75 milligrams
Protein	70 grams	Thiamine	1.5 milligrams
Calcium	1.0 gram	Riboflavin	1.8 milligrams
Vitamin A	5,000 I.U.	Niacin	15 milligrams

Each of the above nutrients is needed for the body to function normally. Our knowledge regarding certain nutrients is more complete than for some of the others. A general statement regarding each of the eight nutrients is given below:

Energy. Food energy units are obtained by the body through the oxidation of carbohydrates, fats, and protein. Energy is necessary to support body activity. The energy needs of a man at light work are much less than one performing heavy work.

Protein. Animal proteins are derived from plant proteins and are necessary for the formation of new tissues, as well as the maintenance of body tissues. A mixed diet of several foods is desirable so the individual will have available all the essential amino acids that go to make up proteins. When a protein is digested amino acids are made available for use by the body. Individual proteins do not have all of the essential amino acids and also vary in digestibility.

Calcium. Most of the material in the rigid or bone structure of the body and teeth is made up of calcium and to a lesser extent from phosphorus. Calcium in small amounts is found in the soft tissues of the body where this mineral performs essential functions.

Vitamin A. This vitamin is stored largely in the liver. It is essential for growth, particularly for teeth during formation, and people low in vitamin A seem more susceptible to colds. Vitamin A is essential for accurate vision and adaptation of the eyes to darkness, sometimes referred to as night blindness. The carotin of plants is spoken of as a precursor of vitamin A since it is chiefly hydrolyzed in the liver to form vitamin A.

Ascorbic Acid. Vitamin C is a dietary essential for the human since we cannot synthesize it as do most other animals. An optimum amount should be supplied to all ages for its therapeutic value in preventing the development of acute or latent scurvy.

Thiamine. A deficiency of vitamin B_1 produces beriberi in man, a peripheral neuritis resulting in paralysis. Thiamine is known to be part of an enzyme system involved in carbohydrate oxidation. Carbohydrate oxidation would be improved by the presence of thiamine only when there is an acute deficiency present.

Riboflavin. Normal growth and health require an adequate supply of riboflavin (vitamin B_2 or G). It is probably involved in certain of the oxidative enzymes in the body and a deficiency may cause a deterioration of skin and eye.

Niacin. This vitamin is an important factor in correcting the deficiency disease called pellagra. The word means rough-red skin, and the tongue also is affected when the person is on a deficient diet. Cellular respiration is affected by niacin and consequently, it is considered a component of certain enzyme systems.

Food composition may be expressed in terms of calories of energy, grams of protein, etc.; but it may be expressed in terms of a man's daily needs for the different nutrients as given previously. Thus, 3000 calories may be considered as an energy unit, 70 grams of protein as a protein unit, 1.0 gram of calcium as a calcium unit, etc. Since vegetables are used as food, the conversion of food value to nutrient units simplifies the use of the data.

If different vegetables are to be compared as to food value, the different resources to be compared must be selected. The housewife and consumer are interested in a resource expressed in terms of nutrients per pound of vegetable. Since this is also a measure of the concentration of food it may be of use when shipping space is limited. From the standpoint of efficiency in the use of land, people are interested in the nutrient units which may be produced per acre; similarly from a labor standpoint, the nutrients produced per hour of labor. Other resources could be considered, such as length of growing season, but it is believed that the above three are a fair basis for comparing different vegetable crops. Such a study has been made of California vegetables[3,4,5] and will be considered briefly in this chapter.

The method of determining the relative efficiency of different vegetables in these papers seems worthy of some explanation. Let us first consider determination of nutrients per pound. Chemical data were available for the composition of these vegetables in terms of the eight nutrients listed previously. These food values were for the edible portion of the vegetables. There is, of course, some waste in preparing the vegetable for the table. Eighty-four per cent of a potato is edible, since in peeling the tuber there is a loss of 16 per cent of the weight. In calculating the nutrients per pound, it seems essential to take into consideration the normal waste in preparation, and also to convert the data to nutrient units. Sweet potatoes possess 24 milligrams of ascorbic acid per 100 grams of edible portion, 86 per cent of this root is edible, and a nutrient unit for this constituent is 75 milligrams. To convert composition data to pounds they must be multiplied by 4.54. This calculation for ascorbic acid content of sweet potatoes is as follows:

$$\frac{24 \times 0.86 \times 4.54}{75} = 1.248 \text{ ascorbic acid units per pound in sweet potatoes}$$

Thus, a pound of raw sweet potatoes would furnish one and one-fourth men with their ascorbic acid for one day, while one pound of watermelon would supply one-fifth of one man's need for one day. Calculation in terms of the cooked food was considered, but abandoned since cooking procedures differ and some vegetables are consumed both raw and cooked. Cooking decreases nutrients per pound. The above type of data was calculated for each of the vegetables and for each of the nutrients. In attempting to compare the different vegetables they were given a rank for each nutrient. The vegetable with the highest amount of nutrient per pound was given a rank of one, and the lesser amounts were ranked with successively higher numbers. Table 26

Table 26*

ASCORBIC ACID NUTRIENT UNITS PER POUND OF SEVERAL VEGETABLES,
AS PURCHASED, WITH THEIR RELATIVE RANK

	Units	Rank		Units	Rank
Artichokes	0.32	25	Cucumbers	0.51	23
Asparagus, green	1.36	9½	Lettuce	0.50	24
Asparagus, white	1.36	9½	Mustard greens	6.00	2
Bean, lima, in pod	0.92	15	Onion	0.68	19½
Bean, snap	0.65	21	Pea, in pod	0.76	17
Beet, with tops	0.22	27½	Pepper, bell	8.89	1
Broccoli	4.63	4	Potato, sweet	1.25	12
Brussels sprout	4.66	3	Potato, white	0.61	22
Cabbage	3.18	6	Radish, with tops	0.74	18
Cantaloupe	0.85	16	Spinach	3.97	5
Carrot, with tops	0.15	31	Squash, summer	1.53	8
Casaba and Honeydew	1.14	14	Squash, winter	0.22	27½
Cauliflower	1.91	7	Tomato, market	1.30	11
Celery	0.23	26	Turnip, with tops	1.20	13
Corn, sweet	0.21	29	Watermelon	0.20	30

* Courtesy, *Calif. Agr. Exper. Sta. Lithoprint Leaflet,* 1943.

gives an example of this procedure for each vegetable, on ascorbic acid per pound.

Nutrient units per acre were determined by multiplying the average yield times the nutrient units per pound. The California average yield of sweet potatoes over the period of 1937–1941 was 6529 pounds per acre. Since each pound has 1.248 units of ascorbic acid, an acre would produce an average of 8148 units. This would be sufficient to supply over 8000 men their ascorbic acid need for one day. In order to determine the nutrients produced per man hour it was necessary to determine the hours of labor required to produce the crop under average conditions. In the case of sweet potatoes, 60 hours are required for cultural labor, 72 hours for harvesting, 10 hours for packing, or a total of 142 hours to produce an average crop. Forty-six pounds of sweet potatoes are produced per hour of labor. Since each pound of sweet potatoes possesses 1.248 units of ascorbic acid, one hour of labor will produce 57.41 units or sufficient ascorbic acid to supply the needs of 57 men for one day. The above figures are for raw sweet potatoes, but Watt and Merrill[7] indicate baked sweet potatoes gain slightly in ascorbic acid due to dehydration while boiled sweet potatoes lose 9 per cent of ascorbic acid upon cooking. The values per acre and per man hour were also calculated for all the vegetables and the eight nutrients. The vegetables in each nutrient column were ranked. Figure 39 gives the data for two vegetables with regard to nutrients per pound and shows that sweet potatoes are higher in all nutrients per pound when compared to watermelons.

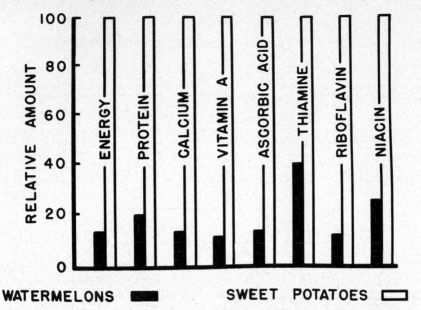

WATERMELONS ■   **SWEET POTATOES** ▭

Fig. 39. Food nutrients may be increased by choice of plant as well as by increased acreage and yield. Sweet potatoes illustrated above contain an average of 6.9 times more nutrients per pound than watermelons; similarly, there are 3.8 times more nutrients per acre; and 2.8 times more nutrients per man-hour.

OUR MOST EFFICIENT VEGETABLE CROPS

The previous paragraphs explain the construction of the tables to compare the vegetables listed in Table 27 on the basis of nutrients per pound, per acre, and per man-hour. As the ranks of the vegetables are compared in these tables, it is found that their relative rank differs for the several nutrients. There was need for some method to summarize these tables if the most efficient crops were to be selected. It was impossible to add the eight nutrient units for the different crops since a calcium unit did not have the same replacement value as an energy unit. In the original paper, comparisons were made as to whether specific vegetables were higher in all eight nutrients or all five vitamins than other vegetables. This procedure is scientifically correct but somewhat cumbersome to use. The original paper gives tables comparing all vegetables considered. Mustard is higher in all nutrients per pound, per acre, and per man-hour than are cantaloupe, cucumber, lettuce, and radish. Likewise, broccoli is higher than cucumber, and sweet potato higher than watermelon (Fig. 39). The nutrients per pound, etc., were further summarized by giving a rank of one to the vegetable which was

Table 27*

CLASSIFICATION OF VEGETABLES BASED ON NUTRIENTS
PER POUND, ACRE, AND MAN-HOUR†

Rank of Nutrients for Fresh Vegetables				*Processed Vegetables*
	Per Pound	*Per Acre*	*Per Man-hour*	
Group 1: ranking 1 to 15 in all three items				
Broccoli	1	5	7	Cabbage (dehydrated)
Cabbage	14	6	4	Tomato juice (canned)
Mustard	2	1	2	Tomato paste (canned)
Spinach	11	12	8	Tomato purée (canned)
Sweet potato	3	13	5	
White potato	8	2	3	
Winter squash	15	11	1	
Group 2: ranking 1 to 15 in two of three items				
Beet, bunch	26	4	15	Carrot (dehydrated)
Brussels sprouts	4	14	24	Onion (dehydrated)
Carrot, bunch	25	7	13	Pea (canned)
Early onion	16½	9	9½	Pea (dehydrated)
Late onion	16½	3	6	Potato, white (dehydrated)
Tomato, market	13	15	17	Tomato (canned)
Turnip, bunch	21	10	12	
Group 3: ranking 1 to 15 in one of three items				
Artichoke	12	30	22½	Asparagus, green (canned)
Cauliflower	20	17	9½	Asparagus, white (canned)
Casaba and Honeydew	27	21	11	Bean, snap (canned)
Celery	24	8	22½	Spinach (canned)
Green asparagus	7	29	26	Spinach (dehydrated)
Lettuce	22½	18	14	Pea (frozen)
Lima bean	10	22	27	
Pea	6	28	29	
Snap bean	5	19	30	
White asparagus	9	31	28	
Group 4: ranking 16 to 31 in all three items				
Bell pepper	19	20	19	Not applicable to any
Cantaloupe	28	24	18	processed vegetables
Cucumber	29	23	25	studied.
Radish	30	25	31	
Summer squash	18	16	20	
Sweet corn	22½	26	16	
Watermelon	31	27	21	

* Courtesy, *Calif. Agr. Exper. Sta. Lithoprint Leaflet,* 1943.
† Interpretation: The accuracy of the data does not permit distinctions between small differences. Vegetables in group 1 are thought to be better than those in groups 3 and 4; group 2 is considered better than group 4.

closest to the highest content in all the different nutrients, and the other vegetables were given similarly lower ranks. After this had been done on the three bases it was possible to prepare Table 27 which indicates the relative efficiency of the various vegetables. These vegetables are placed in four groups and the limits of interpretation are given at the bottom of the table. Following a similar procedure, different processed vegetables were classified in their logical group. If Table 27 is examined it will be noted that most of the nonfruit crops are in the first three groups, and the fruit crops are in the less efficient groups. There are three important exceptions to this statement, winter squash is found in group 1, market tomatoes in group 2, and radishes in group 4. Most of the crops needing punctual harvesting to obtain the best quality are found in groups 3 and 4. Pea, sweet corn, asparagus, and lima bean are typical examples of this characteristic.

EXTREME DIFFERENCES IN COMPOSITION OF VEGETABLES

Previous discussion has indicated that vegetables vary in composition, with respect to different nutrients. Table 28 lists the vegetables with the highest and lowest composition for the different nutrients and the three resources. The table indicates that white potatoes, winter squash, and mustard

Table 28*

VEGETABLES WITH THE GREATEST AND LEAST CONTENT OF THE DIFFERENT
NUTRIENTS PER POUND, ACRE, AND MAN-HOUR

	Per Pound		Per Acre		Per Man-hour	
	Crop	Units	Crop	Units	Crop	Units
Energy	Sweet potato	0.16	White potato	1,895	White potato	16.2
	Cucumber	0.02	Asparagus	61	Asparagus	0.5
Protein	Brussels sprout	0.22	White potato	1,912	Winter squash	16.9
	Watermelon	0.02	Cantaloupe	167	Radish	1.1
Calcium	Mustard greens	0.44	Mustard greens	6,525	Mustard greens	34.8
	Spinach	. .†	Spinach	. .†	Spinach	. .†
Iron	Broccoli	0.85	Celery	10,695	White potato	52.4
	Spinach	. .†	Spinach	. .†	Spinach	. .†
Vitamin A	Winter squash	2.69	Winter squash	40,290	Winter squash	628.5
	Radish	0.00	Radish	0	Radish	0
Ascorbic acid	Pepper	8.89	Mustard greens	90,060	Mustard greens	480.3
	Carrot	0.15	Artichoke	1,104	Snap bean	8.5
Thiamine	Asparagus	0.37	White potato	4,088	White potato	35.0
	Cucumber	0.04	Cucumber	480	Radish	1.4
Riboflavin	Spinach	0.39	Onion	4,004	Onion	22.7
	Watermelon	0.02	Artichoke	155	Radish	0.9
Niacin	Sweet potato	0.28	White potato	4,386	Winter squash	41.9
	Radish	0.01	Bean, lima	129	Radish	0.4

* Courtesy, *Calif. Agr. Exper. Sta. Lithoprint Leaflet,* 1943.
† Calcium and iron contained in spinach are largely unavailable.

greens appear frequently because of high nutrient composition. In a similar way, radish and cucumbers are frequently very low in composition. The differences in composition between high and low vegetables in a single nutrient are frequently very great. A difference of 30 times is common, and in some cases it is as high as 80.

This table may be used to illustrate another consideration regarding foods. If a person's diet were low in ascorbic acid, what vegetable should be emphasized in the diet? Peppers with eight and nine-tenths units per pound would be selected. About one-eighth pound of raw peppers would supply the daily need for ascorbic acid. Of course these crops also contain the other nutrients. If a country's diet were low in ascorbic acid, the units per acre could be increased by growing more mustard greens (90,060 units). If a country's problem were to produce the greatest amount of ascorbic acid with the least use of labor, the vegetables selected would be mustard greens (480 units per hour of labor).

The introduction to this chapter called attention to the fact that food supply could be increased by more acreage, greater yield per acre, or choice of crops of higher nutrient value. The above discussion calls attention to the variation in nutrient value of vegetables, as shown in Fig. 39; there the nutrient composition of sweet potatoes and watermelons is compared. Sweet potatoes are more nutritious than watermelons. There is a smaller increase from the choice of sweet potato for the thiamin than for any of the other nutrients. Instances of other crops that are similarly superior in all three resources have been mentioned previously.

FOOD VALUE OF OTHER AGRICULTURAL PRODUCTS

Since people do and should consume a mixture of foods, it is unfortunate that data are not available for all agricultural foods, so their relative merit from this point of view may be determined. A similar type of work has been published on beef and pork production, but the nutrient consideration has been limited to energy and protein. It is unfair to compare irrigated and range land as to productivity since both need to be used to produce food. The monetary investment in irrigated land is several times that of range land; consequently it should make a greater contribution to our food supply. Guilbert and co-workers[1] have reported on California beef production. Hughes and associates[2] have made a similar report on pork production. The feed for the beef cattle was obtained from range and field clean-up, irrigated pasture, and by-products and other feed consumed in feed lots. The calculations for pork production were based on 274 pounds of barley, 24 pounds of tankage, 16 pounds of alfalfa hay, and six pounds of salt and lime per 100 pounds of gain in weight. Equivalent amounts of other feeds might be used. Table 29 gives the comparative data from this study.

Table 29*

<small>ACREAGE, LABOR, AND FOOD VALUE DATA FOR BEEF AND PORK</small>

	Beef	*Pork*
Acres to produce 100 pounds (live weight)	8.54 acres	0.23 acres
Labor to produce 100 pounds (live weight)	3.30 man-hours	4.30 man-hours
Energy units per acre	2.89 units	238.14 units
Protein units per acre	7.90 units	372.12 units
Energy units per man-hour	7.47 units	11.33 units
Protein units per man-hour	20.44 units	17.70 units

* Courtesy, *Calif. Agr. Exper. Sta. Lithoprint Leaflets,* 1943 and 1944.

There are some interesting differences between the productive capacity of beef cattle and hogs—affected to a large extent by their food habits. Beef cattle are produced largely on range land which would otherwise be wasted. Pork production would give a more favorable picture if part of the feed were garbage. The authors[2] call attention to the fact that near the cities, swine may be produced by using only garbage or garbage and a small addition of grain.

Energy is equally valuable from all sources, but protein varies both as to quantity and quality in different foods. Quality of protein refers to the essential amino acids present and man needs about 11 of these for normal nourishment. A single animal food supplies the different needed amino acids more adequately than does a single plant food. In evaluating proteins in different foods throughout this chapter, no consideration has been given to their amino acid content.

MAN'S NEED FOR DIFFERENT FOODS

The United States Department of Agriculture[6] has divided foods into seven groups and recommends that people eat daily at least one food from each group. The seven groups of food are: "(a) Green and yellow vegetables; (b) oranges, tomatoes, grapefruit—or raw cabbage or salad greens; (c) potatoes and other vegetables and fruits; (d) milk and milk products—fluid, evaporated, dried milk, or cheese; (e) meat, poultry, or eggs—or dried beans, peas, or nuts, or peanut butter; (f) bread, flour, and cereals—natural whole-grain or enriched or restored; and (g) butter and fortified margarine (margarine with added vitamin A)." These recommendations indicate the importance of vegetables in our diet.

This chapter has tended to emphasize the food aspects of vegetables. Their food value has been largely responsible for their increased per capita consumption in recent years. A vegetable producer needs to know the consumer value of the product he produces in order to understand consumption trends.

REFERENCES

1. Guilbert, H. R., L. W. Fluharty, and V. M. Shepard: California beef-production data, *Cal. Agr. Exp. Sta. Lithoprint Leaflet,* 5 p., 1943.
2. Hughes, E. H., Wallace Sullivan, and V. M. Shepard: California pork-production data, *Cal. Agr. Exp. Sta. Lithoprint Leaflet,* 4 p., 1944.
3. MacGillivray, John H., Arthur Shultis, G. C. Hanna, and Agnes Fay Morgan: Food values on a pound, acre, and man-hour basis for California fresh vegetables, *Cal. Agr. Exp. Sta. Lithoprint Leaflet,* 23 p., 1943.
4. MacGillivray, John H., Arthur Shultis, A. E. Michelbacher, P. A. Minges, and L. D. Doneen: Labor and material requirements of California vegetables, *Cal. Agr. Exp. Sta. Lithoprint Leaflet,* 15 p., 1943.
5. MacGillivray, John H., Agnes Fay Morgan, G. C. Hanna, and Arthur Shultis: Food values on a pound, acre, and man-hour basis for California processed vegetables, *Cal. Agr. Exp. Sta. Lithoprint Leaflet,* 15 p., 1943.
6. Sherman, Henry C.: Principles of nutrition and nutritive value of food, *U.S.D.A. Misc. Pub. 546,* 40 p., 1944.
7. Watt, Bernice K. and Annabel L. Merrill: Composition of foods—raw, processed, prepared, *U.S.D.A. Agr. Handbook No. 8,* 147 p., 1950.
8. Recommended dietary allowances, *Nat. Res. Council Cir. 129,* 31 p., 1948.

Chapter 14

Insect and Disease Control

Most growers realize the importance of controlling pests in order to obtain maximum yields. Plant tissue is destroyed so the plant's ability to manufacture carbohydrates is limited. This may be caused by a part of a leaf being eaten by an insect or made nonfunctional through diseased tissue. Still more drastic is for the pest to kill the plant before the crop is produced. Many pests merely lower the total yield. The value or quality of the vegetable may be lowered by insect or disease attack. Such crops are not desired by the consumer and, of course, bring a lower price. Other types of crop injury may result in a violation of the Pure Food Laws which make the product liable to seizure and to destruction. Examples of this type of economic loss are aphids in frozen food and tomato mold in canned tomato products. In some cases there may be spray residues on fresh and processed vegetables. Such conditions may lead to their seizure and destruction by Pure Food Authorities. The grower needs a thorough knowledge of control methods so damage is eliminated without any detrimental effect to the food value of the vegetable. The following treatment of insects, diseases, and other pests is not as complete as may be found in publications limited to this specific subject matter.

Insect control can be successful by application about the time the insects usually appear or when the first ones can be seen. Such a program can be carried out throughout the season for most insects. This also is true of a few diseases, but in most cases preventive procedures must be used. A basic knowledge of the pest and the possible control measures must be known to the operator and he must be alert to make timely applications as well.

INSECTS

Types. Insect pests can be divided into two general groups according to their method of feeding: (1) Chewing insects, and (2) sucking insects. Chewing pests are usually larger than those having sucking mouth parts. They eat noticeable holes in the parts of the plant on which they feed, and in some cases they bore into the part of the plant attacked. This characteristic injury suggests the use of stomach poisons as the best method of con-

159

trol. Since in many cases chewing injury is easy to identify this knowledge will be helpful in selecting insecticides. Some chewing insects are cabbage worms, cutworms, corn ear worms, cucumber beetles, flea beetles, weevils, leaf miners, and grasshoppers. Some of the more important pests for individual crops are given at the end of the crop discussion. Some pests, such as sowbugs, pill bugs, snails, slugs, and land planarians are not insects but since they have chewing mouth parts are controlled as insects.

Another type of insect is the one that feeds with sucking mouth parts. They insert their mouth parts into the plant tissue and suck the juice. This may result in stunted or deformed areas. The plant, if heavily infested, gradually dries up. Some sucking insects excrete quantities of honey dew upon which the sooty mold fungus grows. Sucking insects generally are controlled by contact insecticides and fumigants. Some examples of sucking pests are aphids, thrips, leafhoppers, and squash bugs. Closely related are tomato mite and red spider.

Important steps in insect control are watchfulness, clean culture, and proper use of insecticides. The grower needs to observe his crops for pests and be able to identify them. Remnants of crops and weeds serve as breeding places for many insects so clean culture is helpful. There are three types of insecticides, stomach poisons, contact poisons, and fumigants. In recent years a number of new insecticides have been developed. Some of these have shown unusual promise as controls for certain insects which previously had been hard to control. A brief description of these materials is given in the following paragraphs.

Stomach Poisons. Cryolite (sodium fluoaluminate) is much less toxic to humans and other warm blooded animals than either calcium or lead arsenate.

Calcium arsenate is an effective stomach poison, but is being replaced by other insecticides because of toxicity to man and other warm blooded animals. Its use close to harvest may cause a spray residue problem. When used as a dust calcium arsenate may drift to other fields and cause the poisoning of farm animals and bees.

Rotenone, an insecticide obtained from a plant, is relatively nonpoisonous, but is effective as a stomach poison for some insects and also as a contact poison.

Contact Insecticides. Nicotine (Black Leaf-40) is a tobacco derivative and has been used commercially to control aphids and thrips as a spray or a dust.

Pyrethrum and rotenone are both of plant origin and are effective against aphids, leafhoppers, thrips, and many soft-bodied insects. Dusts containing 0.15 to 0.20 per cent pyrethrins and 2 per cent organic thiocyanate when applied at temperatures below 65° F. give control of leafhoppers, thrips, and cucumber beetles. Rotenone dusts (0.5 per cent) are effective against pea weevil, pea aphid, and cabbage worms.

New organic insecticides are being used more frequently and will be found mentioned for specific insects under the discussion of crops. Some of these are: DDT (dichlorodiphenyl trichloroethane), DDD (dichlorodiphenyl dichloroethane), Methoxychlor (dianisyl trichloroethane), Benzene Hexachloride (666), and Chlordane. Benzene Hexachloride is being replaced by lindane. These compounds kill by contact and some of them also act as stomach poisons.

Two organic phosphates are used as contact dusts or sprays and very likely possess some of the attributes of a fumigant. These insecticides are TEPP (tetra ethyl pyrophosphate) and parathion. Both of these materials are toxic to certain insects and also warm blooded animals including people. The materials may be absorbed through the skin as well as from the vapors so care should be used in their mixing and application.

Fumigants are found practical only for the control of certain underground pests. Dichloroethyl Ether is used for the control of sod webworms, ground mealy bugs, and cabbage maggots. Ethylene Dibromide is very effective for controlling wireworms. D-D is a mixture of three compounds and is used to control nematodes. The proportions of the materials are one-half 1, 3-dichloropropene, one-fourth 1, 2-dichloropropane, and one-fourth 3-carbon tri- and tetrachlorides.

GENERAL INSECTS

Army Worms. Since army worms usually remain on the plants they may be controlled by sprays or dusts (Fig. 40). Arsenical dusts such as calcium

Fig. 40. One of the cutworms which feeds during the day is the yellow striped army worm.

arsenate, DDT dusts and sprays, and rotenone or pyrethrum dusts are all used. Migrating army worms often are checked by means of barrier strips of 10 per cent DDT dusts. The barriers are usually at least one-eighth inch thick and six to eight inches wide. Ditches filled with oil or water sometimes are employed.

Cutworms. These caterpillars are active feeders on several vegetable plants. They usually hide in the ground during the day and cut off the plants near the ground. In certain cases, the worms can climb and remain inside protected places, such as heads of cabbage. Poison bait is used for control and prepared by the following formula:

Paris green (or arsenic trioxide)	1 pound
Bran	25 pounds
Molasses	2 quarts
Water to make a dry mash.	

Mix poison and bran, then add the water-molasses solution while stirring. The replacement of 20 per cent of the bran with citrus meal adds to the attractiveness of the bait. A small amount of amylacetate may be used in place of, or as a supplement to the citrus meal. Either one-half pound of sodium fluosilicate or one and one-fourth pounds of calcium arsenate may be used as a substitute for Paris green. Apply bait in late afternoon at 20 to 30 pounds per acre.

Grasshoppers. This insect is sometimes serious and can be controlled by the same procedure listed for cutworms.

Nematodes. Nematodes are small, worm-like animals but are not insects. There are several types but root knot nematode (Fig. 41) is the one affecting vegetable crops, such as cucumbers, melons, lettuce, carrots and tomatoes. Other crops affected in a minor way are broccoli and cauliflower, while garlic and onion are more or less resistant. The small microscopic worm-like animal lives in the roots of vegetables and causes galls or knobs on the roots. Their prevalence may be reduced by crop rotation, weed control, summer fallowing, and care to prevent soil moving on equipment from an infested field to one not infested. Sometimes early planting will establish the plants before nematodes are active. The soil may be fumigated with D-D or dichloropropene mixture (Shell D-D, Dowfume N) at 200 to 400 pounds per acre (20 to 40 gallons). The material should be drilled into the soil to a depth of six inches with 12 to 15 inch spacings on the surface. EDB, ethylene dibromide mixtures (Dowfume W-10, W-40, Bromofume) may be applied in a similar way with two to four gallons of actual chemical applied per acre.

Slugs and Snails. These pests are not insects but may cause extensive damage to vegetable crops. Poison baits containing calcium arsenate and

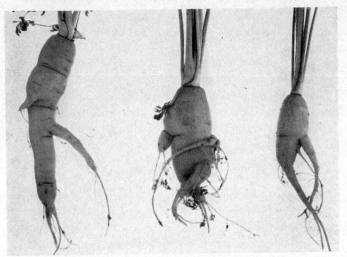

Fig. 41. Carrot roots affected by nematodes. The enlargements on the fibrous roots are caused by nematodes.

metaldehyde give satisfactory control only if applied at intervals since they do not kill the eggs. The following formula has been used successfully:

Calcium arsenate	1 ounce
Metaldehyde	½ ounce
Bran	1 pound
Water	1 pint
Black-strap molasses	2 tablespoons

Repellent mixtures such as hydrated lime, or hydrated lime with 20 per cent monohydrated copper sulfate, have been used with success on some crops.

Wireworms. Underground portions of vegetables, germinating seeds and small plants are damaged by wireworms. Wireworms can be controlled by use of proper rotations of crops and cultural methods but these methods may not always be practical or possible. Other procedures are soil fumigation with dichloropropene mixtures (Shell D-D, Dowfume N) at the rate of 40 gallons per acre; or ethylene dibromide mixtures (Dowfume W-10, Bromofume) at the rate of two gallons of actual chemical per acre. Lindane is used as a seed treatment of vegetable seed to be planted. The 75 per cent material is used with two-thirds ounce per 100 pounds of seed for baby limas and one and one-third ounces for cantaloupe.

DISEASES

Most diseases are caused by fungi, bacteria, or viruses. *Fungi* are microscopic organisms that cause diseases like mildews, rusts, and smuts, as well as molds and rots. In most cases their threadlike filaments, invisible to the eye, grow inside the plant (on the surface in the case of powdery mildews) and weaken or injure it by absorbing food and destroying the tissues. Most fungi spread and reproduce themselves by means of bodies called "spores" which in typical cases like the molds, mildews and smuts, are visible in mass to the eye as a dusty powder. These spores may be blown in the air, splashed by rain or be carried on the bodies of insects, living plants, or seeds, or by other modes of transportation. *Bacteria* are microöganisms even smaller than fungi and are visible only in certain cases as a slimy exudate. They are spread in a manner similar to fungi and are of the same general nature as bacteria or germs which cause animal diseases.

Viruses are foreign substances which invade, spread, and increase in the bodies of plants, often causing specific diseases and great injury. The virus itself is invisible with the ordinary microscope and while in many respects it behaves like a parasitic organism, it has other characteristics which make it seem a nonliving chemical substance. Most plant virus diseases are spread by aphids, thrips, or leaf hoppers which feed on affected plants and then on healthy ones. Some of the materials used for the control of diseases are discussed in the following paragraphs.

Bordeaux Mixture. This material may be applied as a spray or dust. The most common spray is a 5-5-50 mixture as follows:

Copper sulfate (bluestone)	5 pounds
Quicklime	5 pounds
Water	50 gallons

The bluestone is dissolved in a small amount of water. Hot water will increase the speed of dissolving as well as the use of the powdered form. The lime is slaked in a separate container. Wooden containers should be used. Never combine these two solutions in concentrated form. The following procedure is a desirable method: Fill spray tank half full of water and start agitator, pour in bluestone solution, and then after this is mixed add the lime solution through a 20 mesh screen. Add sufficient water to complete the formula. If quicklime is not available, non air-slaked hydrated lime may be used if the amount is increased about one-third. There are prepared Bordeaux mixtures on the market which are never better than the home mixed but may give satisfactory control.

Copper Lime Dust. This material usually is purchased ready for use. A common formula is 20-80 dust which has 20 pounds of monohydrate copper sulfate and 80 pounds of hydrated lime. The material is a dust and 95 per cent will pass through a 200 mesh screen. The material gives better results if applied when the plants are wet.

Sulfur. Finely ground sulfur is used as a dust to control powdery mildew.

This fungicide is used rather generally on vegetable crops with the exception of the Cucurbitaceae. These frequently are injured by sulfur dust particularly in hot interior valleys.

Seed Treatments. These treatments are desirable in protecting seeds against many soil borne organisms. The cost per acre is very small. The recommendation as to material and dosage will be found under the different crops. When the material is to be applied as a powder it usually is placed in a container with the seed and rotated. A 50 gallon drum may be used for large quantities of seed while small packets may be treated in a pint or larger glass jar. Some of the powders used are arasan, new improved ceresan, red copper oxide, mercury bichloride (corrosive sublimate), semesan, semesan bel, semesan Jr., spergon, yellow copper oxide, and zinc oxide. Formaldehyde is a liquid so the material should be handled as outlined under the specific crops.

GENERAL DISEASES

Cottony Mold (Sclerotinia sclerotiorum). This disease affects various plants and under moist conditions causes rotting of stems, leaves, fruit, and other fleshy parts. An abundant growth of pure white, cottony fluffy mold develops upon the affected tissue. The fungus forms no spores, but when there is plenty of moisture, the growth spreads rapidly. On the surface of the rotted tissue are formed roundish, black, solid bodies of various sizes up to about one-half inch long and one-fourth inch wide which are called sclerotia. These sclerotic bodies become embedded in the soil and during moist weather send out small organs which produce spores. In greenhouses or hotbeds the soil may be treated with steam or formaldehyde.

Curly Top. This disease attacks sugar beet, chard, tomato, and to a minor degree spinach, snap bean, pepper, squash, cantaloupe, and watermelon. This is a virus disease which is spread from plant to plant by a small insect, the beet leaf hopper. The virus causes a stunting, mottling, and deforming of the leaves. In the case of sugar beets resistant plants have been developed and may be developed for other crops sometime in the future. The only other control is to prevent infection by the leaf hopper through killing them in the hills before migration to cultivated crops.

Damping Off. Young seedlings often rot at or below the soil surface, fall over, wilt, and die. This disease starts in spots and spreads rapidly particularly in plant beds. Ideal conditions for its growth are high soil moisture, high humidity, high temperature, and a lack of sunshine. Soil fungi like *Pythium, Rhizoctonia,* and *Fusarium* thrive under the above conditions. The usual control measures depend upon the use of disease free soil in the plant beds or soil sterilization by heat or chemicals. Seed treatment materials will help to prevent damping off and are discussed under the individual crops.

Fusarium Wilt. This disease affects many of our vegetables and may cause their death before a crop is produced. Several species of *Fusarium* affect crops like white and sweet potatoes, pea, spinach, tomato, and others. Plants are stunted and the leaves turn yellow. Frequently, one side of the plant is affected and dies before the whole plant exhibits the symptoms. The fungus grows in the water-conducting tissues and causes a brownish discoloration. These tissues become plugged with mycelium so the plant fails to obtain sufficient water. Once a soil becomes infected it will persist for a period of years. Plants become infected from being grown in infected soil, and fields become inoculated from infected transplants. Sometimes seed is another means of introducing the disease. Growers should avoid infected seed, and infected fields. Some varieties have been developed which are resistant to this disease.

Mosaic. Many vegetable crops are affected by this disease which is caused by a virus. Insects are important vectors in transmitting this disease from an infected plant to a normal plant. Aphids usually are responsible for spreading mosaic. Perennial plants and vegetable seed are sources of original infection. Some of the crops affected by mosaic are snap bean, cauliflower, celery, cucurbits (Fig. 42), pea, pepper, white potato, spinach, and tomato.

Fig. 42. Squash mosaic which is transmitted by insects. An insect feeds on a diseased plant and transmits the virus when it feeds on a healthy plant.

The disease affects the leaves and in many cases also the fruit. Any given crop may be affected by several types of mosaics which tend to develop different symptoms in many cases. The affected part usually has a mottled appearance caused by dark and light green areas as well as by yellow patches. Leaves may be deformed and twisted as well as stunted in growth. Reduction in yield is somewhat proportional to earliness of infection.

Spotted Wilt. This is another virus disease and affects celery, lettuce, tomato, and peppers. Usually this disease is more common along coastal areas because there is no freezing weather to reduce the reservoir of infection in winter crops and weeds. No effective control is known.

Verticillium Wilt (*Verticillium albo-atrum*). This disease is soil borne and is contracted through the root system. The woody tissue of the stem is invaded and the fungus ascends to all parts of the plant. This brings about a wilt in the tops which is identical in most respects with severe drought injury. If the stem is cut, the wood cylinder is streaked or stained dark brown. No satisfactory control is known other than planting on non-infected soil. Work is in progress to develop resistant varieties. White potato, tomato, pepper, cantaloupe, and watermelon are usually the vegetables affected.

Alkali, Boron, Salt. Another source of disease-like symptoms is excessive amounts of alkali, boron, and salt. Affected plants usually look yellow and sickly, and the leaves show burning at the margins and between the main veins. Such injuries to plants are caused by harmful chemicals in the soil or irrigation water. Boron may also be present in harmful amounts. These symptoms of excess amounts of alkali, boron, and salt sometimes are mistaken for disease symptoms. A lack of boron causes a stunting of the plant, dying of the growing point, and sometimes a darkening of the tissues. Leaves also may become deformed.

REFERENCES

1. Crowell, H. H., H. E. Morrison, B. G. Thompson, and Don C. Mote: Vegetable garden insect-pest control. *Ore. Agr. Ext. Ser. Bull. 676*, 11 p., 1950.
2. Dana, B. F. and J. C. Dodge: The curly-top disease of vegetable crops in Washington state. *Wash. Agr. Ext. Ser. Bull. 357*, 8 p., 1947.
3. Henderson, W. J.: Fight diseases of gardens, *Colo. Agr. Ext. Ser. Cir. G-5*, 4 p., 1944.
4. McCampbell, S. C.: Kill the bugs, *Colo. Agr. Ext. Ser. Cir. G-4*, 5 p., 1944.
5. Michelbacher, A. E. and E. O. Essig: Ridding the garden of common pests, *Calif. Agr. Ext. Ser. Cir. 146*, 40 p., 1950.
6. Smith, Ralph E.: Diseases of truck crops, *Calif. Agr. Ext. Ser. Cir. 119*, 112 p., 1940.

7. Vorhies, Charles T. and Lawrence P. Wehrle: Pest problems of the small garden, *Ariz. Agr. Exp. Sta. Bull. 203,* 50 p., 1946.

8. Pest and disease control in the home garden, *Wash. Agr. Ext. Ser. Bull. 430,* 12 p., 1950.

Cultural Practices

The first sections of this book have been concerned with the general principles of plant production as they apply to vegetable crops. The following pages deal with the application of these principles to the specific crops. There are several ways that these crops could be arranged for discussion; the temperature classification has been used because of the importance of this factor.

The section on classification pointed out a simple method for separating many of our vegetables into cool and warm season crops. The discussion on Thermo classification of vegetables, developed by Boswell and Jones, gives in further detail the temperature requirements, and relates the time of growing crops to average monthly temperatures as recorded by the Weather Bureau. This treatment, however, should not be taken to indicate that plants may be classified with mathematical accuracy as to temperature requirements. There is also some latitude in adaptability of crops within each group.

Spinach is discussed first because of its ability to withstand cooler temperatures, and sweet potatoes in the last group since they thrive in the warmest weather. This temperature classification gives an indication of climatic requirement, time of seeding, depth of rooting, storage temperature, food value as well as action of physiological processes. The climatic requirement is discussed in more detail under each vegetable. Crops of the same botanical family have been grouped together whenever possible. There are two cases where crops do not appear together. Peas and white potatoes are cool season crops, while the other members of the Leguminosae and Solanaceae are warm season crops.

Chapter 15

Group A. Cool Season Crops Tolerant of Slightly Freezing Weather

Group A. Prefer average monthly temperatures of 60° to 65° F. Intolerant of 70° to 75° F., and tolerant of slightly freezing weather.

SPINACH

The foliage of many plants is cooked for food and these vegetables are referred to as greens and sometimes as potherbs. Spinach belongs to this group of plants as do swiss chard, mustard, kale, New Zealand spinach, and other plants, some of which are used as both greens and salads.

Botany. Spinach, beets, and many weeds are members of the Chenopodiaceae or goosefoot family. Spinach is an annual plant in which the edible portion is the leaves, while they are still in the rosette stage. The roots consist of a large tap-root with many fine feeder roots in the first two feet of soil. The stem at the vegetative stage is short and compact but forms an elongated seed stalk just before the flowers appear. Leaves vary in shape, thickness, and whether smooth or savoyed. Pollen is transferred by means of wind to small inconspicuous flowers which remain receptive for a week or longer. The seed is a one-seeded fruit. The plants are usually dioecious with minor variations. New Zealand spinach and Mountain spinach (orach) are also called "spinach".

The small greenish flowers of spinach (*Spinacia oleracea*) are of three kinds, staminate, pistillate, and hermaphroditic. The types of plants may be classified into, extreme males, vegetative males, females, and rarely monoecious. Prickly seeded varieties possess an abundance of extreme males, while the vegetative male is more common in the round seeded varieties. Seed is produced on the female plants and the male plants die after blooming. Extreme males are smaller in size and bloom earlier than either the vegetative males or females. The latter remain vegetative longer and bloom later in the season and near to the same time. Vegetative males and females are larger in size and seedsmen like to have these types of plants plentiful in their strains so they will exhibit long standing qualities.

Origin and History: The first records are about prickly-seeded spinach, which was used in Europe in 1351. The smooth-seeded form was described in 1552. Records indicate that this vegetable was known in China as early as the seventh century, and it was probably introduced into Europe by the Moors of North Africa. Spinach was first cultivated in the United States about 1806 and the first savoyed leaf variety was introduced in 1828.

Producing Areas: Spinach is grown for fresh market and for processing. The procedures of canning, freezing, and drying are used to preserve the processed product. In general, market production is limited to early areas and those near large consuming populations. The mimeographed reports of the Bureau of Agricultural Economics have been used for the statistical data and these reports contain considerable more details than are found in this book. The 1940–1951 statistical data are given below for the first five most important states:

Spinach for Market

	Acreage	Bushels* Per Acre	Production Bushels	Price Per Bushel Dollars	Farm Value Dollars
United States	62,758	209	13,140,000	$0.82	$10,716,000
Texas	33,858	130	4,414,000	0.94	4,145,000
Pennsylvania	4,542	305	1,386,000	0.82	1,130,000
California	3,967	404	1,603,000	0.64	1,021,000
New Jersey	3,508	334	1,172,000	0.82	963,000
New York	2,458	414	1,017,000	0.90	915,000

(Farm value, other Western states: Washington, $440,000; Colorado, $275,000).
* Approximately 18 pounds.

Spinach for Processing

	Acreage	Tons Per Acre	Production Tons	Price Per Ton Dollars	Farm Value Dollars
United States	33,148	2.58	85,703	$45.99	$3,942,000
California	9,312	4.28	39,908	23.98	957,000
Oklahoma	8,333	1.58	13,167	64.47	849,000
Arkansas	6,146	1.73	10,642	69.81	743,000
Texas	4,958	1.48	7,350	43.40	319,000
Virginia	1,438	2.60	3,745	57.40	215,000

The most active harvest season for the important market states as well as the western states are given below. In the case of Texas, harvest begins about November 15 and ends about April 30, but the active harvest season is December to March. For spinach and also the other crops the active harvest season is only a portion of the entire season. The months for the various states are as follows: Texas, December to March inclusive; Pennsylvania, May and June, also September and October; California, January to March; New Jersey, May and June, also September 15 to November 15; New York, August and September; Washington, January to April, also July to October; and Colorado, July and August.

Food Value. Spinach is found in group one and although high in food value does contain a relatively high amount of oxalic acid. This compound is detrimental since it is said to combine with iron and calcium forming calcium oxalate which makes the calcium unavailable for absorption. While these two nutrients rank low, the other nutrients are high enough to place spinach in the first group. Spinach contains 92.7 per cent water and the food value per 100 grams of edible portion is energy 25 calories; protein 2.3 gm; vitamin A 2,500 I.U.; ascorbic acid 80 mg.; thiamine 0.13 mg.; riboflavin 0.28 mg.; and niacin 0.63 mg. The following data give the relative rank of spinach in comparison to 31 other vegetables on a pound, acre, and man-hour basis; it also gives those nutrients where spinach ranks in the highest ten.

Pound, rank 11:   Riboflavin, 1; vitamin A, 3; ascorbic acid, 5; thiamine, 5; protein, 6.

Acre, rank 12:   Thiamine, 2; riboflavin, 2; vitamin A, 4; ascorbic acid, 4; protein, 5; niacin, 10.

Man-hour, rank 8:   Riboflavin, 2; vitamin A, 3; ascorbic acid, 4; thiamine, 5; protein, 7.

Varieties. Identifying variety characters found in this crop are the smooth versus prickly-seeded, and the early versus late-seeding (long standing) types. A brief description is given of some of the more important varieties, although these will vary with local environmental conditions. Seed catalogues and type books are good sources of variety descriptions and adaptations.

Bloomsdale. Smooth seeded; its dark-green leaves make it a desirable variety for shipment. There are two types of this variety. See also Long-Standing Bloomsdale.

Giant Nobel (Giant Thick Leaved). Smooth-seeded; plants large, vigorous, slow to form seed stalks; and heavy yielder. Used for summer or warm weather production.

Hollandia (Prickly Winter). Prickly-seeded; leaves large, broad, and dark green. Used in California for market gardens and canning. Grown also in other areas of mild climate where spinach is over-wintered.

Long-standing Bloomsdale. Holds 12 to 14 days longer than others before going to seed; smooth-seeded. Plants large, erect; crumpled, dark-green leaves. Used for home, market garden, and shipping.

Viking (also called Northland). Plant is large, and a heavy producer. Leaves are large, dark green with short petioles. Used for both shipping and canning.

Viroflay. Smooth-seeded; vigorous growing with long, broad, smooth leaves of deep-green color. Used for market and canning.

Climatic Requirements. Spinach is placed in the group of vegetables which prefer an average monthly temperature of 60° to 65° F., but it makes good growth at 50° to 60° F. Freezing weather is more harmful to small seedlings and plants approaching maturity than at other stages, when the crop will tolerate subfreezing temperatures for weeks. Young plants will stand 15° to 20° F. without great injury. Sometimes seed is planted on frozen ground and the alternate freezing and thawing will cover the seed. Premature seeding or seed stalk development is caused by both high temperature or long days (**Fig. 43**) and of course this condition makes the crop undesirable for market. With either short days or low temperature, seeding is delayed. There are a

Fig. 43. Spinach, a typical long day plant. The plants with flowers received a long day, and the vegetative plants on the right, a short day.

few areas in the southwest near the ocean where it is possible to grow spinach during the long days of summer. Plants rarely are subjected to high temperatures followed by low temperatures early in their life, but when this does happen there is a rapid development of seed stalks. Some varieties are slightly resistant to premature seeding and these varieties are described as "long standing" types. Temperatures of 70° to 80° produce plants of low market quality. Spinach germination is relatively high at 40° F., and soil temperatures slightly higher.

Soil. Sandy loams to clays are used for this crop. Soils with considerable sand are desirable for winter or early spring crops because they are warmer and are well drained. Harvesting sometimes is possible on sandy soil during rainy periods when it is impossible to get on heavier soils. Muck soil is used to produce canning or main crop spinach.

Fertilizer. Since this crop is grown during cool weather, growth may be slow because of low temperature and little nitrification in the soil. As the soil warms up it is essential to have nitrates available to the plant since these cause a greening of the leaves and improve quality.

The following are suggested fertilizer applications for spinach as given in publications and other sources. Only a brief abstract can be given under each crop and the reader is referred to the publications at the end of the crop discussion. Chemical fertilizers are given in terms of pounds, and manure in

Fig. 44. A spinach fertilizer plot showing the increased growth (on left) from 120 pounds of nitrogen per acre as compared to no fertilizer.

tons per acre. California growers should apply 60 to 120 pounds of nitrogen (Fig. 44) at planting or soon after emergence on the shoulder of the bed. Spinach grown during the rainy season gives best response to ammonium salts or other non-leaching forms of nitrogen. Oregon trials have given an increase of 60 per cent in yield from the use of 30 pounds of commercial borax per acre on boron deficient soils. Other nutrient needs would be expected to be similar to Washington. In eastern Washington, spinach may be a catch crop and require little fertilizer. Fifteen tons of manure and 60 pounds of nitrogen are recommended or 100 pounds of nitrogen plus 40 pounds of phosphoric acid on nonmanured soils. Western Washington growers use green manures or rotted manure on nonmuck soils, plus 600 pounds of 5-10-10 in bands.

Spinach is injured by high acidity; optimum growth was obtained in the East at between pH 6.0 and 7.0. This crop is very sensitive to acid soils below pH of 6.0.

Planting and Spacing. In mild climates, spinach may be planted in the fall and throughout the winter until March. Parker and Royston[3] list the planting dates for commercial fresh market spinach as follows:

California: Los Angeles to San Joaquin counties, July to March, inclusive.

Colorado: Denver area, Routt, Pueblo, Rio Grande counties, March 20 to July 15.

Washington: Puget Sound and southeast, March to June, September to October; Puget Sound, August.

Eight to 15 pounds of seed are used per acre—larger amounts being needed for prickly seed. In areas where there are severe winters, the crop is planted about as soon as the ground can be worked in the spring. Planting is broadcast or in rows varying from 15 to 24 inches apart with a seeding depth of one-half to three-fourths inch. Spinach is planted two rows per bed; plants are spaced 5 to 12 per foot, with the closer spacing necessary for mechanical harvesting. Thinning usually is not practised on the commercial crop. Overwintering of this crop is possible in many areas of the West where there is sufficient snow protection in the winter to prevent heaving of the seedlings out of the ground. The time of planting for most areas where this is possible would be from September 1 to 15.

In recent years seed treatments have been very popular with the growers since they are an inexpensive method of controlling some seed or soil-borne diseases. These diseases cause seed decay or infection of young seedlings, both of which cause poor plant stands. Recommendations are made only after the tolerance is known of the seeds to the fungicide as well as its toxicity to the parasitic organisms. Where recommendations are made they refer to the number of pounds of the chemical which are to be added to a certain amount of seed. The seed is covered with the chemical by rotating in a barrel which is placed diagonally in frame to increase the mixing of the seed and chemical. Small amounts of seed may be treated in a quart glass jar and rotated by hand. Spinach is very susceptible to damping-off, therefore, the use of treated seed is recommended highly. Spinach seed may be treated with zinc oxide at 2 pounds, or yellow copper oxide at one and one-half pounds, per 100 pounds of seed.

Irrigation. Spinach is a shallow-rooted crop and thus is likely to need irrigation. However, a major portion of its growth is made during the rainy season, but ample soil moisture is important near harvest. Adequate soil moisture at this time through rain or irrigation will improve yields and quality. Irrigated areas sometimes use from 6 to 12 inches of water on this crop.

Cultivation. Shallow cultivation is desirable for spinach to control weeds without cutting too large a proportion of the root system. Weeds rob the soil of water and soil nutrients as well as being a nuisance to remove by hand-picking from the harvested crop.

Harvesting. There are several ways of harvesting and marketing this crop. The time of harvest is dependent upon size of plants and the market price. The plants should be harvested after they reach full size for the variety and before any of the leaves turn yellow, form seed stalks, or die. For loose pack, (either market or canning) a blade is run about an inch below the crown in the soil to cut off the taproot. The plants are loaded into crates and washed for market, or delivered to the cannery. In recent years a considerable volume of spinach has been prepackaged in transparent plastic bags for market. In the Los Angeles area some of the spinach is tied in bunches for the fresh market. In recent years, the leaves of the cannery crop are cut just above the crown and bulk-loaded. This decreases costs and may permit the harvesting of one to two crops from the subsequent growth. The crop shipped out of Texas is loaded with ice in the package.

Storage. Normally this crop is stored only for short periods of a week or two. When stored the temperature should be 32° F. and 95 per cent humidity. The use of crushed ice in the packages will increase the storage life and insure a better quality vegetable.

Quality Characteristics for the Retail Buyer[6]. Well-developed stocky plants should have fresh, crisp, and clean leaves of good green color. Small, straggly, or overgrown stalky plants are often tough. Plants with yellow leaves, seed stems, or coarse leaf stems may be woody or tough. Wilted spinach or that showing yellow leaves is undesirable. Decay may be present as a soft, slimy rot.

Insects: *Aphids (Myzuspersicae, Aphis gossypii)*. These insects injure the plant by direct feeding; they cause a curling of the leaves and stunting of the plants. They also do damage as carriers of mosaic virus. Winged forms fly into the spinach fields and give birth to continuous generations. The destruction of malva and other weed hosts may be of value. Nicotine dusts and TEPP dusts will give some degree of control.

Leaf Miners (*Pegomya hyoscyami, Liriomyza spp.*). Spinach leaf miner and serpentine leaf miners damage spinach by eating material between the two leaf surfaces. Maggots of the former species make large blotch mines, whereas the serpentine miners make narrow serpentine mines. The entire leaf may be destroyed. Crop rotation and weed control are of value in reducing injury. Dusting with 2 per cent parathion dust when miners first appear has proved effective in some areas.

Diseases: *Downy Mildew* (*Peronospora spinaceae*) causes the leaves to be puckered or distorted and show pale-yellow spots above with patches of velvety violet-gray fungus growth on the underside. Plants may be injured severely. Resistant varieties are the only control but are not commonly available.

Mosaic blight is a virus disease which causes the young inner leaves of affected plants to become mottled, crinkled, and yellow, and finally die. If the plant is affected when young it is stunted. The virus is spread by aphids. No control method is available.

Curly top is due to a virus carried by the beet leaf hopper (*Circulifer tenellus*). The young leaves become crinkled, rolled, stunted, and deformed and the plants turn yellow and die. There is no control after infection.

Leaf spot (*Heterosporium variable*) is indicated by leaves possessing dead spots and may injure crop severely. It is most severe on winter grown crops subjected to cold, wet conditions.

Damping-off is caused by several species of soil fungi (*Pythium* sp. and others). Seedlings die at an early age or fail to develop from the seed. Seed treatment is a desirable control method.

References

1. Beattie, J. H. and W. R. Beattie: Production of spinach, *U.S.D.A. Leaflet 128*, 8 p., 1948.
2. Bouquet, A. G. B.: Spinach growing and preparation for market, *Ore. Agr. Ext. Cir. 361*, 6 p., (Mimeo.) 1941.
3. Parker, C. O., and R. Royston: Usual dates of planting and harvesting commercial truck crops for fresh market, *U.S.D.A. Bur. Agr. Econ.*, 65 p., 1945.
4. Randall, T. E. and C. D. Schwartze: Commercial spinach in western Washington, *W. Wash. Exper. Sta. Mimeo. Cir. 113*, 3 p., 1943.
5. Gardening for increased commercial vegetable production (eastern Washington), *Washington State Board for Vocational Education. Bul. 1*, 63 p., 1943.

6. U.S. Department of Agriculture, A fruit and vegetable buying guide for consumers, *U.S.D.A. Misc. Pub. 167,* 61 p., 1948.

CABBAGE

Botany. The mustard family supplies a notable group of vegetables such as cabbage (*Brassica oleracea* var. *capitata*), cauliflower, Brussels sprout, broccoli, turnip, and radish. The flowers have four sepals and petals, hence the name Cruciferae from the similarity to the Greek cross. The fruit is a long, slender pod called a silique, but when short and broad is referred to as a silicle. Many of these vegetables have similar-appearing seeds. The flowers are pollinated by insects, so it is possible to have both self- and cross-pollination. However, cabbage tends to be cross-pollinated because most of the plants carry self-incompatibility factors. These factors cause the pollen tube from the plant's own pollen to grow more slowly than a similar tube from another plant. The pollen tubes which grow more rapidly fertilize the ovules in seed production. A cabbage head is made up of numerous, thick, overlapping, smooth leaves which cover a small terminal bud. With the removal of the head there is a development of the buds in the axils of the lower loose leaves. Small heads of two or three inches in diameter are formed which have been called cabbage sprouts, but are of no commercial importance. Cabbage is normally a biennial.

Origin and History. It is believed that cabbage originated from a wild type that occurs at the present time on the chalk cliffs of eastern England, and along the coast of Denmark and northwestern France. Wild cabbage shows variation in general appearance and foliage, but the wild plant sometimes is used as human food. The plant shows no tendency to form heads so it is very similar to our collard plant. Broccoli and cabbage have developed from these wild types. Cabbage has been grown for many centuries and was introduced into America in 1540. By 1806 there were seven early and six late varieties grown in American gardens.

Producing Areas: Cabbage is marketed fresh, dried, and as sauerkraut. While some sauerkraut is sold in bulk most of it is canned. The 1940–1951 statistical data are given on p. 180.

The most active harvest season for some of the important market states are: New York, July to November; Florida, January to April 15; California, February to April; Texas, December 15 to April; Pennsylvania and Colorado, August to October; Arizona, December to March; Washington, June, also September and October; Oregon, November and December; Utah, August and September; and New Mexico, August 20 to September.

Food Value. Cabbage, a leafy crop, is placed in group one on food production efficiency. The pungent sulfur compound is found objectionable by some people. Cabbage probably is used to a greater extent in cooler climates

Cabbage for Market

	Acreage	Tons Per Acre	Production Tons	Price Per Ton Dollars	Farm Value Dollars
United States	171,324	7.3	1,250,908	$28.41	$35,539,000
Florida	15,750	8.3	131,566	35.63	4,689,000
New York	22,766	10.1	229,041	18.98	4,348,000
California	11,616	8.9	104,175	32.29	3,364,000
Texas	31,100	4.6	144,333	19.62	2,833,000
Pennsylvania	7,975	8.3	66,791	31.02	2,072,000

(Farm value, other Western states: Colorado, $1,190,000; Arizona, $657,000; Washington, $474,000; Oregon, $385,000; Utah, $156,000; New Mexico, $129,000).

Cabbage for Processing

	Acreage	Tons Per Acre	Production Tons	Price Per Ton Dollars	Farm Value Dollars
United States	18,107	9.9	179,516	$12.06	$2,165,000
New York	6,675	11.4	76,116	11.41	869,000
Wisconsin	4,633	9.5	44,150	11.59	512,000
Ohio	1,783	9.6	17,166	11.35	195,000
Indiana	1,358	5.9	8,075	13.99	113,000
Michigan	554	8.1	4,508	11.31	51,000

(Farm value, other Western states: Washington, $51,000; Colorado, $28,000).

where competition between vegetables is not so great. Cabbage contains 92.4 per cent water and the food value per 100 grams of edible portion is: Energy, 29 calories; protein, 1.4 gm.; calcium, 45 mg.; vitamin A, 50 I.U.; ascorbic acid, 72 mg.; thiamine, 0.075 mg.; riboflavin, 0.08 mg.; and niacin, 0.3 mg. Cabbage ranks in the highest ten in the following food nutrients:

Pound, rank 14:   Calcium, 5; ascorbic acid, 6.
Acre, rank 6:   Ascorbic acid, 3; thiamine, 5; calcium, 7; riboflavin, 7; energy, 9.
Man-hour, rank 4:   Calcium, 2; ascorbic acid, 2; protein, 4; thiamine, 4; riboflavin, 6; energy, 7.

Varieties. The varieties of this crop are divided into early and late green types, red, and savoy cabbage. The leaves of the savoy are crumpled and possess a distinctive desirable flavor. Some varieties are resistant to yellows disease.

Copenhagen Market: Leaves gray-green in color, stem short; heads round, solid, and of good quality. A few days later than Golden Acre but similar in type and use. Marion Market is a yellows resistant strain.

Danish Ballhead. Most popular late fall cabbage for sauerkraut, shipping and storage; heads (6½ pounds, 7½ inches in diameter) deep, round, and interior compact; plant fairly large, and sturdy; texture of head tender, with good quality. Several strains are available.

Glory of Enkhuizen. Heads medium to large (5 to 6 pounds, 7½ inches in diameter) nearly round, quite compact; plant large, spreading, medium green; used for sauerkraut. Globe is a yellows resistant strain.

Golden Acre. An extra early Copenhagen type with small, round, solid heads of about 3 pounds weight and 6 inches in diameter; plants small, compact and short stem. Green Acre is a strain which holds its green color better after harvest. Resistant Detroit is a yellows resistant strain.

Jersey Wakefield. Popular early variety for general use; plant small, short stems; heads small, compact, conical, 7 inches long. Jersey Queen is yellows resistant.

Mammoth Red Rock. Large strain of red cabbage (7 pounds, 7 inches in diameter); excellent keeper.

Savoy Chieftain. Medium-sized head, nearly round, good quality (Fig. 45).

Slow Bolting Flat Dutch. A valuable slow bolting variety grown in many Pacific coast areas during the cooler months of the year because it is less likely to bolt. Heavy yielder; heads 11 pounds, solid, 8 inches in diameter; good quality for home and market (Fig. 45).

Climatic Requirements. Cabbage is a cool season crop which prefers a

Fig. 45. Heads of Slow Bolting Flat Dutch (left) and Savoy Chieftain cabbage. Flat Dutch is a late type which is resistant to premature seeding. Savoy cabbage is desired for its pleasing flavor. (Courtesy, Ferry-Morse Seed Company.)

cool, moist climate with an average monthly temperature of 60° to 70° F., and is tolerant of some freezing weather. Growth is slow at 55° to 60° F. and also above a mean of 70° F. With the warmer temperature, quality usually is poor. Stocky, well hardened plants not larger than a lead pencil will withstand temperatures of 20° F. but younger or older plants may suffer damage. Low temperatures may cause premature bolting which is considered in a later section. Some frosty weather is believed to improve the quality of cabbage. The plant is a biennial. Seed germination is best at a soil temperature of about 55° to 60° F. The yellows disease of cabbage is more severe at high temperatures such as 75° F. than at low temperatures.

Soil. This crop is grown on all types of soil but a fertile and moisture retentive soil is desirable. The lighter soils are used for the early crop but the heavier soils and muck are used for the main crop.

Fertilizer. Cabbage needs a moderate amount of fertilizer and usually responds well to nitrogen. Supplementary applications when the plants are one-third grown sometimes are desirable. In most California areas about 50 pounds of nitrogen is used per acre, and in addition about the same amount of phosphoric acid is required in Imperial Valley and other areas of phosphate-deficient soils. Oregon suggests the use of 1000 pounds of 4-10-10 or 5-10-10 applied during the spring and worked into the soil for late cabbage. In Western Washington with an application of 10 to 15 tons of manure, the grower should use 500 pounds of a 5-15-5 fertilizer or 800 pounds of 5-10-10 when no manure is used. On irrigated soils in Eastern Washington, the grower should apply previous to seeding about 100 pounds of nitrogen and 40 pounds of phosphoric acid where manure is not used. With an application of 15 tons of manure, 60 pounds of nitrogen is sufficient.

Cabbage does not produce well in an acid soil. A pH of 6.0 to 6.5 is considered desirable; club root of cabbage is less serious when the reaction is near the neutral point.

Planting and Spacing. Field planting dates for commercial acreage are:

Arizona: Yuma and Salt River, September to December.
California: North, Central, and South Coast, November to August; Imperial Valley, September and October; Central Valleys, July and August also November to January.
Colorado: San Luis and Platte Valleys, April 15 to May 15.
Oregon: Willamette Valley, June 15 to July.
New Mexico: Valencia and Otero counties, May 1 to June 20.
Utah: Salt Lake and central, April 20 to May 10.
Washington: Puget Sound and southeast, February to April, May to July.

The crop usually is grown by transplanting although it can be directseeded in the field. Usually three to four ounces of seed are used to grow plants for transplanting an acre of cabbage, and one and three-fourths to two pounds of seed for direct-seeding of an acre. The plants are produced in a coldframe during the cooler part of the year, or in an open bed during the warmer months. Growing a large number of plants in a small area simplifies irrigation, fertilization, pest control, and permits the discarding of poor plants at transplanting time. Plants should be hardened before field setting. Some 8 to 12 weeks are needed to produce the plants. The field planting is done with a transplanting machine. Direct-seeded cabbage does not receive any retardation from transplanting and thus, requires a shorter growing period from seed of about two or three weeks. Sometimes the field seeding can be performed a few weeks earlier than the transplanting of cabbage. Land should be used which is free of weeds since both the cabbage and weed seeds germinate at the same time. Seed is planted thinly and when the plants are five inches tall they are thinned to about 18 to 24 inches apart in the row, according to variety and size of head desired. Rows are three feet apart. Plants that are hardened will stand temperatures of 20° F. in the field for short periods.

Cabbage and other crucifers may benefit in some areas by seed treatment. Semesan at 0.4 per cent (six ounces per 100 pounds) is the most effective dust treatment; but zinc oxide at 2.0 per cent also is used. Cabbage seed produced in the dry areas of the West usually is free of seed-borne pathogens, so that hot-water treatment is unnecessary.

Cultivation and Irrigation. The plant roots are numerous in the top two feet of soil and many roots grow close to the surface. Some roots may extend more than half the distance to the next row. Cabbage is raised on slightly raised beds with an irrigation furrow between the rows or in a humid climate without the use of beds.

Some cabbage may be raised during the rainy season with little or no irrigation. Under arid conditions, 12 inches of water will be adequate for a crop. Cultivation needs to be shallow to prevent cutting of roots.

Premature Seeding. Cabbage plants sometimes go to seed without producing a marketable head and consequently the crop is a total loss to the grower (Fig. 46). Premature seeding is caused by low temperatures near 50° to 55° F. and is prevented by temperatures of 60° to 70° F. Plants are more likely to be affected when they have a stem somewhat larger than the diameter of a lead pencil (6 mm.). Where cabbage is seeded in the fall, the earlier seeded plants are likely to be larger during the cold weather of winter and thus, are more subject to premature seeding. Cabbage plants with mature heads will form seed stalks most rapidly if they are placed at 40° F. for two months followed by placing the plants at 65° to 70° F. Either young or mature plants may be kept in a vegetative condition of forming successive heads by temperatures of 60° to 70° F. Length of day does not cause premature seeding. The grower may grow cabbage only at that time of year when temperatures are favorable for head production. Planting at the proper

Fig. 46. Cabbage planted for market showing a few bolting or seeding plants which are worthless as a fresh vegetable. Low temperature is an important factor causing bolting.

season is very important along the Pacific Coast. The grower may reduce the danger of premature bolting by the selection of varieties which are resistant to bolting such as Slow Bolting Flat Dutch or Early Jersey Wakefield. In contrast the Golden Acre variety bolts very readily. From a historical standpoint, it is of interest to consider some of the reasons given to explain premature seeding before the true causes were known. Miller[4] lists some of these explanations as follows: "(a) Early seeding in the fall; (b) large plants at the time when planting is done in the field; (c) a warm fall and early winter followed by cold weather and rain; (d) extreme changes in temperature; (e) a warm, open winter; (f) excess nitrogen in the plant bed or in the field; (g) poor seed, especially seed of low vitality; (h) heredity; (i) poor soil, either in the plant bed or in the field; (j) relatively low temperature (above freezing) for a considerable period; (k) a check in growth due to low temperature, low moisture, root injury, or other factor which would result in stunting the plants." Some of the above reasons mention temperature so growers in some cases were close to the real cause of premature seeding.

Harvesting. Early cabbage sometimes is harvested before the heads are hard, if the market price is good. Normally the heads are harvested when the head is firm as indicated by pushing the top leaves down with the fingers. The plant is bent over to one side so a knife may be used to cut the head just below the wrapper leaves. Further trimming may be needed to remove any broken or discolored leaves. A few plants in a field may not be harvested promptly and the heads will split open or burst. This condition is not unusual if the plants are growing and it is thought to be caused by the intake of water. The only remedy is to harvest the other heads immediately. In home gardens people sometimes twist the roots of the plant to reduce the intake of water. Heads usually are hauled from the field without packing. Cabbage may be packed in a standard crate (25 to 35 heads), weighing 80 to 100 pounds or in 50-pound green mesh sacks which makes an attractive pack.

Storage. Cabbage stores well and a considerable amount of a fall crop is stored for winter use. In a mild climate the cabbage is harvested from the fields as it is marketed. Under these conditions the heads are really stored in the field unharvested. Considerable cabbage is stored in the northern states for winter use in common storage. Although cold storage is not used commonly because of the low value of the crop, the most desirable conditions for storage are 32° F., 95 per cent humidity for a period of not longer than three or four months. Since most cabbage is stored in buildings without refrigeration, a well insulated building is needed to prevent freezing. Humidity should be high enough to prevent wilting. The use of bins, and slatted floors will help to increase the circulation of air. Cabbage should be handled carefully from the field to storage with the removal of roots and loose leaves. Ballhead types of late cabbage will store the longest, with early varieties sometimes having a maximum period of three to six weeks.

Quality Characteristics for the Retail Buyer. Good heads of cabbage should be reasonably solid, hard or firm, and heavy for their size; heads should be closely trimmed, and all except three or four of the outer leaves should be removed. In early cabbage, the head usually is not so firm as the fall types. When price is high there is a tendency to harvest cabbage before the heads are solid.

Defects of cabbage are worm injury, decay, yellowing of the leaves, and overmature or burst heads. Heads badly affected by these defects should be avoided, but when only slightly affected, the cabbage may be trimmed and utilized to advantage. Soft or puffy heads, although edible, are usually of poor quality.

Insects: *Aphids (Brevicoryne brassicae, Rhopalosiphum pseudobrassicae).* The cabbage aphid which is small, green, and entirely covered with whitish, powdery wax, is a very serious pest. The green peach aphid also is found on cabbage. The aphid population must be kept under control throughout the growing season since it is difficult to clean up a heavy infestation especially after the heads form.

As soon as aphids appear, start control measures. Parathion as a 2 per cent dust, and TEPP dusts are effective and have replaced the use of nicotine in most areas.

Cabbage Looper (*Trichoplusia ni*). These greenish caterpillars are similar in size and habits to the imported cabbage worm. The body tapers to the head. There is a thin but conspicuous white line along each side of the body and two others on the back. When resting or moving the body is humped. From this looping habit, the common name is derived. The same measures used to kill the imported cabbage worm will control the looper, and pyrethrum dusts or sprays can be used. It is important to kill these worms when they are small as the larger ones are more difficult to kill.

Cabbage Maggot (*Hylemya brassicae*). The small white maggots (one-fourth inch long) tunnel in the stems and roots, often killing or severely retarding the plants. The pest is most common in plant beds but it may cause damage in fields and gardens. This maggot can be controlled by treating the soil around the base of the plants with solutions of mercuric chloride (corrosive sublimate), or mercurous chloride (calomel). These materials will kill the maggots present at the time, but will not prevent new infestations. The solutions are prepared by adding one ounce of the chemical to 10 gallons of water and are applied at the rate of one cup of solution per plant, or in seedbeds one gallon to about 35 feet of row. Recent tests have shown that chlordane used as a soil treatment, dip, or field treatment will control cabbage maggot.

Diamondback Moth (*Plutella maculipennis*). The small caterpillars of this moth rarely exceed one-third inch in length, are pale yellowish-green in color, and can be distinguished by their nervous habit of wriggling actively when disturbed.

These caterpillars can be controlled in the younger stages by rotenone dusts but it is not effective against the larger larvae. Arsenicals or DDT will kill it but the same precautions listed under the imported cabbage worm must be observed.

Harlequin Cabbage Bug (*Murgantia histrionica*). This beautiful white, yellow, red, and black bug often causes damage by sucking out the plant juices which results in wilting, curling, and death of the plants. DDT, sabadilla, and lindane dusts give some degree of control.

Imported Cabbage Worm (*Pieris rapae*). The green velvety worms, which are about one inch long when mature, feed upon the leaves and eventually defoliate the plants. A 1 per cent rotenone dust applied preferably when the plants are wet with dew, at the rate of 15 to 25 pounds per acre, is effective on this pest. The active ingredient will deteriorate upon exposure to light and air so it is advisable to buy and use recently compounded materials.

Control also can be obtained when the plants are small by dusting or spraying with lead or calcium arsenate, DDT, or with cryolite. These latter materials are poisonous. They should not be used after the heads start to form, for if the heads contain a poisonous material the product will not be salable.

Diseases: *Alternaria Leaf Spot* (*Alternaria brassicae*) produces concentrically zoned, black spotting of the leaves. Usually not serious nor does it require control practices.

Blackleg (*Phoma lingam*) usually first appears in seedbed two or three weeks before transplanting. Leaf spots are at first indefinite pale yellow areas which later become ashen-gray centers which have many small black bodies. Collar rot lesions may develop on the stem. This is the destructive phase. Control is through the use of clean seed, rotation or a hot water treatment of seed (122° F. for 15 to 30 minutes).

Cabbage black ring is a virus disease that produces dark brown to black spots on the outer leaves of winter-grown cabbage. It is transmitted by the cabbage aphid. This disease is severe on sprouting broccoli.

Club Root (*Plasmodiophora brassicae*). This fungus disease attacks the roots to cause large irregular galls or swellings. Affected plants are stunted and wilt readily on hot days. The disease persists in the soil for many years even though cabbage or related crops are not grown. Club root is spread to clean fields on plants grown in infected seedbeds. Seedbeds should not be located on sites known to be infected and no plants from a seedbed that show evidence of the disease should be planted.

Cottony Rot (*Sclerotinia sclerotiorum*) (**Drop or white blight**). This disease produces a rotting of the stem and head along with a cottony white fungus and black sclerotia. It may cause losses in seed fields and in the crops along the coast.

Downy mildew (*Peronospora parasitica*) may do damage in seed beds and may spot the older leaves of cabbage during moist weather. Spraying cabbage for the control of these leaf diseases has seldom proved successful though Bordeaux mixture (4-4-50) or some of the new organic fungicides might be tried especially in the seed beds.

Mosaic occur on several types and cause different symptoms. Usually not important but only control measure is to prevent infection by spraying for aphids in the plant bed.

Rhizoctonia root rot (*Corticium vagum*) attacks the stems of cabbage plants below the ground level causing hard, dark colored leathery lesions that tend to girdle the stem. The plants become stunted, lopsided and eventually may die. Rotation of the fields and avoiding use of plants affected with damping-off in the plant beds are control measures.

Ring spot (*Mycosphaerella brassicicola*) causes round dead spots on the leaves. The spots are covered with small black dots. It is common only in the coastal districts where crucifers are grown continually. This disease is severe on Brussels sprouts.

Root rot (*Phytophthora megasperma*) is a fungus attacking the roots causing these parts to rot which results in sudden wilting of the plants. Affected plants pull up easily. This disease often is serious on winter crops, as well as cauliflower which is grown in low, wet, or poorly drained areas.

Yellows. This disease which belongs to the Fusarium wilt group, is not common in the Southwest. The stems of affected plants show a brown discoloration of the woody tissue. Marion Market, Jersey Queen, and Globe are yellows resistant varieties that might be used in place of Copenhagen Market, Jersey Wakefield, and Glory of Enkhuizen, respectively.

References

1. Boswell, V. R.: Commercial cabbage culture, *U.S.D.A. Cir. 252,* 60 p., 1945.
2. Bouquet, A. G. B.: Growing late cabbage, *Ore. Agr. Ext. Cir. 313,* 6 p., (Mimeo.) 1948.
3. Knott, J. E. and P. A. Minges: Cabbage production in California, *Calif. Agr. Ext. Ser. Mult.,* 9 p., 1949.
4. Miller, Julian C.: A study of some factors affecting seed-stalk development in cabbage, *Cornell Univ. Agr. Exper. Sta. Bull. 488,* 46 p., 1929.
5. Spangler, Raymond L.: Preparation of cabbage for market, *U.S.D.A. Farmer's Bull. 1423,* 20 p., 1948.
6. Stitt, Loyd L., Leo Campbell, Karl Baur, and John F. Moore: Growing cabbage in Western Washington, *W. Wash. Agr. Exp. Sta. (Mimeo.) Cir. 94,* 4 p., 1950.

SPROUTING BROCCOLI

The late cauliflowers sometimes are referred to as broccolis or cauliflower-broccoli, but sprouting broccoli is quite distinct since the head is small, green in color, and has numerous clusters of flower buds.

Botany. This crop is similar to cauliflower from a botanical standpoint but similar to cabbage with regards to climatic requirements and culture. Sprouting broccoli (*Brassica oleracea* var. *italica*) is grown for its large, thick, green, branching flower stalks which terminate with numerous clusters of flower buds. The edible portion is made up of loose flower buds, stem, and sometimes a portion of the leaves. The first central head (Fig. 47) is large in size and after its removal there are formed numerous secondary or side heads which prolong the harvest season for several weeks. The side shoots develop from the axil of the leaves.

Origin and History. The exact history of this crop does not seem to be known. Some authorities are inclined to believe that sprouting broccoli was known previous to early and late cauliflower. This would lead to the conclusion that the latter developed from sprouting broccoli. This crop has also

Fig. 47. A large, terminal head of Green Sprouting broccoli. (Courtesy, Associated Seed Growers, Inc.)

been called green sprouting broccoli, Italian asparagus, and asparagus-broccoli.

Production Areas. No national statistics are available for this crop, but the importance of sprouting broccoli has increased rapidly in the last 10 years. The crop is grown to some extent throughout the United States in the cooler portion of the year as well as being an important crop in the western states particularly California and Northwest. Sprouting broccoli is an important market and frozen vegetable. The California Crop Reporting Service makes an annual report on sprouting broccoli. In 1951 there were 18,800 acres in California with a value of $7,351,000. Most of the production was in the coastal counties from San Francisco south to Ventura. A small acreage is grown in Imperial Valley during the winter.

Food Value. Sprouting broccoli is high in food value and is found in the most efficient group of vegetables from the standpoint of food production. Cabbage and mustard greens are two other closely related plants which are found in the same group. Sprouting broccoli contains 89.9 per cent water, and the food value per 100 gm. of edible portion is, energy 37 calories; protein 3.3 gm.; calcium 41 mg.; vitamin A 2000 I.U.; ascorbic acid 102 mg.; thiamine 0.077 mg.; riboflavin 0.2 mg.; and niacin 0.75 mg. The following data give the relative rank of sprouting broccoli in comparison with other vegetables on a pound, acre, and man-hour basis as well as those nutrients where the crop ranks in the highest ten.

    Pound, rank 1: Riboflavin, 2; protein, and ascorbic acid, 4; vitamin A, 5; calcium, 6.
    Acre, rank 5:   Ascorbic acid and riboflavin, 5; vitamin A, 6; protein, 8.
Man-hour, rank 7: Ascorbic acid, 5; vitamin A, 7; riboflavin, 8; protein, 10.

Varieties. In recent years there have been developed several strains of this vegetable particularly adapted to time of maturity and use. The early strains are referred to under the names of Calabrese, Di Cico, and Freezers. These types mature their crop two to three weeks earlier than the medium strain. The late strain is planted along the coast about September to December and is used for late winter or spring harvest. This strain usually requires 4 to 5 months to first harvest which consists primarily of the central heads since there are few side shoots.

Broccoli Rab or Italian turnip is similar in some ways to sprouting broccoli since it is grown for tops and tender flower shoots which are used for greens. This plant is related closely to sprouting broccoli but there is an extremely minor commercial production.

Climatic Requirements. This vegetable may be grown under climatic conditions which are less exacting than those essential for early and late cauliflower. Since the climatic requirements are similar to cabbage, sprouting broccoli may be grown more generally than cauliflower. Monthly average temperatures of 60° F. and slightly lower are best for the production of a quality crop. The crop is not affected seriously by temperatures a few degrees below freezing. Best quality is obtained when the crop matures during cool weather.

Culture. Broccoli may be field planted either with plants or by direct seeding in the field. In irrigated areas the plants are grown frequently on beds with 1 or 2 rows. Single rows are used most commonly for freezers' broccoli. When field-seeded the rate is about one and one-half pounds per acre while 4 ounces of seed needs to be planted in a seed bed to produce enough plants for one acre. Field-seeded plants are thinned to 18 inches between plants when 2 to 4 inches tall. If there are two rows per bed it may be desirable to thin the plants so they are alternate on the bed. In this case some of the plants may be closer or about 12 to 18 inches. The plants for transplanting are grown in a similar procedure as that used for cabbage or cauliflower. The usual planting periods for California are central and south coast, June to March; San Francisco Bay area, May to September; Imperial Valley, September and October; San Joaquin Valley, July and August. In the western areas of Oregon planting occurs in early June and July. Western Washington transplants to the field June 10th to June 20th and eastern and central areas at least a month earlier. The cultural practises for broccoli are similar to cabbage.

Harvesting. The heads are ready for harvesting when well developed, but still compact. The buds should not be open and should not show yellow petals. The flower bud, stem, and attached leaves should be cut so they are about 8 inches long. The amount of leaf remaining on the stem varies with the type of pack. Some shippers remove all or most of the leaves so only the stem and unopened buds make up the bunch. The harvested portion is carried out of the field, usually to a packing house in field lug boxes. The heads are tied into uniform sized bunches with the aid of a frame and clamp such as are used for bunching asparagus. The excess stems are cut off and discarded. Each bunch should weigh one and one-half pounds or slightly more. When the crop is shipped, there are usually two layers of broccoli in the crate with ice on each side of the vegetable. Pony cauliflower crates frequently are used for shipment with 28 bunches of broccoli per crate. The weight of a crate is about 42 pounds. Sprouting broccoli for the freezing industry is delivered in field lug boxes without bunching.

Storage. The best storage temperature is 32° F. and the humidity should be 95 per cent. The crop does not keep well in storage and so storage periods should be kept to a minimum of not over two or three weeks. Broccoli in good condition and with good ventilation will keep for this period of time. With longer storage the leaves are likely to discolor and the buds drop off.

Insects. See cabbage.

Diseases. See cabbage.

References

1. Bouquet, A. G. B.: Sprouting broccoli, *Ore. Agr. Ext. Bull. 704,* 7 p., 1950.
2. Knott, J. E. and P. A. Minges: Sprouting broccoli production in California, *Calif. Agr. Ext. Leaflet,* 7 p., (Multolith.) 1948.
3. Moore, John F., Karl Bauer, Loyd L. Stitt, and Leo Campbell: Growing sprouting broccoli in western Washington, *W. Wash. Exp. Sta. Cir. 88,* 4 p., 1950. ·
4. Thompson, R. C.: Cauliflower and broccoli varieties and culture, *U.S.D.A. Farmer's Bul. 1957,* 17 p., 1944.

GROUP A. MINOR CROPS

Beet. The beet (*Beta vulgaris*) is a biennial crop grown primarily for its roots, but the young plants also are used for greens. Cultural and climatic requirements are similar to those of carrots. A seed ball is planted and may have more than one viable seed. Plants are likely to produce seed stalks after temperatures of 40° to 50° F. for 15 days or longer. Cool temperatures,

Fig. 48. (*Top*) The beet varieties are from left to right—Ohio Canner, Asgrow Canner, Detroit Dark Red, Crosby's Egyptian, and Early Wonder. (Courtesy, Associated Seed Growers, Inc.)

(*Bottom*) The radish varieties are from left to right—French Breakfast and Sparkler in the top row, and Saxa, Cavalier, and Early Scarlet Globe in the bottom row. (Courtesy, Associated Seed Growers, Inc.)

without any excess of nitrates, produce a redder or better-colored beet. Beets, graded as one and one-half to three inches in diameter, are bunched; those 2 to 4 inches are sold as topped beets. Detroit Dark Red and Early Wonder are commonly used varieties (Fig. 48).

References

1. Beattie, J. H.: Culture of table beets, *U.S.D.A. Leaflet 127,* 4 p., 1943.
2. Lorenz, O. A., and P. A. Minges: Table beet production in California, *Calif. Agr. Ext. Leaflet,* 5 p., (Multolith.) 1948.
3. Randall, T. E., and C. D. Schwartze: Growing beets in Western Washington, *W. Wash. Agr. Exp. Sta. (Mimeo.) Cir. 122,* 5 p., 1943.

Broad Bean. This crop also is called horse bean, Windsor bean, and faba bean (*Vicia faba*). The crop is produced in the spring about the same time as peas; it is grown both for human food and as a green-manure crop. If fresh peas are high in price the harvesting of broad beans for market is more extensive. The plant is 3 to 4 feet tall, the pods are 10 inches long and contain large flat beans which are green when immature. The beans are used both green and dry. The shelled beans are used as a vegetable. There is considerable variety variation in size of bean.

Brussels Sprout. The plant of this vegetable (*Brassica oleracea* var. *gemmifera*) has cabbage-like leaves and grows 2 to 3 feet tall. In the axil of each leaf occurs a small edible cabbage, a head-like bud which commonly is called a "sprout". These are 1 to 2 inches in diameter. The plant requires cool weather, like the globe artichoke, and will even stand slight freezing. The crop is grown from San Francisco south for about 100 miles along the coast; it also grows in the Puget Sound area and on Long Island. The plants are transplanted to the field in June in the Half Moon Bay area and about a month later in the south-coast areas of California. In Oregon and Washington, plants are transplanted in July and August. The crop is spaced 2 by 3 feet. The culture is similar to that of cabbage. Half-Dwarf Improved is a common variety. Harvest starts 3 months after field setting, or when the buds have made maximum growth and the lower leaves are slightly yellow. The crop usually is harvested about 6 to 8 times, from November until April. The harvesting procedure is first to remove the leaves of the mature buds so there is no damage to the sprouts when they are snapped from the stem. After the buds are removed, they are prepared for market by cutting off any loose, discolored, or yellowed leaves, leaving an attractive firm bud.

Reference

Bouquet, A. G. B.: Brussels sprouts, *Ore. Agr. Ext. Cir. 422,* 3 p., (Mimeo.) 1943.

Kale and Collards. The same scientific name (*Brassica oleracea* var. *acephala*) is used for both kale and collards, although they differ in appearance. Collards are like a nonheading cabbage and are very popular in the South. Their culture is similar to that of cabbage, but with slightly wider spacing. The plant will withstand hot summer weather as well as being hardy to low temperatures. Georgia is a typical variety. Individual leaves may be harvested for market, or the entire plant may be marketed when partially grown. Kale, while similar to collards, is hardy to cold weather but not to hot summers. Both vegetables are planted in August in the coastal areas or may be planted in spring for a summer crop. There are dwarf types and tall types of kale; the tall types develop a main stem. Leaves are curled or smooth; green or bluish-green. Dwarf Blue Scotch and Tall Green Scotch are two varieties of kale. Spacing is 3 by 2 feet. Kale is grown primarily during the cool months and is harvested like collards. It is grown frequently for chicken feed.

Reference

Thompson, Ross C.: Production of kale, *U.S.D.A. Leaflet 143,* 4 p., 1937.

Kohlrabi. Kohlrabi (*Brassica caulorapa*) has an enlarged stem which is the edible portion. The culture and climatic requirements are similar to those of turnip. The plants are harvested when the enlarged stem is about 2 inches in diameter as greater size is accompanied by increased toughness. For market, the main root is cut off and then the leaves with enlarged stem are tied in bunches. Early Purple and White Vienna are varieties.

Parsnip. The parsnip (*Pastinaca sativa*) is a long-season crop which forms a long root, and will withstand winter freezing if left in the field. Viability of parsnip seed is low after the first year, and seedlings are also slow in coming through the soil. The crop is planted at the same time as carrot seed and spaced and grown like other root crops. Hollow Crown is a common variety and has tapering roots which are 2 to 3 inches in diameter at the crown and 12 to 15 inches long. The roots may be loosened with a plow and removed by hand. The roots are topped, washed, and either marketed or stored.

Reference

Beattie, J. H. and W. R. Beattie: Production of Parsnips, *U.S.D.A. Leaflet 154,* 4 p., 1938.

Radish. Radishes (*Raphanus sativus*) are a short-season crop (Fig. 48, *Bottom*) and in a favorable climate it is possible to grow 8 to 10 crops on the same land in one year. There is also the so-called winter radish which is large, and may be stored for winter use. Both are cool season crops and the short season types or spring radishes require about 4 weeks to grow. Two rows are planted per bed; or about 2 feet between rows on the flat; or sown broadcast. The seed is planted with 3 to 4 seeds to the inch of row, and harvested several times so that the larger radishes are removed first. Early Scarlet Globe, French Breakfast, and Sparkler are red varieties; and White Icicle is a white type. Chinese White Winter requires 60 days for growth, is 6 inches long, 2 inches in diameter, and is spaced about five to the foot. The winter types sometimes are peeled before eating and Orientals use them to make pickled radishes.

Reference

Beattie, J. H. and W. R. Beattie: Production of radishes, *U.S.D.A. Leaflet 157*, 4 p., 1938.

Horse Radish. This plant (*Armoracia lapathifolia*) is grown for its pungent compound—allyl isothiocyanate (C_3H_5CNS). This compound, after the pulp is ground, is soluble in water; it is also volatile, so care must be used to retain the pungency of the ground product. The crushed root usually is mixed with white vinegar, and will remain pungent for only about 2 weeks on the store shelves at ordinary temperatures. Pungency will be retained longer if stored at low temperatures. White turnip or white corn meal sometimes are used as adulterants. Since the roots have many secondary or side roots, the greatest factor in economical production of the ground root is the cost of cleaning the roots. Many growers produce the roots for sale without entering into the manufacture of the ground product. The major source of profit is being able to clean the roots economically.

Horse radish grows best in the north temperate sections of the United States, like Massachusetts, Missouri, and Washington. The crop does not thrive in the southern states. There is little choice as to variety, although the usual one named is Maliner Kien. Good, healthy stock should be used. The crop is planted about the time of the average frost date in spring and occupies the land till fall. It is propagated from root cuttings, sometimes root crowns, and rarely produces seed. When the crop is harvested in the fall, the side roots are saved for propagation. Cuttings are 8 to 12 inches long, the size of a lead pencil, and are cut off square at the top and sloping at the bottom. In planting, the square end is placed closest to the surface. The cuttings are tied in small bundles and stored in outside pits, or in moist sand in a cellar. Care should be used to prevent heating or drying. The cuttings are planted 30 by 12 to 15 inches, 5 to 9 inches deep. Horse radish frequently is planted on a slant since in some areas the root is exposed partially during the growing season and the small roots removed by hand. This stripping is done twice and is for the purpose of obtaining roots free from side roots near the crown. Much of the growth is made in the cool months just previous to harvest. The crop is harvested about the time of killing frost, the tops are cut off, and the roots dug by means of a plow. Roots are freed from soil, and placed in piles before removing to a cool storage or outdoor pit. Before marketing, the roots are trimmed of laterals and washed and packed for market. The crop is a perennial but it is grown as an annual to prevent the crop from becoming a weed.

Reference

Beattie, W. R.: Production and preparation of horse radish, *U.S.D.A. Leaflet 129*, 6 p., 1937.

Rhubarb. Pie plant or rhubarb (*Rheum rhapanticum*) is a perennial grown for sauce or pie filling. The petioles or leafstalks are used as food. The crop is typically cool season and in areas of freezing winters it is one of the first vegetables in the spring. Climatic requirements are similar to those of asparagus. The crop does not do well in the South. In the Southwest the crop is produced during the mild winter period and tends to be dormant during the warm, dry season. In a colder climate the dormant period is in winter. The crop may be propagated either from seed or by division of the crown formed the previous season. Seed rarely is used because of the great variability in the resultant plant due to cross pollination. When the crowns are divided care should be used to have one strong "eye" or bud on each root. Division and planting occurs in the spring in severe climates, and in the winter in a mild climate where the ground is not frozen. Plants are spaced 4 by 5 feet and planted 4 inches deep, as the crown needs a covering of soil. Giant Cherry and Crimson Winter are varieties commonly used in the West, and possess attractive red petioles. The seed stalks are removed when they appear. Commercial plantations are reset every third or fourth year. The old crowns which are being discarded sometimes are put in a shed with soil around the roots for forcing. This occurs before the normal harvest season. The roots need to go through a rest period of 6 to 8 weeks commonly broken by freezing weather after which they are watered, and growth is forced by the heating of the shed to 50° to 60° F. Forced rhubarb produces long, pale-pink petioles of excellent quality. Rhubarb is harvested by grasping the leaf close to the main stem and pulling to one side so the stalk with attached stipules comes loose from the plant. Two to five stalks are tied in bunches for market; or a small box may be filled with leaf-stalks for shipment or market.

References

1. Beattie, J. H.: Rhubarb production, *U.S.D.A. Leaflet 126*, 4 p., 1946.
2. Beattie, J. H.: Rhubarb forcing, *U.S.D.A. Leaflet 137*, 4 p., 1940.

3. Bouquet, A. G. B.: Rhubarb growing and forcing, *Ore. Agr. Ext. Cir. 486*, 3 p., (Mimeo.) 1946.

Rutabaga. This crop (*Brassica napobrassica*) has a similar culture to turnip. Most of the production occurs in the northern states and Canada, where the cool season is longer. It requires a longer growing season than turnip, and usually is sold as a topped root. The root is larger, 4 to 5 inches in diameter, and stores well; the quality improves with a short storage period. American Purple Top is a common variety.

Reference

Beattie, W. R.: Production of turnips and rutabagas, *U.S.D.A. Leaflet 142*, 4 p., 1943.

Salsify or Vegetable Oyster. This vegetable (*Tragopogon porrifolium*) is used to make soup which possesses an oyster-like flavor. It is similar to parsnips in culture and also will withstand winter freezing. The roots are harvested when about 1 inch in diameter, topped, and about ten roots are tied in a bundle for market. The roots usually are tied at both ends. Mammoth Sandwich Island is the variety usually grown.

Reference

Beattie, W. R.: Production of salsify or vegetable oyster, *U.S.D.A. Leaflet 135*, 4 p., 1946.

Turnip. Turnips (*Brassica rapa*) and rutabagas are quite similar in culture and use. Both crops have yellow- and white-fleshed roots but turnips usually are white-fleshed and rutabagas yellow. Turnip leaves are usually light green, thin, and hairy; whereas those of rutabagas are bluish, thick like cabbage, and smooth. Turnips are grown in the cooler periods of spring or fall. Temperatures below 50° F. are likely to cause bolting. The fall is preferred since the crop matures in cool weather, while in the spring the weather is sometimes too warm at harvest time for turnips and may cause a bitter or sharp flavor. The crop is grown like other root crops and in a period of 45 to 50 days. Purple Top White Globe is a common variety. The roots are harvested as soon as they are 2 inches in diameter and are sold bunched. When the roots are about 3 inches in diameter they usually are sold as topped turnips. Such roots store better than the bunched turnips. This crop also is grown and used as greens and in this case they are harvested when young and tender with a small root.

Reference

Beattie, W. R.: Production of turnips and rutabagas, *U.S.D.A. Leaflet 142,* 4 p., 1943.

Water Cress. Water cress (*Nasturtium officinale*) is a hardy aquatic perennial which grows in shallow pools of water, but may be grown in greenhouses when provided with ample soil moisture. Beds are started with cuttings or from plants grown from seed. Special care should be used with the seed since it is small and therefore should be covered shallowly and receive ample water. Plants are placed in beds in early spring and they soon spread over the area. When the bed is well established, the young tender shoots are cut for market and tied in bunches. The plant's pungent flavor is desired for mixed salads; the leaves are used as a garnish.

References

1. Beattie, J. H.: Production of water cress, *U.S.D.A. Leaflet 134,* 4 p., 1938.
2. Shear, G. M.: Watercress growing, *Virginia Agr. Exp. Sta. Bull. 424,* 15 p., 1949.

Chapter 16

Group B.   Cool Season Crops Damaged Near Harvest by Freezing Weather

Group B. Prefer 60° to 65° F. Intolerant of 70° to 75° F. Damaged near maturity by freezing weather.

CAULIFLOWER

Botany. In cauliflower (*Brassica oleracea* var. *botrytis*), the edible head is surrounded by leaves similar in texture to cabbage but these leaves tend to be long and narrow. The head is made up of abortive flowers whose stalks are short, fleshy, and closely crowded. When the head is in prime condition there is no trace of flower structure; this condition is followed by a spread of the structures of the curd and the elongation of the flower stalks. Their usual color is white, but purple types are grown. The early cauliflower is grown quite generally over the United States, while the late type is grown primarily on the west coast. These types differ as to length of production season, size of plant, and method of blanching. Late cauliflower is grown for a longer period, has a larger plant and the leaves bend over the heads naturally and blanch the curd (Fig. 49). Late cauliflower is distinct enough

Fig. 49. Plants of early (Snowball variety) and late cauliflower (Christmas). Note the curling of the leaves over the curd of the late cauliflower, on the right. (Courtesy, Ferry-Morse Seed Company.)

in type so it has been called heading broccoli, or cauliflower-broccoli and more recently winter cauliflower. The industry refers to both early and late cauliflower as "flower."

Origin and History. Cauliflower and sprouting broccoli would seem to be closely related and cauliflower probably developed from the green sprouting broccoli. The area of origin does not seem to be known, but the early use of the crop occurred in Europe. There are several types of cauliflower mentioned which vary in color of curd. McMahon in 1806, an American seedsman, listed Roman or Purple, the Neapolitan or White, the Green, and the Black.

There has been much improvement in the color and size of cauliflower in the last hundred years. Danish gardeners have been responsible for much of this improvement and under normal world conditions are an important source of seed. World War II forced American seedsmen to produce most of our cauliflower seed so we are not dependent now upon European sources.

Production Areas. Cauliflower production is limited by climate. Most of the late cauliflower is produced in California. The 1940–1951 statistical data are given below:

Cauliflower for Market

	Acreage	Crates* Per Acre	Production Crates	Price Per Crate Dollars	Farm Value Dollars
United States	34,558	318	10,996,000	$1.27	$14,010,000
California	16,966	321	5,438,000	1.17	6,401,000
New York	7,400	343	2,541,000	1.56	3,965,000
Colorado	3,208	277	890,000	0.79	706,000
Arizona	1,516	309	469,000	1.49	700,000
Michigan	1,275	274	349,000	1.68	587,000

(Farm value, other Western states: Oregon, $440,833; Washington, $305,000).
* Approximately 37 pounds.

The most active harvest season for some of the important market states as well as those in the West are: California, November to April; New York, June to November; Colorado, August and September; Arizona, December and January; Michigan, September and October; Oregon, February and March, also October and November; and Washington, June and July, also October.

Food Value. Cauliflower, a mild, blanched crop, is placed in group three on food production efficiency. The edible portion of this vegetable is approximately 45 per cent of the vegetable as purchased. Cauliflower contains 91.7 per cent water and the food value per 100 gm. of edible portion is energy 31 calories; protein 2.4 gm.; calcium 22 mg.; vitamin A 40 I.U.; ascorbic acid 70 mg.; thiamine 0.2 mg.; riboflavin 0.1 mg.; and niacin 0.57 mg. The following data give the relative rank of cauliflower in comparison with other vegetables on a pound, acre, and man-hour basis as well as those nutrients where this crop ranks in the highest ten.

Pound, rank 20: Ascorbic acid, 7; thiamine, 8.

Acre, rank 17: Thiamine, 3; ascorbic acid, 8.

Man-hour, rank 9; Thiamine, 3; ascorbic acid, 6; protein, 9; riboflavin, 10.

Varieties. The number of varieties is limited. Snowball, the most popular early variety, and Ferry-Morse's strains of late cauliflower generally are used in the West, and the latter are named according to time of maturity. Varieties may be selected to give a continuous supply for several months.

Early Cauliflower. Snowball is used for early crop. Heads medium large, compact, very white, and much used by market gardeners and shippers. There are several strains of Snowball and the following commonly are used: Early Snowball, Snowdrift, Super-snowball, Snowball A, Snowball X and others.

Late Cauliflower. Varieties are named November-December, Christmas, February, March and April to indicate time of maturity. Late cauliflower produces a larger and coarser head than early cauliflower and needs a much longer period to mature the crop in the field. The bulk of the late cauliflower consists of November-December, March, and April strains.

Climatic Requirements. Cauliflower, a cool season crop, is so exacting in its climatic requirements that this crop is produced only in cool, moist areas. Early cauliflower is grown more generally than the late. Like cabbage, it requires mean monthly temperatures of 60° to 70° F., but is less tolerant of extremes of heat and cold. A check in growth may cause the plant to form "buttons" or small unmarketable heads. In the West the crop matures during mean temperatures of 50° to 60° F. High temperatures cause poor quality curds—with defects termed "leafy, ricy, loose, or yellowed curds." Direct rays of sun on the curd produce undesirable brown pigmentation, and sometimes low temperatures cause purpling. Early cauliflower leaves usually are tied for blanching, but the incurving inner leaves of late cauliflower ensure self-blanching. Good seed germination occurs at soil temperatures of 50° to 75° F. Late cauliflower is planted in fall or early winter and there is more variation between these varieties as to length of growing season than for early cauliflower.

Soil. Climate is more important than soil, but cauliflower is a valuable crop that justifies excellent growing conditions. Most types of soil may be used, but all should have good drainage, be rich in nutrients, and provide adequate soil moisture. The root system of this crop is similar to cabbage.

Fertilizer. The fertilizer requirements are very similar to those of cabbage. A steady growth of the plant is important in order to produce good curds, and fertilizer is helpful in accomplishing this purpose. Arizona uses 200 to 400 pounds per acre of a 10-10-0 or 10-20-0 in bands, at planting time, with a side dressing of nitrogen later in the season. California growers use about 100 pounds of nitrogen per acre. Oregon recommends the use of 10 to 15 tons of manure plus some commercial fertilizer, like a 5-10-7 analysis. The use of boron has been found beneficial in preventing hollowness of the stem and browning of the head. The Washington recommendations are similar to those for cabbage.

Planting and Spacing. Cauliflower plants usually are produced in a plant bed or coldframe, and transplanted to the field. The seed usually is more expensive than cabbage; consequently the grower cannot afford the extra seed needed for field seeding. In spite of this serious handicap there has been some direct seeding of cauliflower. Planting distance varies with variety and size of plant. Rows are usually 3 feet apart, and the plants 16 to 24 inches apart in the row. In the Southwest, the shippers desire a curd 4 to 5 inches in diameter and this has caused the growers to use close spacing to reduce the curd size. Spacing between plants under these conditions may be 12 to 14 inches. The planting dates for commercial acreage are:

Arizona: Salt River Valley, August 15 to September.

California: For Snowball variety, July to September. Late varieties, October to December.

Colorado: San Luis Valley, April to June.

Oregon: Willamette Valley, May 15 to July. Douglas County and Willamette Valley, August.

Washington: Puget Sound and Spokane County, February to March, April to May, and June to July.

Seed treatment given for cabbage is applicable to cauliflower.

Irrigation. Much of the plant growth of cauliflower is made during the rainy season, and the irrigation water needed is the same as for cabbage; namely 12 inches.

Blanching. The early cauliflower needs to have the leaves tied near maturity to blanch the head. Some two to three days are required for blanching in warm weather, and eight to 12 in the cooler part of the year. Some growers use different colored twine each time they tie the leaves so the harvesters may easily distinguish the heads needing to be examined for harvesting. Rubber bands have been used to fasten cauliflower leaves. The rubber bands are carried on the worker's left arm and are slipped down over the gathered leaves. In the late type, the leaves naturally bend over for blanching, and this crop matures during the part of the year when there is less sunshine. High quality cauliflower should have a pure-white curd both for appearance and mild flavor.

Table 30*

COST OF PRODUCING EARLY CAULIFLOWER IN
LOS ANGELES COUNTY

Year	Cost Basis	Yield Per Acre Crates	Labor and Field Power	Materials	Overhead, Depreciation, Rent and Interest	Total Costs	Income	Management Income
1948	acre	657	$125.45	$84.11	$62.68	$272.24	$370.93	$98.69
1949	acre	415	142.78	71.23	63.67	277.68	210.94	−66.74†
1948	crate‡	. .	0.19	0.13	0.09	0.41	0.56	0.15
1949	crate	. .	0.35	0.17	0.15	0.67	0.51	−0.16†

* Courtesy, *Los Angeles Co. Agr. Ext. Ser.,* 10 p., (Mimeo.) 1950.
‡ Crate 10 to 12 heads.
† Loss.

Cost of Production. Table 30 gives an example of a cost study made two years in Los Angeles County. Nine coöperators were included each year or about 20 per cent of the acreage in the San Gabriel Valley. A profit was made in 1948, but in 1949 the growers on an average lost money on this crop. In 1949 only one grower made a profit on his crop and the losses of the other growers varied from $6.89 to $193.34 per acre. In the two years the price per crate was about the same but the yield per acre in 1948 was 60 per cent greater. The low yield in 1949 was caused by leaving a large proportion of the crop unharvested due to poor market condition. In the case of the unprofitable crop a large amount was sold to freezers which doubled the labor required for tying, cutting, and packing the individual heads. The original paper furnishes considerable breakdown of the different costs and growers are able to examine these to determine where their costs are excessive. This provides information to be used to reëxamine and to improve their production methods and costs.

Harvesting. In warm weather the heads should be examined every day for harvest, and in cooler weather every three days. Heads are harvested when they reach the proper size and before any head defects are apparent. The curd is cut off low enough with a knife so there are two layers of wrapper or jacket leaves for protection and appearance. After hauling to the roadside or packing shed, they are prepared for shipment. The heads (9 to 13) are placed in a shallow crate, the protruding leaves are cut off with a knife, and the lid nailed on. The crop sometimes is hauled loose to local markets with the wrapper leaves uncut.

There are several defects which may appear in the heads. "Overmaturity" is indicated by spreading of the curds and by yellowish color; this is caused by delayed harvest. "Riciness" is caused by the elongation of the peduncles of the individual flower buds, which causes a granular appearance. Good seed and favorable climate will tend to prevent this condition. "Fuzziness", a somewhat similar condition, is caused by unfavorable growing conditions, and poor seed stocks. "Leafy" heads are indicated by green leaves appearing between the sections of the curd. This defect is caused by inferior seed strain and unfavorable growing conditions.

Storage. Cauliflower is a cool season crop which is stored at 32° F., 90 per cent humidity, and for a period not to exceed two to three weeks. Most of the curds are sold soon after arrival on the market, but an excess supply may be placed in cold storage for short periods. Successful storage depends upon preventing decay, and retarding maturity. Overmaturity is indicated by a browning of the curd and perhaps a yellowing of the leaves. Freezing causes a grayish-brown discoloration and softening of the curd. In shipping the crates should be stacked with the curds down to protect them from discoloration, dirt, and moisture. Top ice is used over loads shipped to eastern markets.

Quality Characteristics for the Retail Buyer. Cauliflower leaves extend beyond the curd (the flower portion of the head) and are trimmed down to within two inches for protection to the head. Number of leaves have no relation to quality since they are merely to protect the very tender curd, which easily is bruised and broken. Sometimes "wrapped and trimmed" heads of cauliflower are found on the markets. Size has little relation to quality.

Fine quality in cauliflower is indicated by white or creamy-white, clean, heavy, firm, compact curd with the jacket or outer leaves, fresh, turgid, and green. A compact curd is solid, with the flower clusters closely united. Riciness is objectionable when it is at an advanced stage of spreading of the flower clusters. Age is indicated by the yellowing of the leaves, and is not important if the curd has all the other requirements of quality. A spotted, speckled, or bruised curd should be avoided unless it can be trimmed without causing too much waste. Presence of aphids or plant lice may be indicated by a smudgy or speckled appearance.

Insects. See Cabbage.

Diseases. See Cabbage.

References

1. Beattie, J. H. and W. R. Beattie: Cauliflower and heading broccoli production, *U.S.D.A. Leaflet 130,* 6 p., 1938.
2. Bouquet, A. G. B.: Cauliflower growing and preparation for market, *Ore. Agr. Ext. Cir. 462,* 7 p., (Mimeo.) 1945.

3. Jones, H. A. *et al.*: The cauliflower industry of California, *Cal. Agr. Ext. Cir. 93*, 32 p., 1935.

4. Schwalm, H. W. and Wallace Sullivan: Cauliflower—cost of production, *Los Angeles Co. Agr. Ext. Ser.* (Mimeo.) 10 p., 1950.

5. Thompson, R. C.: Cauliflower and broccoli varieties and culture, *U.S. D.A. Farmers' Bul. 1957*, 17 p., 1944.

GLOBE ARTICHOKE

Botany. Compositae is one of the largest plant families, and is represented by endive, lettuce, salsify, globe artichoke (*Cynara scolymus*), cardoon, and several other vegetable crops. Many of this family have milky juice and the plants are annuals, biennials, or perennials. The inflorescence is a head made up of many individual flowers.

The globe artichoke plant is a herbaceous perennial in which the tops die down in late spring following the winter crop, or are removed by cutting. Renewed top growth in summer from the crown makes possible the next crop. The marketed portion is a "bud" or immature flower head. These buds range from 1 to 4 inches in diameter. The edible portion consists of the tender bases of the scale-like leaves as well as the receptacle or fleshy base upon which the flowers are borne. The plant grows to a height of 3 to 4 feet, and has a diameter of 6 feet. A mature plant produces 12 or more stems on which are borne 40 to 50 edible buds per plant (Fig. 50). Towards the end of the harvesting season there is a storage of inulin in the fleshy roots for production of the next crop. The trade usually refers to artichokes as "chokes". This vegetable should not be confused with Jerusalem artichoke, a tuberous plant commonly used for stock feed.

Origin and History. The wild form of cardoon is found in southern Europe and towards central Asia. It was used by the Romans as food over 2000 years ago. In cardoon the leaf petioles are eaten while the buds of globe artichokes are the edible part. Artichoke is the cultivated form of cardoon. Records indicate the vegetable was first used in Naples and was carried to Florence in 1466. There were three varieties of artichoke listed in 1612, and it appeared in American seed catalogues in 1806. The French people of Louisiana and the Italians of California are responsible largely for the popular use of this vegetable in this country. Half Moon Bay District of San Mateo County, California had the first commercial planting about the turn of the century.

Producing Areas. The production of artichokes is located in an area along the California coast from about San Francisco south to Santa Barbara. Artichokes are sold both fresh and canned. The marketing season extends from late September till the first part of May with the most active harvest period from December to February inclusive. The 1940–1951 statistical data for

Fig. 50. Harvesting of Globe Artichokes. (Courtesy, Henry Washburn.)

California are as follows: acreage, 7916; yield per acre in boxes (40 pounds), 94; production in boxes, 746,000; price per box $3.04; farm value, $2,272,000.

Food Value. Artichokes are a unique type of food that adds variety to our meals. It is placed in group three in food production efficiency. Globe artichoke contains 83.7 per cent water and the food value per 100 gm. of edible portion is energy, 63 calories; protein, 2.9 gm.; calcium, 47 mg.; vitamin A, 200 I.U.; ascorbic acid, 10 mg.; thiamine, 0.18 mg.; riboflavin, 0.05 mg.; and niacin, 0.7 mg. Artichokes rank in the highest ten in the following food nutrients:

Pound, rank 12: Thiamine, 6; iron, 7; energy, 10.
Acre, rank 30: All nutrients rank 11 or lower.
Man-hour, rank 22: All nutrients rank 11 or lower.

Varieties. This crop is propagated vegetatively; seeds rarely are used, because they do not breed true. There are two general types, referred to as the Italian and the French varieties. The buds of the Italian type tend to be long and slightly pointed, while those of the French type are almost round or somewhat flattened at the ends. Extreme flattened types are difficult to pack so the Italian type is preferred. Seedmen sometimes list the variety Green Globe.

Climatic Requirements. This crop is apparently very exacting with respect to climatic requirements. Production is limited to counties in Central California along the coast in the so-called fog belt. In this area the buds make a desirable development, the bracts become thick, fleshy, fit together tightly, and the floral development is slow so high quality buds are produced. This area has an average monthly temperature of 55° to 65° F. The rootstock will survive freezing weather but the aerial portion of the plant is injured by temperatures near freezing. A light frost does not destroy the edible quality of the buds but produces a blistered appearance which reduces their marketability. Freezing temperatures may kill the buds (28° to 30° F.). After low temperatures, harvest is delayed two to six weeks. If low temperatures kill the aboveground growth, harvest is delayed from six to eight weeks. A hot, dry climate produces tough buds, the petals tend to spread, and the period of harvest is shortened.

Soil. Rather heavy loams or light clays are used for the production of artichokes. Very likely a wide range of soils could be used for this crop if located in a desirable climatic area, however best production is obtained on a deep, fertile, well-drained soil.

Fertilizer. California growers use manure at the rate of 10 to 12 tons per acre, usually with an application of 60 to 100 pounds of nitrogen per acre in addition. The fertilizer ordinarily is applied in one application before the buds begin to form.

Irrigation. After a field has been dormant from a previous crop, irrigation is used to start growth for the fall crop. Water is applied in furrows between the rows, with 3 to 5 applications. Approximately 12 inches of water are applied. Since the crop is grown near the ocean the water loss from the plants to the air as transpiration is small. The artichoke plant is deep-rooted and in deep soils will extend to a depth of 6 feet.

Planting and Spacing. Plants will grow almost indefinitely, but after a few years the production and quality decrease. In order to prevent this, plantings are renewed every four to seven years. Young offshoots or suckers were the primary source of plants in the past. These were removed from the mature plants from November to March, when 12 to 18 inches high, and stored in a cool, moist place to prevent drying. More recently, the practise is to divide the old crown into pieces, with a stem per piece of crown. This procedure gives a young plant, with more reserve food.

The rows are spaced 8 feet apart with plants 6 feet apart in the row, or 975 plants per acre. Planting of the new fields occurs in February and

March; since the harvest season starts in September or October, early plantings will have greater production the first year. The plants are set 6 to 8
inches deep when starting a new field.

Culture. Weeds are controlled by cultivation as in other crops. After
harvest is complete, about May, the leaves and stems are cut off several
inches below the level of the ground. To do this the soil usually is plowed
away from the plants, and equipment with a cutter bar is used to cut off the
tops. If the leaves and stems are not cut off they will die at about the time
that the seeds mature. These leaves and stems sometimes are allowed to dry
for burning. They may be placed in a furrow to rot and thus, increase the
organic matter of the soil. In some cases the tops are sold for silage to the
livestock industry. Some three to four tons of silage are produced per acre
which is about equal to corn in feeding value.

Harvesting. Harvest begins with the maturing of the first buds in fall and
continues throughout the winter into spring. Pickings usually are made
weekly except during periods of cold weather. The buds are selected for
harvest on the basis of size, compactness, and age. Buds which are old and
not compact are fibrous and inedible. Each stem has several buds, with the
terminal one the most desirable. When all the buds have been harvested
from a stem it is removed to allow for the formation of new stems and pro-
longation of the harvest season. The buds are cut to include one and one-
half inches of stem, and are placed in sacks for hauling to the packing house.

Packing. At the packing house, defective buds are removed and the remainder sized accurately by machine. A large box ($9\frac{3}{4} \times 11 \times 20\frac{5}{8}$
inches) is used for shipment and may contain a bud count of 48, 60, 72,
84, 96, 110, or 125. For local markets the artichokes are packed in lug boxes.

Storage. A temperature of 32° F., relative humidity of 90 to 95 per cent,
and a limit of three to four weeks' storage would be applicable to this crop.
When shipped the cars are iced with 25 to 30 blocks of ice, each weighing
300 pounds, these are placed on top of the load.

Quality Characteristics for Retail Buyer. A compact, heavy globular,
plump artichoke which yields slightly to pressure, and which has large,
tightly clinging, fleshy leaf scales of a good green color, is the most desirable.
Freshness is indicated by green color, which, with age or injury, becomes
brownish. Overmaturity is indicated when the artichoke is open or spreading; the center may be fuzzy and a dark pink or purple color; the tips of
the scales are hard. When cooked the flavor is strong and the scales are
tough and woody. Discolored artichokes are generally old or stale, or may be
bruised. Bruises appear as dark discolored areas at the point of injury. Worm
injury occurs mainly at the base of the bud. Size is not important as far as
quality and flavor are concerned.

Insects: *Artichoke Aphids* (*Myzus braggii* and *Aphis fabae*). The artichoke aphid is a yellowish-green plant louse with dark markings, which

feeds on the undersides of the leaves of the plant. It causes serious injury to the plant by sucking out the sap, but may be controlled with a dust containing 2.5 per cent nicotine as alkaloid (nicotine is not poisonous in these concentrations) or a 2 per cent parathion dust. A nicotine oil spray using one pint of nicotine sulfate to one gallon of light-medium oil emulsion to 100 gallons of water also is effective. The bean aphid is a black species commonly infesting artichoke. It is controlled similarly to the artichoke aphid.

Artichoke Plume Moth (*Platyptilia carduidactyla*). The most common pest of artichokes is the artichoke plume moth. The moth is generally of a brown or buff color and has narrow wings with an expanse of three-fourths inch. The larvae are less than one inch long, and yellowish with black heads. They feed on the leaves and stems, but mainly on the developing buds, tunneling into them and at times causing severe crop losses. There are three over-lapping broods during the year, and larvae may be found at any time of the year.

Field sanitation assists in the control of this moth. Experimental work in California indicates that a 2 per cent parathion dust or 1 per cent lindane dust properly timed on the second brood will give a good control. State restrictions make it necessary to apply dusts two weeks before harvest.

Diseases: *Botrytis Rot* (*Botrytis cinerea*). The end scales are rotted and covered with a brownish-gray, dusty growth which is composed of mycelium and spores of the causal fungus, *Botrytis cinerea*. Disease is greatly favored by rain, fog, or high humidity. No specific control, but affected buds should not be shipped.

Curly Dwarf. Affected plants are stunted, shoots are spindly, curled and sometimes yellowed. Buds on infected plants are small, may have dead areas at the tip of bud scales and are generally worthless. The disease is a virus and is spread by unknown vector or insect and by planting infected transplants.

Leaf spot (*Ramularia cynarae*) causes older leaves to be disfigured by large dead spots. Disease is of minor importance and requires no treatment.

References

1. Bouquet, A. G. B.: The globe artichoke, *Ore. Agr. Ext. Cir. 252*, 3 p., (Mimeo.) 1943.
2. Tavernetti, A. A.: Production of the globe artichoke in California, *Cal. Agr. Ext. Ser. Cir. 76*, 19 p., 1947.

LETTUCE

Botany. Lettuce (*Lactuca sativa*) is an annual plant with milky juice, and is a member of the Compositae family. There are several types of lettuce which are called leaf lettuce because they are nonheading, cos lettuce which forms a loose upright head, and both butter, and crisp heading types. The last type most generally is eaten and sometimes is incorrectly called "Iceberg" lettuce. The leaves are alternate and grow from a short stem. Lettuce leaves vary in shape and color. Several minor varieties have leaves with reddish color. The inflorescence contains many separate flowers, each (or all) with strap-shaped corollas. The flowers open shortly after sunrise and they exhibit two or more cycles of flowering, over a period of two months. There is usually a period of six hours between pollination of the stigma and fertilization. Lettuce is self-pollinated almost entirely but is visited sometimes by insects which may carry pollen.

Origin and History. Records indicate that lettuce was used both as a food and for its medicinal properties as early as 550 B.C. Lettuce appeared on the tables of Persian kings. By 164 A.D. lettuce was in general use and was very popular with the Romans. In China, the presence of this crop has been known since the fifth century. Lettuce was cultivated in Haiti in 1565 and in Brazil in 1647. In 1806, some 16 sorts or varieties were listed by seedsmen in America. Evidently, cos lettuce first was grown in Italy as early as 1570. Heading types of lettuce have been known since the sixteenth century.

Production Areas. Lettuce is used generally throughout the United States but the production is located primarily in two western states. The 1940–1951 statistical data are given below:

Lettuce for Market

	Acreage	Crates* Per Acre	Production Crates	Price Per Crate Dollars	Farm Value Dollars
United States	179,937	166	29,956,000	$2.76	$82,879,000
California	109,025	175	19,116,000	2.88	55,154,000
Arizona	40,891	153	6,253,000	2.88	18,051,000
New York	4,408	228	1,007,000	2.22	2,239,000
New Jersey	2,933	229	671,000	2.67	1,798,000
Texas	3,958	106	418,000	3.19	1,332,000

(Farm value, other Western states: Washington, $1,016,000; Colorado, $927,000; Idaho, $472,000; Oregon, $465,000; New Mexico, $98,000.)
* Approximately 70 pounds.

The most active harvest season for some of the important market states as well as those in the West are: California, January and February, April and May, July to November; Arizona, December and January, March 15 to April 15; New York, July and August; New Jersey, June, and October 10 to November 15; Texas, December to February; Washington, May and June, also October and November; Colorado, August and September; Idaho, June, also October; Oregon, June and July, also October 5 to November 15; New Mexico, October.

Food Value. Lettuce is found in group 3 on food production efficiency. Even though it is a very popular salad crop and one in which a vegetative part of the plant is used as food, it does not rate as high as many other cool season crops. Lettuce contains 94.8 per cent water and the food value per 100 gm. of edible portion is energy 18 calories; protein, 1.2 gm.; calcium, 40 mg.; vitamin A, 210 I.U.; ascorbic acid, 12 mg.; thiamine, 0.037 mg.; riboflavin, 0.037 mg.; and niacin, 0.5 mg. The following data give the relative nutrient rank of lettuce:

Pound, rank 22: Calcium, 10.
Acre, rank 18: Calcium, 9.
Man-hour, rank 14: Calcium 9.

Varieties. There are two types of head lettuce, crisp and butter; leaf lettuce; and romaine or cos lettuce (Fig. 51). Most of the lettuce shipped is of the crisp type and the Great Lakes and Imperial strains are used most commonly. There is also some production of leaf, butter-head type, and cos lettuce. A description is given of the more important types and varieties of lettuce.

Big Boston. Butter-head type, for greenhouse or outdoor culture; head medium size, with creamy yellow heart; leaves smooth, glossy, with noncrisp texture; white seed.

Great Lakes. This type produces heads under more unfavorable conditions than other varieties. Some variation in type; hard heads, slow to bolt; leaves light green, finely cut, distinct from Imperial strains; some resistance to tipburn and marginal burning of outer leaves. There are several well defined

Fig. 51. Two types of lettuce. White Boston (*left*) is a butter head type, and Black Seeded Simpson (*right*) is a leaf type. (Courtesy, Ferry-Morse Seed Company.)

strains which differ in maturity and head characters. Great Lakes is used throughout the West as a summer variety.

Imperial Strains. Developed originally for Arizona and California areas. Resistant to brown blight, some variation in green color, and size of head; both white- and black-seeded strains. Important strains are Imperial 152 and 44 for fall lettuce in the Southwest and Imperial 615 and 101 for winter lettuce.

Simpson's Early Curled. Leaf lettuce used in home gardens; loose, large leaves; early, hardy, and dependable; white seed.

White Paris Cos. Large self-folding sort, with erect, concave leaves forming a loose head. Leaves excellent flavor; white seed. There is also a dark green strain.

Imperial Strains have a comparatively narrow climatic adaptation, hence each area has a rather definite planting schedule. Few vegetable crops seem to exhibit this characteristic. Planting schedules of Salinas and Imperial Valleys, also Arizona, are given in Table 31 as examples of this characteristic.

Table 31

LETTUCE GROWING SCHEDULES FOR CALIFORNIA AND ARIZONA (1952)

Districts and Varieties	Planting Dates	Periods to Maturity
Imperial Valley, California:		Days
Great Lakes	September 15–25	85–95
	October 15–November 10	120–130
Imperial 152	September 15–25	85–95
Imperial 615, 101	September 25–November 1	100–120
Salinas-Watsonville, California:		
Imperial 615, 101, K-1	November 10–December 10	120–145
Great Lakes	November 25–August 15	70–145
Yuma, Arizona:		
Great Lakes	September 1–15	80–85
	November 20–December 1	120–130
Imperial 44	September 7–20	70–85
Imperial 152	September 15–22	75–85
Imperial 615	September 20–November 15	90–120
Imperial 101	October 1–November 5	100–120
Imperial 749	October 28–November 28	120–130
Salt River Valley, Arizona:		
Great Lakes	August 20–September 1	80–85
	November 10–January 10	90–120
Imperial 44	August 27–September 10	80–85
Imperial 152	September 15–October 10	95–120
Imperial 615	October 1–December 15	95–110

Climatic Requirement. Lettuce is a cool-season crop. The climatic requirements of head lettuce are much more critical than for leaf lettuce. Since the commercial crop is primarily of the crisp heading type it will be considered more in detail here. Crisp-heading varieties or strains differ in their climatic requirements and tolerances. The Great Lakes variety has changed this situation to some extent, and Great Lakes seems adapted to a wider set of climatic conditions than previous heading types. Winter lettuce comes from Salt River Valley, in Arizona, and Imperial Valley, with temperatures of 50° to 60° F. Summer lettuce in the West is grown at 60° to 65° F., and in New York State at 65° to 70° F. Heading is prevented and seed stalks form at 70° to 80° F. Cool nights are essential for lettuce production, with an average temperature of not over 70° F. High temperature causes bitter flavor, as well as seeding. The relationship between carload shipments and average monthly temperatures is shown in Table 32. This indicates that most shipments occur in months with average temperatures of 54° to 63° F. Temperatures previous to the shipping month also affect production. Small, immature plants will tolerate mild freezing, but similar temperatures damage mature plants and are likely to cause injury to the leaves, with the development of slime. Lettuce seed germinates well at soil temperatures of from 45° to 75° F.

Table 32*

RELATION OF AVERAGE MONTHLY TEMPERATURES TO AVERAGE
MONTHLY SHIPMENTS OF LETTUCE

Month of Shipment	Salinas		Brawley	
	Average Temperature in Degrees F.	*Average Shipments in Carloads*	*Average Temperature in Degrees F.*	*Average Shipments in Carloads (Brawley and El Centro)*
January	49.0	0	52.8	3,006
February	51.2	0	55.7	2,451
March	53.3	2	63.3	875
April	55.7	2,483	69.6	1
May	58.6	3,350	77.0	0
June	60.8	1,416	85.0	0
July	61.8	2,566	91.0	0
August	62.0	2,708	90.7	0
September	62.0	2,656	84.5	0
October	58.9	2,294	73.0	0
November	54.2	2,674	61.3	0
December	50.3	236	53.6	451

* Courtesy, *Calif. Agr. Ext. Cir. 128.*

Soil. Most soils are suitable for this crop if they are located in a favorable climatic area, particularly as to temperature. Mucks are used in the East for head lettuce while sandy loams to clay loams are used in other areas. Fertile loam soils high in organic matter are most desirable. Where the crop matures in warm weather a heavier type of soil is desirable. Usually they are cooler and hold more available moisture. Lettuce has a small root system, therefore adequate moisture and good drainage are essential.

Fertilizer. Nutrients are used in moderate amounts on lettuce, and there is need to use nitrogen with care the last half or last third of the growing season. Excess nitrates late in the growing season tend to force growth and cause loose heads. Arizona uses the same amount and analysis of fertilizer as listed under cauliflower for that state. Imperial Valley in California uses 40 pounds of nitrogen and 80 pounds of phosphoric acid. Salinas Valley used 60 pounds of nitrogen in the spring and fall, but fertilizer is unnecessary on the summer crop. Some of the foothill soils of Salinas Valley respond to an application of phosphorus. On light Salinas soils ammonium nitrogen is preferred because it is more resistant to leaching than the nitrate form. Oregon suggests the use of animal manure to increase the yields of lettuce. Nitrogen should be applied if the soil is deficient in this element. A 3-10-10 fertilizer has been used with success in several areas of Oregon. The use of manure also is recommended in Washington with the addition of 60 pounds of nitrogen per acre in the west and 700 pounds of 3-10-10 in the east on irrigated soils. Without manure 100 pounds of nitrogen and 40 pounds of phosphoric acid per acre are recommended in the west and 1000 pounds of 5-10-10 per acre in eastern Washington.

Seeding. In irrigated areas, the crop is raised on beds (Fig. 52) with two rows per bed. The seed may be planted in dry soil and the seeds germinate after they are irrigated—or as often expressed, "Irrigated up". Another procedure is to preirrigate the beds so the seed is placed in moist soil a few days after irrigation. During the rainy season the seed is planted one-half inch deep, and about an inch deep under irrigation conditions. One to one and one-half pounds of seed are used per acre. Rows should not be less than 10 inches apart, and usually are 14 to 17 inches so as to obtain larger heads. To obtain successive harvests, the fields should be sown 10 to 14 days apart. Irrigation is important for adequate germination; and since the beds are irrigated by "subbing", high beds require more water. Lettuce is planted with rows 16 to 24 inches apart on land without beds. Planting dates for commercial acreage are:

Arizona: Salt River and Yuma, September to December 15.

California: Central and south coast, December to August; Imperial Valley, September to November; central valleys, August to September, December to January.

Colorado: San Luis Valley, Routt County, and Denver, March 20 to July 10.

Idaho: Canyon County, March and July 25 to August 5.

New Mexico: Otero and Valencia counties, April to July 10.

Oregon: Willamette Valley and Klamath County, February to April, July 15 to August 10.

Fig. 52. (*Top*) The first operation in making beds for row crops. Later beds are shaped with a sled and perhaps seeded in the same operation.

(*Bottom*) Planting beds with small seed using four seed drills so that two beds are planted in one operation.

Washington: Puget Sound, Spokane, southeast and Clark County, February to June 15, July 15 to August 10.

Some lettuce is overwintered in the mountain states and planted September 1 to 15.

Commercial plantings of lettuce usually are not treated with fungicides, and there is little evidence that such a procedure is needed. In heavily infested soil, damping-off can be reduced by seed treatment with red copper oxide, or zinc oxide at the rate of 2 pounds per 100 pounds of seed.

Thinning. In order to obtain a good stand, it is important to plant seed thinly and cut out the excess plants before they are slowed in growth from crowding. This operation also includes the removal of any weeds as well as lettuce plants that are not true to variety or for some other reason will not make a good head. Thinning usually is done three weeks after seeding, in warm weather, and eight weeks in the cooler part of the year. In cooler weather the heads tend to be small so the plants are spaced 14 inches apart to encourage growth. When warmer weather prevails the heads tend to be too large so the plants are crowded by spacing 12 inches apart. Five dozen size heads are desired. Most lettuce is thinned by hand with a short handled hoe. Thinning sometimes is preceded by cultivation, and beds sometimes compacted with a 1000-pound roller to aid subbing and thinning. Rolling lays the plants on their side and is an aid in thinning. Plants frequently are side-dressed with fertilizer about this time. Thinning of overwintered lettuce should be delayed until spring.

Irrigation. This practise varies with soil type, age of plant, and climatic conditions. Where beds are high, large amounts of water are used in order to wet the seed or the root system of small plants. Water application to maturing heads will tend to make them loose, open, and spongy. A wet soil surface or water on the lower leaves of the head in the last two weeks before harvest is likely to cause rot and slime. With careful irrigation, winter crops may be grown with 6 inches of water along the coast, or 18 to 24 inches in the Imperial Valley, and 18 inches in areas like Salinas Valley in summer.

In Salinas Valley recent research[7] indicates lettuce roots grow to a depth of at least two feet, but the soil is not thoroughly permeated. Consequently, the soil is not reduced to the permanent wilting percentage before there is a need for irrigation. Studies in Arizona[8] indicate that a wet soil surface is an important factor in lowering the temperature of the top 3 inches of the soil. Warm weather makes it difficult to germinate lettuce seed so a cooler soil is an important consideration.

Cultivation. Weeds should be eliminated by cultivation; those in the row are removed at the time of thinning.

Premature Seeding. Sometimes seed stalks will form before the plant produces a marketable head. High temperature is the most influential factor causing this condition, as discussed under "Climatic Requirements."

Harvesting. Lettuce is allowed to become slightly dry previous to harvest so the plants are not turgid. This reduces transportation injury. The mature lettuce plant is cut just below the surface of the soil by hand. The tool has a V-shaped blade which is bent at an angle where it is attached to the handle. The head is examined with the finger tips to test whether it is hard and fully developed before harvesting. Two rows are cut at a time by each worker for loading into trucks. Trimming the outer leaves is performed at the packing shed. The interval that lettuce is in good condition for harvest is shorter during warm than cool weather. Frosty weather is likely to kill the leaves and cause slime.

Packing. At the packing house the outer leaves are removed leaving two wrapper leaves to protect the head in shipment. The crate is lined with heavy waterproof paper, and 3 layers of heads are placed in the crate. Usually, these layers contain 16, 20, or 25 heads corresponding to a four, five or six dozen crate (Fig. 53). The stem end of the head is placed up and crushed ice is placed between each layer. Crushed ice also is placed over the top so that when the lid is nailed on there is a distinct bulge. Crates are placed in refrigerator cars and 4500 to 7500 pounds of crushed ice are blown over the top of the load, the amount depending upon weather conditions.

The so-called "dry pack" is used for local markets. Three dozen heads are placed in a crate with more wrapper leaves than for eastern shipment. No ice is used in this pack.

Storage. Two to three weeks is a maximum storage period. Lettuce from California requires some 9 to 10 days to reach New York markets. A shorter shipping period would improve the quality of the lettuce. Temperatures of 32° F. and relative humidity of 95 per cent are considered best for storage. Lettuce sometimes is placed in cold storage when there is a surplus on the market. The addition of crushed ice tends to keep the crop fresher and prevent wilting. Tip burn is a troublesome disease because it may affect interior leaves and is followed by a slimy bacterial decay.

Quality Characteristics for the Retail Buyer. Head lettuce to be of good

Fig. 53. Head size of lettuce is designated as 4, 5, or 6 dozen indicating the number of heads per crate. The crate on the left is a 5 dozen pack, and the other a 4 dozen.

quality should be fresh, crisp, tender, and fairly firm to hard. It should be free from decay without an excess of outer or wrapper leaves. Lettuce with seed stems is objectionable because of bitter flavor and waste. Unexposed seed stems can be detected by wide spaces between the outer leaves at their base and a knob-like swelling protruding beyond the normal contour of the head. The swelling is usually at the top, but may be at the side of the head; the hard core may be detected by applying pressure. Dead and discolored areas on the outer leaves may be an indication of decay. Sometimes a soft rot is found that penetrates the interior of the head. Broken, ragged, bruised, or wilted outer leaves are unattractive, but usually do not affect the quality of the head. Trimming lettuce to remove defects and improve its appearance is a common practise on all markets. Such lettuce is often economical to purchase.

Insects: *Alfalfa Semi Looper (Autographa Californica).* This worm is common on leaves of young lettuce and in 5 to 10 days green larvae appear which move in semi-looping fashion. Larvae development occurs in 12 to 42 days depending upon the temperature. Pupation occurs above ground, usually on the plants in a silken cocoon. The larvae feed on the leaves of the young plants, and damage is most noticeable just following thinning when the larvae congregate on the remaining plants. If the plants are not dusted immediately, many are deformed permanently so that normal head development is prevented. Control with cryolite dust at 15 to 30 pounds per acre, or a 5 per cent DDT dust at the same rate.

Beet Root Aphid on Lettuce (Pemphigus betae). The wooly masses of aphids clinging to the roots are characteristic. Winged aphids fly into the fields from dock or other weeds in late spring. These winged migrants crawl down cracks in the ground and give birth to living young. Winged forms appear in a month and spread the infestation. Probably three generations are produced on lettuce in a mild climate. Meanwhile continuous asexual generations are produced on the roots of dock. Control is difficult. A predacious chloropid fly maggot and a syrphid fly maggot prey on this aphid and often control the infestation. Farm practises such as even irrigation or frequent cultivation will reduce cracking and damage. Aphids are more damaging in heavier soils. No practical chemical control has been developed.

Other Aphids. Usually control is not necessary; but they can be controlled by applying nicotine dust or TEPP dust. Free nicotine (80 per cent), used to make a 2.5 per cent dust, has proved satisfactory in Salinas Valley, where dusting temperatures usually run below 70° F.

Corn Earworm (Heliothis armigera). This insect (see sweet corn, page 299) occasionally attacks lettuce, and no adequate control is known as the larvae usually are found inside the heads at harvest time. Dusting and spraying the small plants as described under alfalfa semi looper may give some control.

Diabrotica (Diabrotica undecimpunctata), or Cucumber Beetle. Sometimes damages small lettuce sufficiently to require control measures. Same control as for vegetable weevil, but do not use after heads have begun to form.

Garden Centipedes (Scutigerella immaculata). Sometimes damage young plants and dichloropropene-dichloropropane (D-D), a soil fumigant, at 40 gallons per acre has proved of value in certain cases.

Pea Leaf Miner (Liriomyza flaveola). This miner has caused losses to young lettuce. Lindane and chlordane sprays are used with some success.

Vegetable Weevil (Listroderes costirostris obliquus). These insects often damage young plants. Dust with DDT or 40 per cent cryolite dust.

Woolly-bear Caterpillar (Estigmene acrea). In the fall these caterpillars migrate and eat lettuce, particularly young plants. Barriers and ditches seem the best control.

Disease: *Anthracnose (Marssonina Panattoniana)* causes small dead areas on leaf blades and stems and death of flower leaves. Dead areas on the leaf blades may later fall out leaving small holes bordered by dead tissue, producing a shot-hole effect. No control measures used because disease is rare in Southwest.

Aster yellows produces leaves which are yellow, dwarfed, and narrow. Center leaves are extremely stunted and affected plants do not head. Virus transmitted by the six-spotted leaf hopper.

Basal Yellowing. The lower leaves sometimes exhibit a yellowing of the interveinal areas and a corky texture of the affected tissue. This condition is most common on plants that have had a long growing season. Applications of magnesium have not corrected this condition which may be due to the normal movement of materials out of the lower leaves when the plants reach a certain physiologic age. Basal yellowing is not a disease caused by an organism and damage is slight.

Big vein causes the area along veins to lose their green coloring matter and their translucence causes the veins to appear enlarged. Affected plants are stunted and heading is delayed. Disease is soil borne and is more common in cool weather. No practical field control.

Downy mildew (Bremia lactucae) produces angular light colored or yellow areas on the upper side of leaves and white downy growth on the underside of these areas. Yellowed areas later die and provide an entrance for organisms causing rot in the heads. In some areas resistant strains can be used to reduce damage from this disease.

Lettuce Drop (Sclerotinia sclerotiorum). Plants are affected at any age but more often on headed plants. Older, outer leaves turn pale yellow and wilt, lying flat on the ground. Under moist conditions a dense white mycelial growth and black sclerotia are formed underneath the head near the ground level. Control has been attempted by flooding and soil treatment with calcium cyanamide without complete success.

Mosaic causes light green to yellow-green mottle of leaves. Necrosis may occur along the veinlets of affected leaves giving the plant a slightly browned or bronzed appearance. On older plants the mottling is indistinct. Caused by a virus which is seed borne and is transmitted by aphids. No adequate control demonstrated but the use of disease-free seed and control of aphids is desirable.

Spotted wilt attacks plants at any stage of growth. Numerous brown spots develop in intermediate leaves and petioles, and midribs may develop sunken necrotic pits. There is a one-sided effect. Disease is a thrips transmitted virus which overwinters mainly in ornamentals. Avoid planting near infected plants.

Tip Burn. Brown necrotic areas appear at the margins of younger leaves and dead areas may also develop in the interior of the head. Most common occurrence during periods of hot weather and it is nonparasitic. Some varieties such as Great Lakes are resistant partially, otherwise avoid having a crop mature during hot weather.

References

1. Bouquet, A. G. B.: Lettuce growing and preparation for market, *Ore. Agr. Ext. Cir. 358*, 8 p., (Mimeo.) 1948.
2. Carstens, M. W. and T. E. Randall: Lettuce growing in western Washington, *W. Wash. Exp. Sta. Cir. 114*, 5 p., (Mimeo.) 1943.
3. Griffiths, A. E. and A. H. Finch: Further studies on the response of lettuce to fertilization, *Ariz. Agr. Exp. Sta. Bull. 199*, 42 p., 1945.
4. Knott, J. E. and A. A. Tavernetti: Production of head lettuce in California, *Cal. Agr. Ext. Ser. Cir. 128*, 51 p., 1944.
5. Schneider, G. W. and Rufus Stroud: Head-lettuce tests, *N. M. Agr. Exp. Sta. Bull. 301*, 16 p., 1943.
6. Thompson, R. C.: Lettuce varieties and culture, *U.S.D.A. Farmers' Bull. 1953*, 42 p., 1951.
7. Veihmeyer, F. J. and A. H. Holland: Irrigation and cultivation of lettuce, *Cal. Agr. Exp. Sta. Bull. 711*, 52 p., 1949.
8. Wharton, M. F. and Charles Hobart: Studies in lettuce seedbed irrigation under high temperature conditions, *Ariz. Agr. Exp. Sta. Tech. Bull. 33*, 281–303, 1931.

PEA

Botany. The Leguminosae family is widely distributed and is of value because the plants are rich in protein as well as the fact that bacteria (*Pseudomonas radicicola*) live on the roots in nodules and enrich the soil by fixing nitrogen from the air. Both peas and beans are legumes and are members of the above family. The vegetables are mostly annual herbs, but some such as climbing lima beans are perennials grown as annuals. Both bush and climbing varieties occur in many of the crops. Peas and beans are distinguished by their method of climbing or means of attaching themselves to a support. Peas use tendrils and beans climb by twining of the stem around a support. The leaves are alternate and compound. The white flowers are borne singly or in pairs. The stamens form a tube inclosing the pistil, which tends to insure self-pollination. The fruit is a legume, or pod. Peas may be grouped as shelling or edible-pod types. The shelling peas are most common, vary in height of plant from 1 to 6 feet, and the dry seed is either smooth or wrinkled. The latter type of seed produces a better quality crop but will not germinate at as low soil temperatures as the round or smooth-seeded types. Edible podded peas are also distinct in type and are used like snap beans; that is, both the pod and seed are eaten. *Pisum sativum* is the scientific name of peas.

Origin and History. Peas are native to Europe, and northern Asia, as well as being used in India in early times. This vegetable was used by the ancient Egyptians and spread to many countries in the world. The seed was first eaten in the dry state. Records indicate they were eaten as immature peas about 1536 and by the last of the seventeenth century were very popular in this form. Peas were brought to the American Continent and were being grown by the Indians near Montreal as early as 1613. By 1690 the Indians of Mexico were also growing this plant. Records seem to indicate that smooth and wrinkled peas, tall and bush peas, as well as the edible podded types were all available about 1550. McMahon, an American seedsman, lists 22 varieties in 1806, but there was a rapid increase in the number of varieties after 1850.

Production Areas. Peas are an important crop in many sections of the country. They are grown for fresh market, canning, and freezing. A disadvantage of the fresh crop is the operation of hand picking and shelling. They also are used dried. The 1940–1951 statistical data are given on p. 222.

The most active harvest season for some of the important market states as well as those in the West are: California, February to May, also October to December 15; Colorado, July 15 to August 31; New York, July; Washington, June; Florida, December to February; Oregon, June to September; Idaho, June, also August 1 to September 15; New Mexico, September and October; and Utah, August and September.

Food Value. Peas, in common with other legumes, are particularly high in protein and are placed in group 3 on food production efficiency. Only 45 per cent of the pea pod in shelling varieties is edible. Dry peas, and beans form an important item in the diet of the working classes in the world, particularly when they cannot obtain meat. Shelled peas contain 74.3 per cent water and the food value per 100 gm. of edible portion is energy 101

Peas for Market

	Acreage	Bushels* Per Acre	Production Bushels	Price Per Bushel Dollars	Farm Value Dollars
United States	56,262	92	5,199,000	$1.86	$9,680,000
California	26,679	93	2,471,000	2.30	5,697,000
Colorado	10,050	98	987,000	1.31	1,302,000
New York	3,500	108	378,000	1.87	710,000
Washington	1,560	204	318,000	1.67	532,000
Florida	1,887	71	134,000	1.86	250,000

(Farm value, other Western states: Oregon, $263,000; Idaho, $246,000; New Mexico, $46,000; Utah, $14,000.)
* Approximately 30 pounds in the shell.

Peas for Processing

	Acreage	Pounds Per Acre	Production Tons	Price Per Ton Dollars	Farm Value Dollars
United States	416,160	1988	413,883	$78.71	$32,579,000
Wisconsin	132,316	1938	128,313	76.35	9,797,500
Washington	46,883	2182	51,182	82.86	4,241,000
Oregon	42,530	2146	45,662	75.73	3,458,000
Minnesota	40,141	1820	36,554	83.24	3,043,000
New York	33,866	1750	29,660	79.53	2,359,000

(Farm value, other Western states: Utah, $1,343,000; Idaho, $558,000; California, $388,000; Colorado, $266,000.)
Farm value for freezing peas in United States: $5,647,000.

calories; protein, 6.7 gm.; calcium, 22 mg.; vitamin A, 700 I.U.; ascorbic acid, 28 mg.; thiamine, 0.25 mg.; riboflavin, 0.15 mg.; and niacin, 2.10 mg. The following data give the relative nutrient rank of peas:

Pound, rank 6: Protein, 2; niacin, 3; thiamine, 4; energy, 6.

Acre, rank 28: All nutrients rank 11 or lower.

Man-hour, rank 29: All nutrients rank 11 or lower.

Varieties. The several varieties of peas may be grouped as having smooth and wrinkled seed, as well as into bush and tall types. Fresh market and freezing types (Fig. 54) should have a good green color; whereas canning pea varieties have a clear or colorless skin. Not only is the juice of regular

Fig. 54. Pods of pea varieties vary in size and shape. The above varieties are, from left to right, Alderman, Number 40, Pride, Shasta, and Wyola. (Courtesy, Associated Seed Growers, Inc.)

canning pea varieties more clear, but the peas are also more attractive after canning than are the green-seeded types. In market peas, varieties tend to be selected which have pods widely separated on the vine, so there will be several pickings. In processing varieties, types are used which have a concentration of the pods on the stem so a larger percentage of the peas will be of good quality when the vines are cut for harvest. Some varieties have two pods per fruit stem. Some of the important varieties are given below.

Alaska. Smooth-seeded; light-green foliage; 30 inches high, pods single, 2½ inches long. Some strains resistant to wilt. Canning and market variety which may be planted when soil is cool.

Alderman. Excellent for home gardeners, shipment, and freezing; plants dark green, 60 inches high, pods single, large pod (4½ inches) with peas of excellent quality. Seed is wrinkled.

Giant Stride. A large-podded, late shipping variety. Vines are about 2½ feet tall, dark green; pods 5 to 5½ inches long, dark green, pointed, and slightly curved; wilt resistant. Morse's No. 60 and No. 40 are improved types. Seed is wrinkled.

Improved Gradus. Used extensively for freezing. Plant medium green, stocky; pods single, broad, pointed, 4 inches long with 6 to 8 large sweet peas.

Laxton's Progress. Used for market gardens and shipping for early peas. Vines dwarf (18 to 22 inches), dark green; pods 4 inches long, 3/4 inch wide, plump, tapered at end; seed wrinkled. Another strain is Morse's Progress No. 9 which is wilt resistant.

Little Marvel. An old market variety. Good quality and yield; plant dark green; pods 3 inches long, blunt, with 7 to 8 tender peas. Seed is wrinkled.

Mammoth Melting Sugar. Edible-pod type; plant light green, 54 inches high; pods single, broad and transparent, 5 inches long.

Perfection. Important canning type; resistant to fusarium wilt; concentrated in pod development, and productive; plant medium green, 30 inches tall; pods double, medium green, blunt, slightly curved, 3¼ inches long; seed green. There is also a dark seeded type for freezing. Seed is wrinkled.

Shasta. Recent variety used by freezers. Follows T. Laxton in season, and is resistant to wilt. Plant medium size; pods dark green, borne in pairs, almost 4 inches long, with dark green high quality peas. Seed is wrinkled.

Stratagem. Late garden and market type. Resistant to wilt. Stocky plant; pods nearly round, 4½ inches long, pointed; with 8 to 10 peas. Seed is wrinkled.

Surprise. Early canning type; plant medium green, slender, 28 inches tall; pods single, light green, plump, blunt, 2⅝ inches long; seed small and wrinkled; green; tender skin and sweet flavor.

Thomas Laxton. General purpose variety; plant deep green, heavy, 36 inches tall; pods single, deep green, plump, broad, blunt, 3½ inches long; seed cream and green; excellent quality. Seed is wrinkled.

Wyola. A midseason freezing type. Plant medium in size, prolific, wilt resistant. Pods dark, blunt, 3 inches long with 7 to 9 peas, dark in color. Seed is wrinkled.

Climatic Requirements. The optimum mean monthly temperature for peas is 55° to 65° F., which is a little lower than for cabbage. Peas are damaged more seriously by frost. The blossoms and pods are more susceptible to frost damage than the leaves and stems; but a frost usually will cause the pea vines to stool out which usually results in an uneven crop. A temperature of 80° F. for even one day is very destructive of quality of canning peas. Thus, short periods of either heat or cold can be injurious to the crop. Warm weather speeds up the rate at which peas mature and reduces yield. The Alaska variety is tolerant of some heat. Variety differences in adaptability are partly the result of different length of periods required to mature the crop. Root rot is exaggerated by excessive rainfall, and aphids become more serious in hot dry weather. Good seed germination occurs in soil temperatures of 40° to 75° F.

Soils. Grown on most soil types; climate however, is the important factor in quality production. Lighter soil types favor early production; good fertile soils are necessary for good yields. In the East, a pH range of 5.5 to 6.7 is preferred since peas are sensitive to acidity.

Inoculation. Since this crop is a legume, yield, quality, and greenness of plants is increased frequently if bacteria are present on the roots which fix nitrogen from the air. Bacteria present in the soil dissolve the cellulose wall at the tip of the root hair and thus enter the root to form nodules. If the bacteria are not in the soil, the vetch group IV may be used to produce nodules on the roots. Inoculation is not always necessary or worthwhile; but usually it is advisable to determine whether the bacteria are in the soil. Nitrogen may be added to the soil in this way very cheaply. Experiments in California and Utah have failed to show any increase in yields of peas from inoculation; the soils apparently are supplied with the proper bacteria.

Fertilizer. Pea seed is very sensitive to fertilizer injury (Fig. 55) so it is essential to place the fertilizer several inches from the row and below the seed level. Nitrogen and potash are the materials which largely are responsible for the harmful effect.

In Imperial Valley 50 pounds of phosphoric acid are applied per acre. On these soils nitrogen usually is not required. In many northern and central California soils, peas should be fertilized with about 60 pounds of phosphoric acid per acre. On light soils and during seasons of high rainfall, the plants also will require from 50 to 80 pounds of nitrogen per acre. The ammonium form is preferred under these conditions. An 11-48-0 fertilizer sometimes is used in Oregon at the rate of 200 to 300 pounds per acre; or if phosphorus alone is needed the application may be 100 to 125 pounds of treble phos-

Fig. 55. Fertilizer injury to pea plants on the right, where seed and fertilizer were mixed. On the left, the fertilizer was placed in bands on both sides of the seed. Legume seeds are sensitive to fertilizer injury. (Courtesy, New York [Geneva] Agricultural Experiment Station.)

phate. If a complete fertilizer is used it should have a ratio of 1-4-1 such as a 4-12-4 fertilizer. Market gardeners sometimes side-dress with nitrogen when the plants are young. The fertilizer should be put on about 2 inches from the row and 2 inches below the seed. On canning peas in Utah it is recommended that 40 to 60 pounds of nitrogen along with 60 to 80 pounds of phosphoric acid, be applied per acre. If manure at the rate of 10 tons per acre is used, no other nitrogen is recommended. On irrigated soils in eastern Washington 40 pounds each of nitrogen and phosphoric acid should be used for crops grown without manure and applied broadcast. No commercial fertilizer is needed where 10 to 15 tons of manure is used. Under most western Washington soil conditions, an application of 65 pounds of phosphoric acid is recommended to be applied in bands on most mineral soils. With muck soils or mineral soils deficient in potash including the Buckley loams and soils of Chehalis valley, 70 pounds of phosphoric acid and potash should be used in bands. Nitrogen does not increase significantly yield on processed peas. Super-phosphate is used in Idaho for peas.

Planting. Commercial planting dates for the various areas are as follows:

California: Imperial Valley, September, and November to December; San Luis Obispo to Yolo County, December to March; Santa Clara and Tulare counties, July to September.

Colorado: San Luis and Arkansas valleys, April 15 to June 15.

Idaho: Western part, March 15 to April 10 and May.

New Mexico: Colfax and Sandoval counties, June 15 to July.

Oregon: Northwestern part, February 20 to June 15.

Utah: South-central areas, May 25 to June.

Washington: Puget Sound area, March to April.

In any given area, smooth seeded peas may be planted in cooler soil with more success than the wrinkle seeded peas. Thus, where there are severe winters, Alaska types are planted first for early peas even though poorer in quality. Many peas mature in weather slightly too warm. Correct time of planting under such conditions greatly affects yield. The data in Table 33 illustrate the importance of correct planting period as well as temperature on the yield of peas. The quality of the peas is not considered in this table, but it is poorer as the yield decreases, primarily because the period of maximum quality is shorter with warm weather. Peas planted March 29 and April 3 produced greater yields and required a longer growing period due to cooler weather than peas planted May 8th. These weather conditions are typical of a large amount of pea acreage, and warm weather is an important factor causing standard canned peas. Where the harvest period is uniformly cool, better quality is obtained and is an essential condition for producing pole peas for market. If peas are planted in too hot weather the crop may be a total loss.

Table 33*

INFLUENCE OF TEMPERATURE UPON THE GROWTH AND DEVELOPMENT OF PEAS
PLANTED AT WEEKLY INTERVALS OF THE ALASKA VARIETY

Date Planted	Number of Days			Mean Temp. ° F.			Days from Seeding to Harvest	Average Weight or Number		
	Planting to Emergence	Emergence to First Blossom	Blossoming to Harvest	Emergence to First Flower	Blossoming to Harvest			Weight of Plant gms.	Number of Pods	Weight of Pods Per Plant
March 29	16	29	29	59.4	64.7		74	22.6	4.3	13.0
April 3	13	28	28	60.4	64.6		69	25.9	4.9	14.5
April 9	12	26	28	63.1	66.1		66	21.8	4.1	12.5
April 16	12	24	27	63.3	66.1		63	22.3	4.1	11.7
April 24	11	23	28	63.9	65.6		62	20.9	4.4	10.6
April 30	8	22	23	64.0	68.3		53	17.5	3.3	7.6
May 8	8	21	22	63.3	70.5		51	13.2	2.5	6.5

* Courtesy, *Md. Agr. Exper. Sta. Bulletin* 306

Seed is planted one to one and one-half inches deep. Row distances depend upon height of pea vines, and upon method of cultivating and harvesting. Rows may be spaced from 2 to 6 feet, with the wider spacing used for tall peas trained on a trellis. Where rows are spaced for cultivation, one and one-half to two and one-half bushels (90 to 150 pounds) of seed are used per acre. Market peas are picked by hand. Processing peas are mowed, and put through a viner to obtain the podded peas. In this case rows usually are closer together (8 to 24 inches) and the seed requirement is 3 to 5 bushels. Some western Washington growers produce early pole peas by transplanting. Three weeks before transplanting, the seed is sown thickly in rows 2 inches apart in a coldframe or sash house. Plants are transferred to the field in February and March, when 2 to 3 inches high, and planted 6 inches apart in the row. Care should be used to avoid breaking the long taproot during the transplanting operation.

Seed decay is so severe in this crop that seed treatment commonly is practised. Spergon at 3 ounces per 100 pounds of seed is used most commonly because it provides satisfactory protection under nearly all conditions. It is easy to apply, has a low toxicity to man and animals, requires no lubricant for machine planting, and is safe to use on seeds that will be planted under different conditions or held in storage. Semesan also is used.

Support of Vines. There are several methods of providing support for climbing peas, snap beans, and lima beans, but the following procedure commonly is used. Large heavy stakes are put at the end of the row and braced. Light stakes which are 1 x 1 inch and 7 to 8 feet long, are placed every 4 or 5 feet with a slightly heavier one replacing every eighth stake. A wire is stretched horizontally at the top (No. 14) and bottom (No. 16). Vertical strings are tied between the two wires for supporting the vines. The string may be tied to the top wire at the beginning of the row, passed under the bottom wire, and sometimes a half hitch is made around the plants in the hill in the case of snap beans. Sometimes a half hitch is made on the wire so, if the twine (No. 4) breaks, the row does not fall over entirely. Some shorter types of peas are supported on brush, for the home or market garden. Two rows may be placed 8 inches apart for shorter varieties, as a means of support. In the case of processing peas tall types are planted closely and grown without support.

Irrigation. Many pea crops are started during rainy weather, but are harvested in the dry season. Adequate soil moisture is desirable for good production and quality, particularly for the last third or last half of the growing season. Imperial Valley, for instance, depends entirely upon irrigation for soil moisture, and needs 18 inches of water, as does the fall crop in other areas of the state. The winter crop outside of Imperial may be grown with 6 inches of water. In some other western areas irrigation is desirable for a good yield of high quality.

Harvesting. Market peas are picked by hand. The peas are able to get some nourishment from the pod, and so store better than shelled peas. Peas are a high quality product, and care must be used to obtain the best possible product. Under cool conditions peas will remain in the proper stage of maturity for several days, while in warmer temperatures they will be in best condition for only a day or less. Market peas are harvested once and sometimes twice, which are green, well filled, but contain no hard, starchy peas. Yield per acre is greater for the mature peas but quality is so poor that they are unusable.

For processing, the peas are mowed when the greatest yield of quality peas may be obtained. If the individual peas are pinched and they break into their two cotyledons they are too old. Peas should be large but crush when pinched in the fingers. Ordinarily the field representative of the canning or freezing company will check on the maturity of the peas. He is able to base his judgment on a tenderometer machine which measures the tenderness of the peas. He will request the peas be harvested when they are in their prime quality. The mowed plants are put through a viner which removes the peas from the pod mechanically. These are hauled to the cannery or freezing plant where the older peas may be sorted out by passing them through tanks with brines of different specific gravity. In these tanks the old peas sink and the young peas float. Canned peas are sold by size, varying from $1\frac{8}{64}$ to $2\frac{4}{64}$ of an inch in diameter. There are four sizes. While old peas generally are larger than the young peas, this really only holds true early in the season; for as the stage of maturity advances for the field, the quality of even the smaller sizes decreases. Hence, it is possible to have large peas within the same variety which will be very tender. Inasmuch as the grower is paid according to the tenderometer grade, it is important that he harvest the peas when he will make the most money per acre. This will be while the majority of the peas are in the stage of prime quality, since the price is higher for the best quality peas.

Precooling of peas is desirable and could be practised more generally with benefit to the quality obtained by the consumer. Quality of peas is impaired when they become starchy. This occurs after harvest, particularly if the weather is warm. Precooling will slow down this change.

Storage. Prompt cooling of peas after picking to 32° F. is essential to prevent the loss of sugars and deterioration of quality. Shelled peas suffer more rapid loss of quality than do peas in the pod. Peas shelled mechanically have a coating of pod and vine juice on each pea which is an ideal media for the development of organisms, causing heating and poor flavor. Cooling and washing of the peas immediately upon vining will reduce these changes. Unshelled peas may be stored one to two weeks if properly cooled. Crushed ice may be used in the package.

Quality Characteristics for the Retail Buyer. Peas of best quality are young, fresh, tender, and sweet. Quality is indicated by the color and condition of the pod, which should be bright green, somewhat velvety to the touch, and fresh in appearance. The pods should be fairly well to well filled, and the peas contained therein well developed. Pods of immature peas usually are flat, are dark green in color, and may have a wilted appearance. Pods that are swollen, of poor color, or more or less flecked with grayish specks, may be in an advanced stage of maturity and the peas may be tough and of poor flavor. A yellowish appearance indicates age or damage. Water-soaked peas should be avoided as well as those that show evidence of mildew, for the peas are likely to be warty and may prove to be very poor in quality.

Insects: *Lygus Bugs* (*Lygus* spp.) These bugs may damage the developing pods. DDT gives satisfactory control.

Pea Aphid (*Macrosiphum pisi*). It is one of the most damaging of pea insects, causing a curling of the leaves and pods; more important, carries pea mosaic which often is very severe. The plants become stunted, the pods curl, and have rough spots and fail to fill and a typical mosaic leaf pattern occurs. DDT as 5 per cent dusts with 50 to 70 per cent sulfur are effective at 25 to 35 pounds per acre.

Pea Leaf Miner (*Agromyza flaveola*). This insect is similar to the bean leaf miner. It is a severe pest to fall peas grown in certain coastal districts. The pupae usually occur in the ground instead of on the leaves as for the bean miner. A dust containing 2 per cent chlordane, 5 per cent DDT, and 50 per cent sulfur controls this insect and other pea pests when used from three to five times during the growing period at 25 to 30 pounds per acre. Chlordane as a 5 per cent dust also is effective, but does not control other pests as well as the combination. This pest breeds in sugar beet fields, and peas grown next to sugar beets may become heavily infested.

Pea Weevil (*Bruchus pisorum*). The elongate, yellow eggs are laid on small green pods in the spring of the year. In 5 to 18 days the eggs hatch, and the larva burrow through the pod into the pea. They develop inside the peas in a period of 30 to 50 days. They construct an exit tunnel so the adults can emerge, then pupate. In 10 to 15 days the adults emerge and leave little "windows" where they emerge. Period from egg to adult is 45 to 60 days. Some adults leave the peas in the summer and fall; others remain in the stored seed or other protected places or can overwinter inside the stored peas. Control consists of sanitation, use of insecticides, and fumigation.

Sanitation and cultural methods used in pea weevil control consist of the prompt harvesting of seed peas when mature, burning of stubble, and growing seed and green pea or cannery peas in different areas. Green peas can be dusted with a derris dust at 20 to 30 pounds of 0.75 per cent rotenone content at about the time the peas flower. This is followed by 2 or 3 applications at 6 to 10 day intervals. DDT as a 5 per cent dust often is substituted for rotenone. Fumigation of all dry peas with methyl bromide or other fumigant usually is necessary to kill all weevils in the peas. Ordinarily peas are fumigated at the warehouse soon after harvesting.

Soil Insects. Wireworms and garden centipedes may damage pea seed at the germinating period. The plants are tolerant of these pests if once established. Pea seed can be treated with 0.25 to 0.50 per cent of 25 per cent lindane for wireworm control, and can be combined with Spergon or Arasan.

Diseases: *Ascochyta Blight (Ascochyta pisi, A. pinodella, Mycosphaerella pinodes).* The stem becomes spotted with purplish-black spots and the underground stem is blackened and shriveled. Dark brown or tan-colored spots may also develop on the leaves and pods. Caused by three species of Ascochyta. Disease is seed borne. Use disease free seed and avoid infested land for at least three years.

Bacterial blight (Phytomonas pisi) causes plants to develop watery, olive-green blisters on stems and leaf bases and water-soaked, oily spots upon pods and leaves. Disease is favored by cold wet weather, and is most severe after frost injury. Disease is seed and soil borne.

Cladosporium Leaf Spot, Scab (Cladosporium pisicola). Leaves, stems, and pods of affected plants are marked with dark-colored spots which, in moist weather, are covered by mycelium and spores. Causal organism is seed and soil borne.

Downy mildew (Peronospora viciae) causes leaves to be curled downward, yellowed on the upper surface and covered with a violet-colored fungus on the lower surface. Pods also are affected. Disease development favored by cool, moist weather.

Fusarium Wilt (Fusarium oxysporum, f. *pisi)* and *Near Wilt.* Affected plants are stunted and turn yellow, the leaves curl, and the plants die. The stem may be swollen slightly near the ground and the vascular bundles in the lower stem and taproot may have an orange-brown discoloration. Control measure is the use of resistant varieties.

Symptoms of near-wilt are similar to those of wilt. Disease occurs on varieties resistant to wilt. Vascular bundles may be deep red instead of orange-brown as in wilt. Both diseases controlled by resistant varieties.

Powdery mildew (Erysiphe polygoni) causes pods and leaves of affected plants to become covered with a white growth composed of mycelium and spores. Plants often are stunted and badly injured. Dusting with powdered sulfur controls powdery mildew.

Seed decay, damping off, root rot are caused by *Rhizoctonia, Fusarium* and other soil borne organisms which cause a rotting of the plants. Use spergon as seed treatment.

References

1. Baur, Karl and F. T. Tremblay: Commercial fertilizers for canning and freezing peas in Western Washington. *Wash. Agr. Exp. Sta. Bull. 503,* 19 p., 1948.
2. Beattie, W. R., L. L. Harter, and B. L. Wade: Growing peas for canning and freezing, *U.S.D.A. Farmers' Bull. 1920,* 22 p., 1942.
3. Boswell, Victor R.: Factors influencing yield and quality of peas—biophysical and biochemical studies, *Md. Agr. Exp. Sta. Bull. 306:* 341–382, 1929.
4. Bouquet, A. G. B.: Growing green peas for market and manufacture, *Ore. Agr. Ext. Cir. 451,* 8 p., (Mimeo.) 1945.
5. Campbell, Leo, Loyd L. Stitt, Karl Baur, and John F. Moore: Growing pole peas for fresh market in Western Washington, *W. Wash. Agr. Exp. Sta. Cir. 91,* 3 p., (Mimeo.) 1950.

POTATO

Botany. The family Solanaceae includes several vegetables which are important: White (or Irish) potato; tomato; pepper; eggplant; and a minor crop, the pepino. The plants are succulent in the case of potatoes and tomatoes, and are woody shrub-like plants in the case of peppers and eggplant. The leaves are alternate; flowers perfect, with color; and, in the case of eggplant large and showy. In all vegetables the fruit is a berry.

The potato (*Solanum tuberosum*) is a bushy, herbaceous annual, 2 to 4 feet in height, with both underground and aerial stems. The tuber, a swollen rhizome, is a shortened, thickened, underground stem. The eyes of the potato are buds which are more numerous at the apical end of the tuber, opposite the point of attachment to the plant. The apical bud is the first to grow if the tuber is planted without being cut into pieces. Tubers are formed about the same time as bud formation or 3 or 4 weeks after the plants appear above the ground. Most commercial varieties have white flesh, but there are varieties which are yellow, purple, and other colors. Potatoes are shallow-rooted. The flowers may be white, yellow, purple, or blue. Pollen is carried by the wind. Propagation is by means of tubers, although the true, small, kidney-shaped seed is used almost exclusively in the development of new varieties. Seed is produced only with long days, cool temperatures, and high humidity.

Origin and History. The potato is of American origin and had been cultivated in northern Chile and Peru by the Inca Indians before the coming of the white man. They are also native to Colorado. Potatoes were introduced into the colonies along the Atlantic coast as well as being sent to England

and Europe in the sixteenth century. The crop is adapted admirably to cool climates of north central Europe and Ireland and has become one of the principal food sources there. By 1848, there were some 100 sorts or varieties of white potatoes in the United States. The "Rough Purple Chile" was introduced from Panama about 1852, and has been the parent, through selection of seedlings, of many commercial varieties.

Producing Areas. Potatoes may be grown in practically all states sometime during the year. The data in Figure 56 indicate that potato yields have increased gradually since 1900 with a rapid increase the last five years. Increases in yield are likely due to more general use of certified seed, new production areas, as well as other better farming practices. Potatoes are mainly used fresh or after storage; only minor amounts are canned and dried. Other uses for potatoes are live stock feed and for the manufacture of starch and alcohol. Potatoes are the most valuable vegetable crop in many states. The 1940–1951 statistical data are given below:

Potatoes for Market

	Acreage	Bushels* Per Acre	Production Bushels	Price Per Bushel Dollars	Farm Value Dollars
United States	2,390,900	169	404,803,000	$1.21	$491,743,000
Maine	171,300	343	58,811,000	1.08	63,704,000
California	96,916	363	35,169,600	1.32	46,426,000
New York	164,000	195	31,978,000	1.24	39,492,000
Idaho	153,200	250	38,376,000	0.91	34,937,000
Pennsylvania	129,000	147	18,991,000	1.40	26,645,000

(Farm value, other Western states: Colorado, $20,202,000; Oregon, $14,230,000; Washington, $12,123,000; Utah $3,528,000; Montana, $2,926,000; Wyoming, $2,675-000; Arizona, $1,862,000; Nevada, $704,000; New Mexico, $357,000.

* Approximately 60 pounds.

The most active harvest season for the late crop is before killing frost in the fall or before wet weather in other areas. Most of the digging occurs in the months of September and October. The most active harvest period for early potatoes in California is April 20 to July 15.

Food Value. White potatoes have the greatest consumption per capita of any of our vegetables, and are found in group 1 on food production efficiency. Potatoes contain 77.8 per cent water and the food value per 100 gr. edible portion is: energy, 85 calories; protein, 2.0 gm.; calcium, 13 mg.; vitamin A, 40 I.U.; ascorbic acid, 12 mg.; thiamine, 0.11 mg.; riboflavin, 0.06 mg.; and niacin, 1.18 mg. In spite of its excellent qualities as a food, the potato tuber

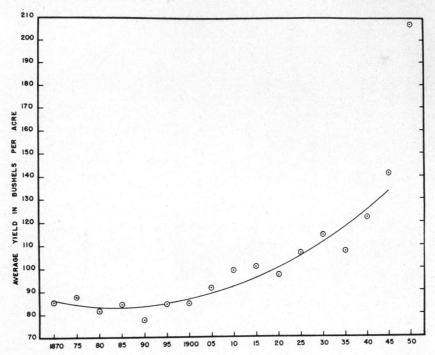

Fig. 56. The average yield per acre of potatoes has increased since about 1900. Increases in the last few years have been affected by the government potato support program. The data are in five year averages.

may contain an alkaloid (solanine) if it is exposed to light. This compound is poisonous and is associated with greened potatoes. Seventy per cent of solanine is removed when the potatoes are peeled. This alkaloid may cause sickness or death to both livestock and people. The following data give the relative nutrient rank of potatoes:

Pound, rank 8: Energy, 2; niacin, 2; thiamine, 7; protein, 7½.
   Acre, rank 2: Energy, 1; protein, 1; thiamine, 1; niacin, 1; riboflavin, 6.
Man-hour, rank 3: Energy, 1; thiamine, 1; protein, 2; niacin, 2; riboflavin, 7; ascorbic acid, 9; calcium, 10.

Varieties. Potatoes have hundreds of so-called variety names and about 25 years ago Stuart classified all these varieties into 12 groups. Some of these synonyms are listed under variety descriptions. Clark[5] gives a recent description of potato varieties. Potatoes are grown widely throughout the United States although the varieties used and the amounts produced vary greatly

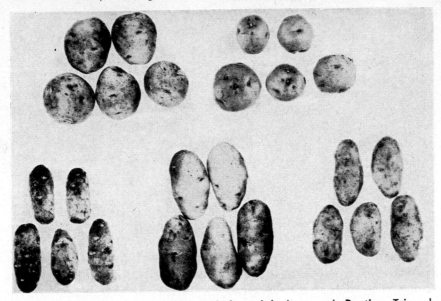

Fig. 57. Varieties of white potatoes. Left to right (*top row*), Pontiac, Triumph; (*bottom row*) Netted Gem, White Rose, Calrose.

in the different areas. (Fig. 57) The United States Department of Agriculture has worked since 1910 to develop better varieties and varieties which are resistant to the ravages of plant diseases. Katahdin, Chippewa, and Sebago have been introduced since 1923; all are resistant to mild mosaic. Chippewa is an early variety and the other two are late types.

Cobbler. Origin is unknown. Plant is medium in size; stems thick to medium; nodes slightly swollen; internodes slightly pigmented; leaves medium in length, breadth, and type, and light bluish green. Tubers roundish, medium to large in size, with blunt ends. Skin smooth, creamy white, with white flesh. An important early variety of wide adaptation.

Green Mountain. Plants large, spreading; stems thick; nodes slightly swollen and internodes slightly pigmented or green; leaves long, medium in breadth and green in color. Tubers are oblong, broad flattened, ends usually blunt; skin smooth, or often netted, white; eyes medium in depth; flesh white. Leading late variety in the Northeastern states.

Katahdin. Developed by United States Department of Agriculture. Plants are large, stems thick, prominently angled; internodes slightly pigmented or green; stipules large to medium in size; leaves green in color. Tubers are large, short, elliptical to roundish; skin smooth, dark creamy buff; eyes shallow; flesh white. A late-maturing variety adapted to a wide range of conditions and widely grown.

Pontiac. Developed by the United States Department of Agriculture from a cross between Triumph and Katahdin. Plants are large, spreading, stems thick, dark green. Tubers are large, oblong to round, blunt at ends, skin smooth or sometimes slightly netted, red; eyes medium in depth, flesh white. A high yielding, late variety of value where red varieties are in demand. Adapted to peat soils.

Red McClure. Used at high altitudes in Colorado and New Mexico; tubers are medium size, round and flattened; skin red; few eyes; flesh white; susceptible to virus diseases.

Russet Burbank (Synonym Netted Gem). Late potato grown in Idaho, Washington, Oregon, and California. Tubers large, long, cylindrical; skin russeted, heavily netted; eyes numerous, shallow; flesh white; desirable for baking. Somewhat resistant to common scab but susceptible to virus diseases.

Sebago. Originated by United States Department of Agriculture from a cross between Chippewa and Katahdin. Plants are large, erect to spreading; stems thick, prominently angled; nodes slightly swollen, slightly pigmented; stipules mostly large to medium; leaves long, medium in breadth and green in color. Tubers are large, elliptical, medium in thickness; skin smooth, "ivory yellow"; lenticels frequently conspicuous; eyes shallow; flesh white. Grown in Northeastern and Western states.

Triumph (Synonym Bliss Triumph). An early variety used widely. Tubers large to medium, round; skin smooth, red; eyes medium depth; flesh white. Susceptible to most or possibly all potato diseases.

White Rose (Synonyms American Giant and Wisconsin Pride). Grown throughout California and southern Oregon; tubers large, long, flattened, usually irregular; skin smooth, white; eyes numerous, medium depth; flesh white. Under adverse conditions subject to second growth and susceptible to wart.

Climatic Requirements. Temperature is an important factor in potato production, and the principal production areas are characterized by cool weather. Average mean temperatures of 60° to 65° F. are preferred, although previous to tuberization slightly higher temperatures give the best growth. Tuberization is best at a soil temperature of 64°, is decreased at 68°, and inhibited at 84° F. Certified potatoes are produced in cool areas, since at 77° F. or higher the mosaic-infected plants cannot be identified. High temperatures also may injure the tuber, causing heat necrosis. Cold weather may affect a few leaves, or even kill the plants back to the ground. When the latter occurs, new stems appear from unfrozen buds below the ground. High temperatures, long days, and abundance of nitrogen favor plant growth in all plant parts except tubers. Low temperature, intermediate day length, and deficient nitrogen cause early tuberization. Tubers are produced at high temperatures if nitrogen is withheld, and at unfavorable temperatures if the days are ten and one-half hours long. True potato seed is not essential to propagate the crop, but plant breeders are interested in the most desirable conditions for the production of seed. Flowers commonly are found on potatoes but plants form very few fruits which are a berry and similar to small tomatoes. A day length of 16 to 17 hours, cool temperatures, and high relative humidity seem most desirable for true seed development. Ample soil moisture is essential for maximum yields.

Soil. The most favorable soils for potatoes are fertile, well-drained, and of rather loose texture. In poorly-drained soils, or in the heavier types such as clay, the tubers frequently are deformed, subject to growth cracks, and often not attractive in appearance. While potatoes are grown on many soil types, the best yields are obtained on sandy loams, silt loam, and peat.

Fertilizers. Most California soils need 60 pounds of nitrogen per acre for potatoes; on light soils this should be increased to 100, or even 150 pounds. Also, on light soils the ammonium form should be used and, if leaching is serious, potatoes may be fertilized efficiently by applying some additional ammonium nitrogen in the irrigation water. The fertilizer should be placed in bands 2 inches to the side and below the seed piece at planting time. A 16-20 fertilizer is used where soils are phosphorus-deficient. Only in the case of peat soils of the Delta is potash needed and consequently a complete fertilizer is used, such as 1000 to 1500 pounds per acre of 10-10-10 fertilizer. Colorado growers are advised to apply manure to an alfalfa field before the last cutting for best results. Response to commercial fertilizer on different farms is variable, but 150 to 200 pounds of high analysis fertilizer can be used to advantage. Idaho soils are rich in minerals with nitrogen likely to be the most deficient element; in only a few cases is phosphorus deficient. Sometimes treble phosphate is applied to alfalfa a year or two previously with favorable response in the potato crop. New Mexico suggests preceding the potato crop with green manures or animal manure. Some areas do not respond to fertilizer, but at Deming, nitrogen alone or in combination with phosphorus gave the greatest increased yield. In Eastern Washington on irrigated land 80 pounds of nitrogen are used with 15 tons of manure, or 100 pounds of nitrogen and 60 pounds of phosphoric acid without manure, or 60 pounds of nitrogen and 60 pounds of phosphoric acid following an alfalfa crop. Western Washington uses 1000 to 2000 pounds of a 5-10-10 on mineral soils and 800 to 1200 pounds of 3-10-20 on muck soils. In the Hood River Valley of Oregon on a Parkdale Loam the most economical fertilizer was 575 pounds of ammonium sulfate and 1523 pounds of super-phosphate.

Planting. The date of planting depends on the district where the crop is grown, the most profitable season of marketing, and the hazard from frost. Kern County, California, plants from November to March with most of the planting in January. The Delta area plants from March to July but mainly March and April. At Tulelake, planting is in May. In southern New Mexico most of the potatoes are planted the last of March or the first of April. The Blue Water area plants during May. Fall potatoes in the south are planted the last of July and the first of August. In the northern states, the dates are about early May to June, with Idaho planting a few potatoes in early July.

Planting usually is done by machines, which plant one, two, or four rows at a time. Rows are generally 32 inches apart. From 8 to 20 sacks of seed are needed per acre, according to the locality, variety, and the practises of the individual grower.

Since pieces of potato tubers are used for propagation they are referred to as seed or seed potatoes. This is a misuse of the word seed, but causes little confusion since potatoes rarely form true seeds in most climates.

Certified Seed. Most growers use "certified" seed since thereby they obtain greater yields (Fig. 58) and better quality; or they use it for every second crop. In most areas potatoes tend to become infected with diseases, such as mosaic, mild mosaic, spindle tuber, leaf roll, and yellow dwarf. Most states have an agency which certifies seed potatoes. These standards usually include trueness to variety, freedom from varietal mixtures, relative freedom from diseases, and good yield per acre. Certified seed is produced in cool climates where diseases, particularly mosaic, may be identified. Standards of different certification agencies are not necessarily identical.

Tuber indexing refers to the numbering of a tuber, growing a portion of the tuber to learn whether it carries disease and, if disease-free, to use the remainder of the tuber to start a line of seed for certification. The section used for indexing may be grown in the greenhouse during the winter, so the tubers which are disease-free may be planted at a normal time. There also is considerable production of seed by the tuber unit method. In this case the potato is cut into four pieces and these are planted adjacent to each other in the row. If disease appears in any of the plants all four plants from this tuber are destroyed. Both tuber indexing and the tuber unit methods have the same objective of providing better seed. The latter method is more rapid but results in some waste of land where the potato plants must be destroyed.

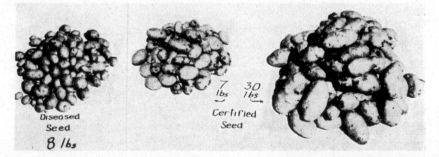

Fig. 58. Effect on yield by using certified seed as compared with diseased seed. Certified seed produced 30 pounds of marketable potatoes and 7 pounds of culls, and the diseased seed produced only culls.

Whole vs. Cut Seed. Small potatoes, one to two ounces, from high yielding fields may be planted whole; but the supply usually is inadequate. Cut pieces of about one to two ounces give greater yields than one-half ounce pieces or smaller. The increase is sufficient to recompense the grower for the additional seed used. Each seed piece should have at least one eye or bud. The apical end of the potato usually has the largest number of buds so the apical end should be cut to make more than one piece (Fig. 59). Sometimes they are cut without regard to eye position, which results in about 10 per cent of the pieces having no eyes, but with a saving in the cost of cutting. Machine cutting of potatoes is not as satisfactory as hand cutting, but with high cost of labor it may be desirable. A Colorado Bulletin[11] describes a double-edged stationary cutting knife with an attachment for sterilizing the blade.

The cut surfaces should be sealed over by suberization, which proceeds most rapidly at 68° F. and 90 per cent relative humidity. Some two to three days' delay in planting results from this treatment, but gives the seed piece protection against drying and rotting.

Tubers infected with *Rhizoctonia* or scab should be treated, before cutting,

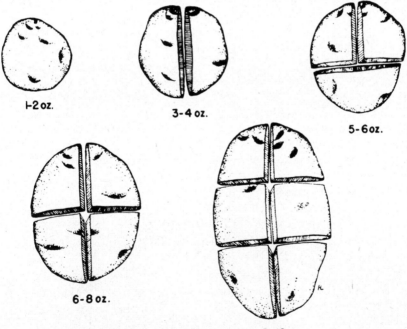

1-2 oz.

3-4 oz.

5-6 oz.

6-8 oz.

9-12 oz.

Fig. 59. Size of potato tubers affects the position of the cut as do the numerous buds at the apical end. The diagram illustrates the usual method of hand-cutting potatoes. (Courtesy, New Mexico Agricultural Experiment Station.)

in one of the following solutions: Mercuric chloride (corrosive sublimate) : Use at a one to 1000 dilution (4 ounces to 30 gallons of water). Soak for one and one-half hours at 50° to 75° F. Dry the tubers; then store them whole, or cut and plant them. Cold formaldehyde: Soak the tubers for one and one-half hours in a solution made by dissolving 1 pint of commercial formalin in 30 gallons of water. Semesan Bel: Mix 1 pound of the powder in seven and one-half gallons of water. Dip the tubers long enough to wet the surface thoroughly. Drain, cut, and plant them; or dry and store them.

These treatments will not protect the potato plants against *Rhizoctonia* or scab infection from the soil. Nor will they prevent virus diseases or bacterial ring rot, which are carried inside the tubers; against these the use of certified seed is the best assurance.

Green Sprouting. If uncut potatoes are exposed to indirect sunlight there form tough, thickened, green sprouts. This procedure is termed *green sprouting* and results in earlier emergence of plants from the soil, better stands, and increased yields. The period of exposure is about 1 to 3 weeks and the tubers should be in shallow layers so light may reach them. Exposure to light gives a short, stubby sprout and the warm temperature is also beneficial. This practise is used more commonly by small producers.

Dormancy. Potatoes require a rest period after digging before they will sprout readily and this condition is called *dormancy*. This rest period is about 6 to 8 weeks in length. Dormancy may be broken by the use of chemicals, storage, or breaking the skin of the potato near the eyes. Treatment varies slightly with variety, but 6 cc. of ethylene chlorhydrin (40 per cent solution) per liter of water will suffice if cut tubers are soaked in it for 1 hour. Storage for 4 to 6 weeks at 70° F. will give similar results. The length of dormancy period varies with variety. White Rose has a short and Netted Gem a long period. In areas where another crop of potatoes may be grown soon after harvesting of the spring crop, dormancy is an important consideration in obtaining seed germination.

Cultivation. Cultivation controls the weeds, prepares the land for irrigation, and the tubers are covered with soil to prevent sunburn or greening and reduce tuber moth infestation. Cultivation should be shallow to prevent root pruning.

Irrigation. Almost every conceivable practise is followed in the various districts of the West, ranging from culture under winter rainfall and summer dry-farming, to irrigation on alternate days in the Shafter-Wasco district of California, and almost continuous subirrigation in the Delta. The amount of water required to grow a crop and the frequency of irrigation vary so much with local climatic and soil conditions that a general discussion is futile. Potatoes respond to frequent irrigation (Fig. 60) under conditions of high transpiration and the grower also should use care to provide adequate water in other climatic areas. In general it is recommended that a total of 30

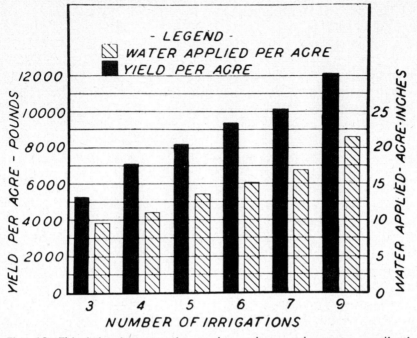

Fig. 60. This irrigation experiment shows that as the water application increases, there is an increase in yield. (Courtesy, New Mexico Agricultural Experiment Station.)

inches of water be supplied the early crop, and about 20 to the late crop.

An excess of water frequently causes reduced yields because of poor aeration and the tubers have large corky lenticels. The grower should be careful to follow irrigation practises which will give a uniform growth of tubers. If the soil becomes too dry, the skin of the tuber sets and subsequent irrigations may cause growth cracks. Second growth or knobby tubers were thought to be due to irregular soil moisture but more recent work[9] indicates this is caused by an excess of top growth to the amount of tubers. Plants with 3 or 4 stems produce less deformed tubers than plants with one stem.

Harvesting. The yield of marketable potatoes increases rapidly as the plants approach maturity, even increasing somewhat after the vines have turned yellow. New potatoes or tubers whose skin will slip sometimes will bring a big enough premium for the grower to sacrifice some increase in yield. Immature potatoes have a thin skin which is rubbed off easily. As the potatoes approach maturity, the skin becomes thicker, tougher, and more firmly attached to the tuber. Potatoes for storage should be mature unless there is danger of freezing.

Potatoes are harvested by tractor-drawn mechanical diggers which harvest 1 or 2 rows at a time. The digger is followed closely by "pickers" who pick the potatoes off the ground and put them in sacks (Fig. 61). Each sack is filled half full, and the workers generally are paid by the "half sack." Many new mechanical harvesters are being used with varying degrees of success. In general, they are quite satisfactory and save a considerable amount of labor. The potatoes are hauled on trucks from the field to grading and packing sheds. The load usually is covered by a canvas to prevent windburn and subsequent darkening of skinned areas on the tubers.

In recent years, growers are inclined to destroy the aerial portion of the plant previous to harvest. The foliage of the plant tends to clog the diggers and cover the tubers laying on the ground that are being picked up. This practise is followed on plants which are either dead or have green tops. A few days should intervene between killing of vines and digging. This permits the skin to set on the tubers. The vines are killed by beaters (mechanical), or spraying and dusting with chemicals.[10] Both ammonium sulfate and Sinox, a weed spray, have been used to kill vines. Ammonium sulfate is used at the rate of one pound per 100 to 200 gallons of water sprayed on the plants in the warm part of the day. Sinox is used in combination with ammonium sulfate.

Grading and Packing. On arrival at the packing shed the potatoes are put through a mechanical washer to remove all surface dirt. Then they are passed over a mechanical grader which separates the potatoes according to size into U.S. No. 1, U.S. No. 2, and cull grades. Workers generally are stationed along side the graders to pick out potatoes of the various grade sizes which have unacceptable surface blemishes. After grading, the potatoes are put in 100-pound sacks and loaded directly for shipment to market or for transport to storage. Most graders will handle 200 to 400 sacks per hour.

Storage. Cooking quality, palatability, and composition of potatoes are influenced markedly by storage temperature. Table stock is stored at 38° to 50° F. with 90 per cent relative humidity for 12 to 20 weeks. Potatoes exposed for several weeks to temperatures just above freezing turn sweet because starch is converted to sugar, which accumulates. Such potatoes are unpalatable, but the surplus sugar may be removed by storing the potatoes at 60° to 70° F. At this temperature the excess sugar is removed primarily by respiration. The tubers should have adequate ventilation to prevent the occurrence of blackheart. After potatoes have been stored for several months the eyes tend to produce sprouts which cause the tubers to wither. Sprouting of table stock can be held back by treating with the methyl ester of alpha-naphthaleneacetic acid applied in Pyrox Talc dust or by putting impregnated shredded paper among the tubers. Should not be used on seed potatoes.

For seed stock the most satisfactory storage conditions are obtained at approximately 40° F. with sufficient ventilation to insure adequate oxygen. If the storage period is relatively short, the temperature should be increased to 50° F.

Fig. 61. A picking belt is used to free both hands for picking up potatoes. When the man bends over, the sack is close to the ground and the mouth is open to receive the tubers. Extra sacks are carried on the back of the belt. (Courtesy, Union Pacific Railroad Company.)

Quality Characteristics for the Retail Buyer. During early spring or early summer, potatoes may be either new or old stock. New or immature potatoes will not stand rough handling; the skin is broken easily and often presents a discolored and feathering appearance. Potatoes that are sound, smooth, shallow-eyed, and reasonably clean are usually of good quality. Potato varieties vary as to shape, size, and color of the skin, and as to cooking qualities. It is often economical to buy and cook a small sample before buying in quantity. Dirty potatoes are unattractive, but eating quality is not affected. Wilted, leathery, discolored potatoes should be avoided. Occasionally potatoes show a green color on the surface which is known as sunburn; these have a bitter taste and should be avoided. Hollow heart and blackheart are two defects causing waste but can be detected only by cutting. Frozen tubers after some storage are wet and leaky, and usually turn dark upon cooking. Both wet and dry decay may affect the surface and interior flesh. Wireworms may cause numerous small perforations on the surface, with considerable waste in preparation. Shriveled, sprouted, badly formed, and misshapen potatoes also may cause considerable waste.

Insects: *Colorado Potato Beetle (Leptinotarsa decemlineata)*. Adults of this insect are three-eighths of an inch long, plump, yellow and black striped. The young insects are reddish, hump-back larva about one-half inch long. The color changes to an orange as they mature, with two rows of black spots along each side of the body. Both adults and the larva feed on the foliage of potatoes. Plants should be watched for the appearance of the beetles. Either a calcium arsenate dust or spray may be used as a control measure. One part of calcium arsenate and three parts of inert carrier such as talc is used for the dust or 4 pounds of calcium arsenate is mixed with 100 gallons of water for a spray. A 1 per cent dust of DDT also is used as a control.

Potato Aphid (Macrosiphum solanifolii). Large uniform green or pinkish aphids infest the young shoots and terminal growth of the potato plants. They are sucking insects and in their feeding they carry virus diseases from plant to plant.

The green peach aphid, a most troublesome species in much of the potato-growing area, can be controlled by applications of DDT dust. These should be applied at intervals of 7 to 10 days during the season of infestation, beginning when plants are 4 to 6 inches high. The organic phosphate parathion would give excellent control when applied as a dust, but the hazards of applying this material must be considered. It is extremely toxic to animals, including man.

Potato Flea Beetle (Epitrix cucumeris). These tiny, flealike beetles are shiny black or brown. They perforate the leaves of the plant early in the spring. Their larvae burrow into or feed on the tubers, causing pimply potatoes. Early-planted potatoes are damaged most, and small fields are damaged more than large plantings.

The only practical control is directed against the adults. If infestation warrants, dust with 5 per cent DDT.

Potato Psyllid (Paratrioza cockerelli). This insect sucks the cell sap from the leaves, and injects a toxic substance into the plant which causes the condition known as "psyllid yellows". The plant becomes stunted, the leaves curl and turn yellow, and the condition results in poor development of the tubers.

Damage is caused by the immature forms, or nymphs, which are yellowish orange to green in color, and flat and elliptical in shape. The nymphs secrete quantities of white wax.

Best control is obtained by dusting thoroughly with sulfur.

Potato Tuberworm (Gnorimoschema operculella). Caterpillars of the potato tuber moth burrow through the tubers, either in the field or in storage. The full-grown caterpillars are white or pinkish and not over three-fourths inch long.

Pupation occurs in white silken cocoons on the plant, in the surface soil, in sacks or storage bins. The adult moths are small and gray with silvery bodies and minute dark specks on the forewings. Each female may lay from 150 to 200 oval, pearly white eggs, any place on the potato plant or in storage.

To prevent infestation of the potatoes in the field, hill up well around the growing plants, remove the potatoes from the ground as soon as dug, and destroy all volunteer potato plants. Packinghouse sanitation should be practised. Plant only clean seed. A 5 per cent DDT dust applied when the miners are in the foliage, using two applications 3 to 4 days apart and a third a week later, at 30 pounds per acre, will give adequate control. The bags can be treated with a 1 per cent DDT solution.

Diseases: *Bacterial Ring Rot (Corynebacterium sepedonicum)*. Disease causes leaves to turn brown, and may be followed by wilting and death of the plant. If a cross section of the stem or tuber is squeezed there may be an exudate which is yellowish white, somewhat thickened and which emerges from near the vascular tissue. In extreme cases the tuber shows a slimy secondary rot. Certified seed should be free from this disease and clean seed is the most important method of control. Disinfection of storage walls, containers, and implements, including cutting knives, is a desirable precaution.

Blackleg (Erwinia atroseptica) can be identified by a black, slimy, foul-smelling rot of the stem just above the seed-piece. The leaves near the top of the stem become curled upward, stunted, and yellow. Aerial tubers may form in the leaf axils. New tubers may become infected, and develop soft rot in storage, and transmit the disease to next year's crop. Diseased plants and tubers should be rogued from seed fields. Seed treatment as for scab also will help in control as well as crop rotation.

Early blight (*Alternaria solani*) causes brown, circular, dead areas to develop on the leaves, blighting and killing them and also defoliating the plants. Use Bordeaux mixture for control.

Late blight is likely to occur in areas of moderate temperature, and also in foggy, moist climates. Large, brown, dead areas develop in the leaves and under favorable conditions, the entire foliage and tops of the plants may be blighted and killed by the fungus *Phytophthora infestans*. Tubers may be affected and show dark-colored, slightly sunken, rotted areas on the surface which may cause serious losses in storage. Spraying with Bordeaux or dusting with a copper-lime dust before the disease usually appears prevents the development of blight.

Rhizoctonia Disease (*Corticium vagum*). A fungus disease causing small, black particles of fungus tissue up to one-third inch in diameter on the potato. Presence of the disease is indicated by the leaves, which tend to roll upward and may turn yellow. Small aerial tubers may develop in the axils of the leaves on severely affected plants. Young sprouts in the soil are rotted or burned off below the surface. The roots may be corroded by the fungus.

Crop rotation and seed treatment are the principal methods of keeping this disease under control.

Scab (*Actinomyces scabies*). Round, brown, rough areas are seen on the surface of the tuber. These areas may be few or numerous enough to cover the entire surface. The fungus causing this scab thrives under high temperatures and in alkaline or very slightly acid soil. Some success in controlling scab has been reported by the use of sulfur to increase the acidity of the soil.

To control scab use clean seed, disinfect seed thoroughly, and plant in clean soil. Methods of seed treatment are given on page 240. Crop rotation should be practised when no new potato lands are available. When planting new land, treat all seed very carefully, even though it may not show scab. This will help prevent infestation of the soil.

Virus Diseases. At least 10 virus diseases of potatoes have been recognized in the West. They cause the foliage to be more or less mottled, dwarfed, crinkled and distorted, and the vigor and yield of the plants to be reduced. These diseases are transmitted in the seed potatoes, and are spread from plant to plant by aphids and other insects.

No one can tell by looking at potatoes whether or not they are affected with virus diseases. Inspection of the growing plants is necessary for identification. Virus diseases are controlled by planting seed which is free from the disease, such as adequately certified potato seed.

Wilt may be caused by two soil fungi, *Fusarium oxysporum* f. *tuberosi* and *Verticillium albo-atrum*. The leaves lose their bright-green color, curl upward, turn yellow, and dry up. The plant is stunted and finally killed. Brown discoloration is seen internally in the woody portion of the stem, this extends into the tuber and often forms a dark ring in the flesh at the stem end. Crop rotation, use of clean seed, and seed treatment are helpful control procedures.

References

1. Bennett, E. R.: Growing the Idaho potato, *Idaho Agr. Ext. Bull. 141,* 31 p., 1942.
2. Blodgett, Earle C. and Avery E. Rich: Potato tuber diseases, defects, and insect injuries in the Pacific Northwest, *Wash. Agr. Exp. Sta. Pop. Bull. 195,* 116 p., 1950.
3. Bloodgood, Dean W.: The effect of the frequency of irrigation on potatoes grown in Mimbres Valley, New Mexico, *N.M. Agr. Exp. Sta. Bull. 205,* 28 p., 1932.
4. Brown, Gordon G.: Influence of commercial fertilizer on yields, grades, and net value of potatoes in Hood River Valley, Oregon, *Ore. Agr. Exp. Sta. Bull. 343,* 29 p., 1936.
5. Clark, C. F., and P. M. Lombard: Descriptions and key to American potato varieties, *U.S.D.A. Cir. 741,* 50 p., 1946.
6. Davis, Glen N.: Growing potatoes in California, *Cal. Agr. Ext. Ser. Cir. 154,* 23 p., 1949.
7. Edmundson, W. C. *et al.:* Potato production in the Western States, *U.S.D.A. Farmers' Bull. 2034,* 58 p., 1951.
8. Enzie, J. V., and J. R. Eyer: Increasing Irish potato yields in New Mexico, *N.M. Agr. Exp. Sta. Bull. 342,* 35 p., 1947.
9. Kraus, James E.: Influence of certain factors on second growth on Russet Burbank potatoes, *Amer. Potato Jour. 22:* 134–142, 1945.
10. Kraus, James E., and Carl F. Dietz: Hastening potato tuber maturity by killing the vines, *Ida. Food Production for War Cir. 26,* 4 p.
11. Paschal, J. L., George H. Lane, and W. A. Kreutzer: The double edge stationary potato cutting knife for saving labor, reducing the spread of ring-rot, and reducing equipment costs, *Colo. Agr. Exp. Sta. Bull. 493,* 12 p., 1946.
12. Raeder, J. M.: Diseases of potatoes in Idaho, *Ida. Agr. Exp. Sta. Bull. 254,* 39 p., 1944.
13. Shull, W. E. and H. C. Manis: Potato insect control, *Ida. Agr. Ext. Ser. Bull. 150,* 10 p., 1945.

CELERY

Botany. The family Umbelliferae obtains its name from the fact that the flowers are borne on an umbel. Several stems for individual flowers arise at the same place on the stem. These flower stems look like the ribs of an umbrella, hence the name. The flowers usually are insect-pollinated and consequently there is considerable crossing—indicating the need for particular care in selecting a good source of seed. The fruit or seed tends to be ridged, and, in the case of carrots, has spines. Celery (*Apium graveolens* var. *dulce*) is grown for the thick, fleshy leaf stalks (petioles). Celery forms a mass of fibrous roots and many of these are located in the top 6 inches of soil, but some roots extend to the depth of 2 feet. If the plants have been transplanted the tap root is lacking. The first year the plant is made up mostly of roots and leaves together with a short compact stem which may be less than an inch in length. The second year the stem elongates to several feet in length to bear the flowers and the seed. The plant is normally a biennial. There are both self-blanching and green types as well as celeriac, or turnip-rooted celery (*A. graveolens* var. *rapaceum*).

Origin and History. The wild form commonly is found in marshy places from Sweden southward to Algeria, in areas like Egypt, Abyssinia, and parts of Asia. Celery first was used about 1542 as a medicinal plant upon the basis that it would purify the blood. There are Chinese records of a plant similar to celery as early as the fifth century—listed as a cultivated plant in 1640. Celery probably first was used as food about the last of the sixteenth century. Early food types possessed a hollow petiole and for many years were preferred to plants with a solid petiole. At present we do not cultivate varieties with hollow leaf stalks. The first celery was eaten green and then most of the varieties were blanched and were selected for their ease of blanching. In recent years there has been an increased use of nonblanched green celery which is higher in vitamin A content. Cultivated varieties were listed in France about 1623 and an English variety in 1726.

Producing Areas. Celery is produced in many states which have a cool period for growth and maturity during part of the year. The 1940–1951 statistical data for market celery are given below:

Celery for Market

	Acreage	Crates* Per Acre	Production Crates	Price Per Crate Dollars	Farm Value Dollars
United States	40,530	515	20,882,000	$2.16	$45,119,000
California	14,575	641	9,349,000	2.08	19,508,000
Florida	10,070	518	5,213,000	2.49	13,000,000
Michigan	5,616	468	2,628,000	1.63	4,299,000
New York	4,025	389	1,566,000	1.97	3,091,000
Ohio	1,691	428	724,000	2.65	1,919,000

(Farm value, other Western states: Colorado, $1,040,000; Utah, $562,000; Oregon, $409,000; Washington, $377,000.)

* Approximately 65 pounds.

The most active harvest season for some of the important market states as well as those in the West are: California, January to March, also May and June, also November and December; Florida, January to May; Michigan, July to October; New York, June 20 to August 15, also September and October; Ohio, July to October; Colorado, September to November; Utah, September 10 to October 31; Oregon, July to October; Washington, September and October.

Food Value. Celery is placed in group 3 on food production efficiency. The fleshy petioles of the celery leaf are consumed almost every month of the year and are in particular demand from Thanksgiving Day to New Year's. Celery contains 93.7 per cent water and the food value per 100 gm. edible portion is energy, 22 calories; protein, 1.3 gm.; calcium, 75 mg.; vitamin A, 50 I.U.; ascorbic acid, 6 mg.; thiamine, 0.037 mg.; riboflavin, 0.05 mg.; and niacin, 0.3 mg. The following data give the relative nutrient rank of celery.

Pound, rank 24: Calcium, 3.
Acre, rank 8: Calcium, 2; protein, 7; energy, 10; riboflavin, 10.
Man-hour, rank 22: Calcium, 5.

Varieties. There are two main types: Golden Self Blanching which tends to blanch easily; and the Utah type, which has become popular in recent years for its good quality, but is green in color and is either grown without blanching or with a very small amount of blanching. Various strains of Utah and Golden Self Blanching are available which vary in height of leaves.

Golden Self Blanching. Plants medium in height, stocky, compact, foliage yellowish green; stalks solid, broad, and blanch readily to golden yellow. Some of the other varieties used are Golden Plume and Cornell No. 19.

Utah. Green type which is stocky, full-hearted, and compact; stems thick and broad and free from strings. Good quality and nutty flavor. Used primarily in the West. Some of the other varieties used are Giant Pascal, Summer Pascal and Utah No. 15.

Climatic Requirements. Celery is rather exacting with respect to temperature and soil moisture. While it is grown in many areas the bulk of the market production is grown in a few areas because of the limitations of climate and also the high cost of production per acre. Most of the winter and spring crops are grown in California and central Florida with the late summer and early fall crops being grown on the muck soils of New York to Michigan and other states. Celery seems largely to be grown in an area with average monthly temperatures between 60° and 70° F. The crop is subject to premature seeding although some varieties show some resistance to this physiological effect. Exposure for 10 days or longer to temperatures of 40° to 50° F. is likely to cause seed stalk formation before a marketable plant can be produced.

Soil. Celery commonly is produced on muck or peat soils. This organic soil with proper fertilization will provide the celery plant with an ample supply of nutrients and soil moisture. Rich loams and clay loams are used but need to possess the above characteristics for good growth. Celery produces a large amount of plant tissue per acre. Plant growth of 60 tons or more is not unusual. Such plant growth requires a large amount of material from the soil and it is essential that celery make a uniform growth.

Fertilizers. Large applications of fertilizer are used on this crop. Florida growers sometimes use as high as three tons per acre. Where large amounts are used it should be applied several times, particularly the nitrogen carrier. The California growers in the Chula Vista and Santa Monica areas use 3 to 5 tons of an 8-8-4 fertilizer per acre. There is evidence that the same yields could be obtained from 1 ton per acre of ammonium sulfate applied in two applications. Half or more should be applied at time of field planting and the remainder about 6 weeks before harvest. Heavy fertilizer applications are used in these districts to force growth when climatic conditions are unfavorable. The Salinas district uses 200 to 400 pounds of nitrogen per acre; the Tulare district uses 400 pounds of nitrogen; the Terminous region needs no fertilizer on the good soil, but needs 200 pounds of nitrogen on the poor soils. In Oregon, on sandy and silt loam soils, it is desirable to apply 15 to 20 tons of manure as well as some commercial fertilizer in the spring, thoroughly working it into the soil. On peat soils several hundred pounds of a 3-10-10, 2-8-10, or 5-10-10 are applied broadcast. Some growers also side-dress with 200 pounds per acre of sulfate of ammonia. In Western Washington on muck and peat soils the growers use 2000 to 3000 pounds of a 5-10-10 per acre. Celery is another crop which is benefited by an application of boron on a deficient soil. Celery petioles are likely to crack if boron is deficient.

Planting and Spacing. The planting dates for commercial areas are:

California: South coast, August to November; Los Angeles County, January to March; Sacramento, San Joaquin, Santa Clara and Los Angeles counties, June to August.

Colorado: Denver and Canyon City areas, May 10 to June 15.

Oregon: North Willamette Valley, March 15 to July.

Utah: Salt Lake area, May 10 to June.

Washington: South Puget Sound area, March to July.

Celery is harvested almost each month of the year somewhere in the West. Most celery throughout the United States is grown by the transplanting method. There is some acreage in the Santa Maria and Salinas Valleys which are grown by direct seeding. In this case, care must be used to keep the field soil very moist and the plants are thinned similar to lettuce. The seed is planted in coldframes or in beds in the field according to the time of year. Eight to 12 weeks are required to produce the plants. To obtain good germination it is necessary to keep the soil moisture near "field capacity". Sometimes seed is sown broadcast in flats in the greenhouse and subsequently transplanted to other flats. These may be transplanted to the field with dirt on the roots. Most plants are pulled, the lower leaves pulled off, and the tops cut short in preparation for field planting. Plants are 4 to 6 inches high when ready for transplanting. The plants are set in the field by means of a transplanting machine, with an application of water. Plants are set in single rows, 6 to 8 inches apart. Rows are placed 18 to 24 inches apart for close culture, and 3 to 5 feet for other methods. Celery is a member of the Umbelliferae family so Stoddard's solvent may be used when the plants have 2 to 3 true leaves (up to field transplanting), to kill weeds (see Table 6).

Seedlings of celery are not very susceptible to damping-off, hence, seed treatment seems unnecessary. Either early-blight or late-blight may be carried on, or in the seed parts. This can be eliminated either by seed treatment or use of seed more than two years old. Seed may be pre-soaked for 15 to 30 minutes in water; then treated for 15 minutes in a formaldehyde solution made by adding 1 tablespoonful of commercial formalin to 2 quarts of water; and finally dried and planted.

Irrigation. The roots of celery are shallow; there is a large amount of plant growth per acre, and the need for continuous growth results in the use of considerable water. A crop may be produced with the use of 30 inches of water.

Premature Seeding. This condition formerly was attributed to many factors, such as poor seed, seed lacking in vitality, early sowing, checking of growth due to freezing, drought, crowding, disease, and exposure to low temperatures. The research results of Starring[3] in Montana and Thompson[4,5] in New York have shown premature seeding was caused by exposure of plants to low temperatures (Table 34). Premature seeding or bolting is caused by 10 days or more exposure to 40° to 50° F. and older plants are

Table 34*

EFFECT OF DIFFERENT TEMPERATURES ON THE SEEDING OF CELERY

Treatment	Average† Temperature ° F	Number of Plants	Per Cent Producing Seed Stalks
February planting, set in cold frame early	44	386	59
March planting, set in cold frame early	44	394	34
February planting, kept in greenhouse	61	824	2
March planting, kept in greenhouse	61	905	0

* Courtesy, *Mont. Agr. Exper. Sta. Bull. 168,* 1924.
† Data was for 1918, seed stalk data for 1916 and 1917 are also included.

more likely to be affected. Long chilling is more detrimental than short chilling, as is also low temperature above freezing. Subsequent temperatures of 55° to 70° F. accelerate seedstalk formation; but higher temperatures of 70° to 80° F. tend to prevent bolting. High growing temperatures reduce vegetative growth and the production of high quality celery. Under field conditions, high temperatures rarely prevent bolting. Thus, it is dangerous to harden plants. Some varieties are resistant to bolting.

Blanching. This procedure refers to the exclusion of light several weeks before harvest so the stalks will be whitish yellow in color. This tends to make the celery milder in flavor. Varieties such as Utah, or green types (Fig. 62) are usually blanched less than those such as Golden Self Blanching; there is a trend away from any blanching in the Utah types. Light is excluded by the use of paper, boards, or dirt along the side of the plant, or by close planting so the tall plants shade each other. Ten to 21 days are required for blanching in summer, and slightly longer for the fall and winter crops. Paper or boards 10 to 12 inches wide are used for the summer crop, and are placed alongside the row. Boards are fastened by stakes and cleats, and the paper by the use of U-shaped wires. The lower part of the U is up and the ends of the wires are pushed into the ground on the outside of the paper. In the case of fall and winter crops, dirt is thrown up against the

Fig. 62. Unblanched (*left*) and blanched (*right*) celery. In the center are celery hearts in a consumer package.

stalks at two or three different times, but they require a wide spacing of the rows. By performing this operation several times, it tends to prevent dirt from getting into the heart of the celery. The use of soil is the cheapest and also gives some frost protection.

Pithiness. All celery tends to become pithy before going to seed. Sometimes this condition occurs early, so the plants cannot be marketed. It has been shown that some seed strains are more likely to produce pithy celery than others.

Blackheart. This is a physiological condition that causes the young leaves to turn brown and at older stages they are black in color. The affected tissue dies and the plants are not marketable. Observations would indicate it is most prevalent during hot weather and also with high soil moisture. Some growers feel a fluctuating soil moisture or soils with high salt content also may cause this condition. Serious financial losses may result from blackheart.

Harvesting. A field is prepared for the harvesting crew by cutting the roots off just below the crown. A sugar-beet lifter may be used for this purpose. The plants are pulled and the outer, loose leaves stripped off and the base of the crown cut into a four-sided pyramid. Some celery is harvested at the present time by the equipment shown in Fig. 63. This equipment cuts the roots below the crown and also cuts off the leaves at a uniform height above the ground. Crates may be packed in the field, but usually the celery is taken

Fig. 63. A celery harvester which cuts the roots of the plants and also cuts off the leaves at the desired height. (Courtesy, The Conveyor Company.)

to a packing house for washing. The stalks are laid on a moving belt which passes underneath sprays of water. The stalks are packed in a celery half-crate, 16 to 24 inches high, with one and one-half to five dozen per crate. The tops are cut off and the crate lidded. Various crates are used such as upright celery half-crate, "Sturdee" crate, wire-bound celery crate, and standard vegetable crate. Net weights vary from 46 to 65 pounds.

Storage. States in the East harvest a considerable amount of their fall celery and place it in cold storage to be sold after frost up to Christmas time. Much of the Western celery moves directly into trade channels because it may be harvested up until Christmas because of the milder climate. Some Western celery is placed in storage when there is a surplus on the market. The crop can be stored for a period of 2 to 4 months, but care should be used to provide good storage conditions. The humidity should be high (90 to 95 per cent) to prevent wilting and the storage temperature should be 32° to 31° F. Since celery may heat because of respiration, there should be sufficient air movement to maintain uniform low temperatures. The plants make some growth in storage at the expense of the food stored in the stalks, and some blanching may occur in storage. Celery may be trimmed and washed upon removal from storage before it is put on the market.

Quality Characteristics for the Retail Buyer. The most desirable celery is of medium length, thickness, and solidity, with stalks or branches that are brittle enough to snap easily. Pithy or stringy celery is undesirable. Pithiness can be detected by breaking. Freezing injury may cause a browning and drying of the tops, which may later decay. Rot, if present, can be seen by separating the branches and examining the heart, as can insect injury. Celery that has formed a seed stem has poor flavor and may be more or less bitter. The seed stem can be seen by separating the stalks or branches—the typical heart formation is replaced by the development of a solid roundish stem of varying size, depending on the stage of development.

Insects: *Aphids.* The rusty-banded aphid and a number of other species damage celery, and also carry *western celery mosaic*. Parathion, or TEPP, or lindane as sprays or dusts will control this aphid. The use of "celery free" periods also assists in controlling mosaic.

Celery Leaf-tier (Phlyctaenia rubigalis). This moth is one of the most injurious insects attacking celery. The small, scale-like eggs are laid singly or in overlapping groups of 2 to 15 on the undersides of leaves. The mature caterpillar is green with longitudinal white stripes and characteristic black spots on each side of the prothorax. The larva makes a cell among the leaves, where it pupates, and the adult moth emerges. The larvae web and eat the foliage, completing their cycle in 20 days to 3 months depending upon temperatures. There may be 4 to 6 generations, and the severity of damage depends upon the date of harvest in relation to the age of the worms. The older worms consume more food than the younger ones. Many other plants are hosts of this moth and damage may occur to cabbage, cucumber, lettuce, peas, and many garden plants. DDT as a spray or 5 per cent dust can be used on small celery. Pyrethrum-oil sprays are effective and can be used on older celery.

Celery Looper (Anagrapha falcifera). This semi-looper may damage celery occasionally. DDT or pyrethrum-oil sprays will control it.

Leaf Hoppers. Various species may damage celery and carry *aster yellows*. Pyrethrum and oil will control them adequately.

Western Parsley Caterpillar (Papilio Zelicaon). These beautifully marked caterpillars may damage celery. Control with pyrethrum or rotenone sprays or dusts.

Diseases: *Aster Yellows.* The leaves of affected plants are twisted, stunted and yellow. Same virus is responsible as aster yellows in lettuce. Disease is spread by six-spotted leaf hopper (*Macrosteles divisus*) from other plants and has a wide host range. No satisfactory control is known.

Cottony Rot, Pink Rot (Sclerotinia sclerotiorum). Plants sometimes wilt and die on account of a soft rot of the stems and roots, usually starting near the crown on the outer stalks. At this point, a white, cottony fungus, grows out over the surface and may spread from plant to plant. Affected tissues show a light-pink color. No good control procedure. Rotation of plantings and removal of affected plants are recommended.

Fusarium Yellows (Fusarium oxysporum var. apii). Plants are stunted and yellow, usually more so on one side. There is a brownish discoloration of the woody tissue of the stems. This disease is soil-borne and soils containing the disease should be avoided for seed beds or field planting. Some celery varieties are resistant to this disease.

Late Blight (Septoria apii). The leaves and stems are blighted and have dead areas dotted with small, black, spore pustules. Causes stunting of plants and slimy rot in shipment. Repeated spraying with 5-5-50 Bordeaux mixture beginning in the seed bed will control the disease. Throughout the season it may be necessary to spray once a week. A somewhat similar disease is called early blight.

Mosaic is a virus disease causing malformations of the leaves. Control of aphids may reduce spreading of the disease and in one area control has been attempted by establishing a celery-free period of 3 months when no celery can be grown.

Root Rot (Phoma apiicola). A black rot sometimes attacks the crown, leafstock, and roots of the plant usually near the ground level. Plants are stunted and the center leaves or the whole plant is killed, or the roots may rot off. Where serious, noninfected soil should be used in seed bed, and plants should not be put in infested fields.

Soft Rot, Slime (Erwinia carotovora). Disease caused by bacteria entering through dead areas or cuts and bruises. Field spraying and the stripping off of leaves which have blemishes or cuts at packing time will help reduce losses.

References

1. Beattie, W. R.: Celery growing, *U.S.D.A. Farmers' Bull. 1269,* 45 p. 1944.
2. Bouquet, A. G. B.: Celery growing and marketing, *Ore. Agr. Ext. Cir. 421,* 9 p., (Mimeo.) 1943.
3. Starring, C. C.: Premature seeding of celery, *Mont. Agr. Exp. Sta. Bull. 168,* 16 p., 1924.
4. Thompson, H. C.: Factors affecting early development of seed stalk of celery, *Amer. Soc. Hort. Sci. Proc. 20:* 219–225, 1924.
5. Thompson, H. C.: Temperature as a factor affecting flowering of plants, *Amer. Soc. Hort. Sci. Proc. 30:* 440–447, 1934.

CARROT

Botany. The fleshy storage root is the part of the carrot (*Daucus Carota*) plant used for food. The edible portion of roots varies in length from one and one-half to eight inches, as well as in shape. Roots include those that are white, yellow, orange-fleshed, red, and purple. The outside portion of the root usually has the best color, is higher in sugar content, and possesses the most typical carrot flavor. Seedsmen have improved varieties through obtaining a more uniform color throughout the root. The stem in the carrot, like in celery, is very short and, of course the leaves arise from the stem. There is a transition stage in morphological development of the stem below the leaves so we may eat not only the true root but also a portion of this transition region between the root and stem. Seeding is sometimes a problem because of poor germination, some of this low viability is due to seeds with immature embryos which will germinate only after months in the germinator. The flowers usually are pollinated by insects and the presence of nectar increases the number of insect visitors. The crop is a biennial.

Origin and History. The carrot is a native of Europe and adjacent areas in Asia. This plant was introduced early into North and South America as well as into China. The root is slender, aromatic, and sweetish. The wild carrot is an annual, but the cultivated type is a biennial and is believed to have been developed from the wild type. Vilmorin, in France, was able to develop a desirable garden type from the wild plant in a period of a few years. Besides being used raw and cooked, the roots also have been considered as a source of sugar and as a substitute for coffee. The carrot has been used for many centuries as a source of food. The plant was grown in 1609 in Virginia and soon was grown by the American Indians for food.

Producing Areas. The value of carrots has increased from two and one-fourth million dollars in 1923 to its present value. Much of this increase has been due to better appreciation of the health-giving qualities of carrots, particularly with regard to vitamin A. The 1940–1951 statistical data for market carrots are given below:

Carrots for Market

	Acreage	Bushels* Per Acre	Production Bushels	Price Per Bushel Dollars	Farm Value Dollars
United States	72,691	344	24,998,000	$1.36	$34,073,000
California	26,842	411	11,027,000	1.67	18,494,000
Arizona	6,350	355	2,255,000	1.85	4,187,000
Texas	17,092	177	3,017,000	0.65	1,986,000
New York	4,542	480	2,178,000	0.77	1,681,000
Ohio	1,658	503	834,000	1.46	1,225,000

(Farm value, other Western states: New Mexico, $966,000; Washington, $774,000; Oregon, $606,000; Colorado, $500,000; Utah, $220,000; Idaho, $79,000.)
* Approximately 50 pounds.

The most active harvest season for some of the important market states as well as those in the West are: California, January to July, also October to December; Arizona, April to June, also December to February; Texas, January to May; New York, July and August, also October and November; Ohio, August and September; New Mexico, August to November; Washington, August to October; Oregon, August to October; Colorado, August and September; Utah, September and October; Idaho, September and October.

Food Value. Carrot, one of our popular root crops, is placed in group 2 on food production efficiency. The calculations were made for bunched carrots, which are 63 per cent edible as compared to 88 per cent for topped carrots. The root possesses a characteristic flavor which a few people find objectionable, particularly when raw. Carrot contains 88.2 per cent water and the food value per 100 gm. edible portion is energy, 45 calories; protein, 1.2 gm.; calcium, 42 mg.; vitamin A, 12,000 I.U.; ascorbic acid, 4 mg.; thiamine, 0.042 mg.; riboflavin, 0.043 mg.; and niacin, 0.21 mg. The following data give the relative nutrient rank of carrots:

Pound, rank 25: Vitamin A, 1.
Acre, rank 7: Vitamin A, 1; energy, 5; calcium, 5; iron, 6; protein, 9; thiamine, 10.
Man-hour, rank 13: Vitamin A, 1; energy, 8; calcium, 8.

Varieties. In recent years production has been concentrated in the larger, later varieties. French Forcing and Early Scarlet Horn are early small-rooted varieties. Most of the shipping carrots (Fig. 64) have a long tapered root like the Imperator; the Chantenay is used more by market gardeners and short distance shippers. Morse's Bunching and Streamliner are two other varieties with short leaves which are used for shipping.

Chantenay. Root 5 inches long, 2 inches in diameter, smooth, and tapered, and of reddish orange color. Several strains are available which vary in root length and the Red Cored strain also is widely used, as well as being the principal variety used for processing.

Danver's Half Long. A carrot of general use. Roots 6 inches long, one and three-quarter inches in diameter, uniformly tapered to a blunt end and orange in color.

Imperator. The type used almost exclusively for shipping in the West. Root 8 inches long, one and one-half inches in diameter, tops medium but strong enough for bunching, and color deep orange. A strain with a longer root also is available.

Nantes. High-quality root used in home or market garden. Root cylindrical, 6 inches long, one and one-half inches thick; flesh bright orange, core inconspicuous.

Fig. 64. Carrot varieties differ in size and shape of root. The above varieties are, from left to right, Imperator, Morse's Bunching, Red Cored Chantenay, Long Chantenay, and Nantes. (Courtesy, Ferry-Morse Seed Company.)

Climatic Requirements. The carrot, like the beet, grows best at 60° to 70° F. but in the seedling stage is more sensitive to extremes of high and low temperature. Carrots also require a longer growing season than beets. Mild freezing weather at the market stage is more likely to harm carrot leaves than those of beet. The roots of both crops will stand mild freezing weather. The best color development for carrots occurs at 50° to 60° F. and lower temperatures cause poor carrot color. The best temperature for seed germination is 45° to 65° F.

Soils. This plant will grow on practically all soils, but most of the production for market carrots is on the looser types of soil such as sandy loams, loams, and muck. Deep, moderately rich soils produce a smoother and more rapid-growing carrot.

Fertilizer. Root crops sometimes are thought to require more phosphorus and potash than most vegetables. Imperial Valley in California uses 60 pounds of nitrogen and 50 pounds of phosphoric acid per acre, while in other areas of California about 60 pounds of nitrogen, and sometimes some phosphoric acid are used. Eastern Washington growers on irrigated soils use 100 pounds of nitrogen and 60 pounds of phosphoric acid per acre without manure. When 15 tons of manure are applied only 60 pounds of nitrogen need be added. On mineral soils in Western Washington 1000 pounds of 5-10-10 are used per acre or 600 to 800 pounds of 4-12-8 in addition to 10 to 12 tons of manure. Muck soil growers use 700 to 1000 pounds of a 3-10-10 or 350 to 500 pounds of a 6-20-20.

Planting. Commercial planting dates for the different areas are:

Arizona: Salt River and Yuma, August 20 to October; Salt River, December 15 to February.

California: Imperial Valley, September to November; Imperial, Los Angeles, and Monterey counties, November to February; Monterey to Los Angeles County, March 15 to August.

Colorado: Denver and Pueblo counties, April to June.

Idaho: Canyon, Valley and Teton counties, April to August.

New Mexico: Valencia and Otero counties, April to August.

Oregon: North Willamette Valley, March to May.

Utah: Iron, Sevier, and Utah counties, May to August.

Washington: March to July.

In the West, carrots frequently are raised with two rows to the bed. In some areas a single narrow row is planted with or without thinning. In the West the seed is scattered thinly in a row 3 to 4 inches wide which permits production without thinning. The weeds that germinate with the crop seed are killed by spraying with Stoddard's solvent at the rate of 35 gallons per acre. The plants should be sprayed when they have at least 1 true leaf but not more than 4.

The amount of seed planted per acre varies with the percentage germination and number of seeds per ounce, but usually is about three and one-fourth pounds. The seed is planted one-half to three-fourths inch deep according to type of soil and the weather. For hand-cultivation without beds the rows are drilled 12 to 18 inches apart. Carrot seed is somewhat slow to germinate and care should be used to have adequate soil moisture.

In most areas satisfactory stands of carrots are secured without seed treatment. As a precaution against seedling infection, Spergon may be used at a rate of 6 ounces per 100 pounds of seed or Semesan at 4 ounces per 100 pounds. In the few tests conducted there has been little difference in the stand between treated and nontreated seed.

Irrigation. Adequate soil moisture is essential both for quality production and good germination of the seed. Most of the roots are found in the top 4 feet of soil and require 24 inches of water in Imperial Valley and 18 inches in coastal areas. Seed germination is increased and accelerated by soil moisture close to field capacity—or the soil filled with available water. Carrot roots should grow rapidly for good quality and perhaps for mild flavor. An inadequate supply of soil moisture increases roughness, decreases root size, and many times can be detected only through a slowing or cessation of growth.

Cultivation. The first weeds are killed by the use of oil, but this must be used only on young plants or the flavor of the root will be affected. Some western growers run a chisel 3 times down the middle of the bed between the rows. In the last cultivation, dirt is thrown over the crown of the root to prevent the formation of chlorophyll and thus improve the appearance of the root.

Cost of Production. Carrots are sold topped on the fresh market and also for canning and dehydration. The cost of raising the crop in Willamette Valley[2] is given in Table 35. The average cost for about one-fifth of the acreage was $13.30 per ton for graded roots. The contract price was about $18.00 per ton. Harvesting costs made up about one-half of the total costs with hand weeding being the most important cultural item. Twenty-seven of the 31 growers used sprinkler irrigation and the remaining fields were not irrigated.

The 1943 labor requirement for producing California[4] bunch carrots also has been reported. In order to produce 11.3 tons of carrots there were required 330 hours of labor or 29 hours per ton of roots. The Oregon data show that 9 hours of labor were used to produce a ton of topped carrots. About one-half of the labor used in California was for the bunching operation or 155 hours. A larger number of hours also was required for cultural operations. Since the carrots were grown for different types of markets it would be expected that the labor requirement would be different. Bunch carrots need to be tied in uniform bunches and the roots usually are smaller than those of processing roots.

Table 35*

COST OF PRODUCING CARROTS FOR PROCESSING IN THE WILLAMETTE VALLEY OF OREGON, 1946
(THIRTY-ONE FIELDS AVERAGING 7.1 ACRES PER FIELD AND 16.2 TONS OF GRADED CARROTS PER ACRE.)

Operation	Man-hours Per Acre	Labor Cost Per Acre	Machinery Cost Per Acre	Seed and Fertilizer Cost Per Acre	Overhead, Taxes, and Interest Cost Per Acre	Total Cost Per Acre	Per Ton
Soil preparation and planting	6.3	$ 6.10	$ 4.70	$ 3.70	...	$ 14.50	$ .90
Hand cultivation	27.8	22.50			...	22.50	1.40
Machine cultivation	5.0	4.60	2.40		...	7.00	.40
Oil weding	1.8	1.60	1.60	4.90	...	8.10	.50
Fertilizing	0.6	.60	.30	5.70	...	6.60	.40
Irrigation	4.9	4.50	10.00		...	14.50	.90
Cover crop	0.3	.20	.10	.70	...	1.00	.10
Preharvest total	46.7	40.10	19.10	15.00	...	74.20	4.60
Pulling and topping	76.1	71.10	15.00	.10		86.20	5.30
Hauling crop and workers	9.1	8.70	13.70			22.40	1.40
Harvest total	131.9	79.80	28.70	.10		108.60	6.70
Overhead	11.1	10.40	3.20		2.30	15.90	1.00
Taxes and interest					16.10	16.10	1.00
Total	143.0	$130.30	$51.00	$15.10	$18.40	$214.80	$13.30†

* Courtesy, *Ore. Agr. Exper. Sta. Bull. 467*, 1949.
† Carrots were grown under contract and usually sold for $18.00 per ton.

Harvesting. A tool with a blade is run under the roots to loosen them for pulling. The equipment is similar to the root lifter used for sugar beets. The two rows of roots are pulled out and laid in one row. The carrots are sorted as to size, and tied into bunches weighing from one to one and one-fourth pounds for roots and tops. Recently the bunches have been fastened with "Twistems" which are a piece of wire covered with paper tape. Roots of uniform size are put together in a bunch; a pound bunch therefore may contain anywhere from 4 to 20 roots. The carrots are placed in boxes or hauled loose to the packing house. Here they are washed and packed 6 dozen bunches to a crate with package ice (Fig. 65). After the cars are loaded, ice is blown over the top of the load. The standard vegetable crate is used, which weighs 72 to 90 pounds filled.

Carrots may be topped in the field, washed, and sold as topped carrots. These are marketed in 50-pound sacks, bushel tubs, or half-crates. Roots with poor tops that will not meet U.S. No. 1 grade, sometimes are sold as topped carrots. Although the tops are not eaten, they have been left on the roots to indicate to the buyer the fresh condition of the bunch. Leaves constitute about 17 per cent of the weight of bunched carrots.

Storage. Carrots are stored with tops removed or shipped in refrigerator cars with the green tops attached to the root. The roots with tops removed keep longer in storage which may be storage of the common type, without refrigeration. Roots may be stored until late winter or early spring, but should be protected from freezing. High humidity is essential to prevent wilting. Bunch carrots will retain good appearance for about 2 weeks if stored

Fig. 65. At left is shown one-pound bunches containing 4, 6, and 10 carrots. On the right is a packed, iced crate of carrots, top view.

at 32° F. and 95 per cent humidity. These carrots are shipped to eastern markets. Crushed ice is desirable to keep the bunches in good condition. If icing is impossible in cold storage the bunches should be loosened so as to allow good air circulation.

Quality Characteristics for the Retail Buyer. Good quality carrots are firm, clean, fresh in appearance, smooth, well-shaped, and of good color. Usually, although not always true, poor color of carrots is associated with poor quality. The tops of bunched carrots should be fresh and green. The condition of the tops is an indication of quality, but is not always a trustworthy one since the tops may be damaged and the roots still be in prime condition. Carrots that are wilted, flabby, soft, or shriveled are undesirable; they usually lack flavor. Those that are excessively forked or pronged, or rough, or have deep growth cracks, are wasteful. Carrots showing excessively thick masses of leaf stems at the point of attachment or "neck" usually have undesirably large cores or hearts. Decay is seen easily. It appears usually as soft or water-soaked areas, which may be more or less covered with mold.

Insects. *Carrot Beetle (Ligyrus gibbosus).* Larvae and adults are general feeders and may eat carrots. Adults are beetles of the June beetle type and are reddish-brown in color. The whitish larvae or grubs feed only on the roots, but adults feed below and above ground. Clean farming practises and crop rotation will reduce injury to carrots.

Cabbage Looper. See Cabbage.

Carrot Rust Fly (Psila rosae). Affects carrots in coastal areas of Oregon and Washington. The slender, legless, yellowish-white maggots, one-third inch long when fully grown, destroy the fibrous roots and tunnel in the fleshy roots. Infestation can be reduced by planting so roots are harvested before July 15th and the late planting is seeded after June 1st. Crude naphthalene flakes may be broadcast on the soil surface at 3 weekly intervals about as the flies emerge. Naphthalene affects flavor of roots so there should be an interval of 1 month before harvest. A suspension of calomel may be used to control the fly by applying to growing carrots.

Six-spotted Leaf Hopper (Macrosteles divisus). This insect is the means of transmitting the virus causing aster yellows.

Vegetable Weevil (Listroderes costirostris obliquus). The adults and larvae feed on the foliage and on the roots occasionally in California and Texas. The legless larvae are green grubs one-half inch long when mature. The adult is a brown to buff colored snout beetle. In the winter and spring when damage commences, dusting with a 70 to 80 per cent sodium fluosilicate dust or a 30 to 50 per cent cryolite dust or 5 per cent DDT dust at the rate of from 15 to 50 pounds per acre, depending upon the density of the foliage, often gives satisfactory control. After treatment, tops should not be feed because of poisonous residue. Control of weeds particularly malva will reduce the weevils.

Western Parsley Caterpillar (Papilio zelicaon). The beautiful green, black, and orange caterpillars of a butterfly often feed on carrot foliage. Control with calcium arsenate, DDT or cryolite.

Diseases: *Aster Yellows*. See Celery.

Bacterial Blight (Phytomonas carotae). Occurs mostly on plants grown for seed. Irregular dead spots appear on the leaves, petioles, and stems, and flower heads. Crop rotation and use of clean seed are possible control procedures.

Cottony Rot. See Celery.

Heat Injury. In hot weather, young plants sometimes shrivel and turn brown just at the surface (Fig. 66) of the soil and may wilt and collapse as in damping off. Unlike damping-off, this is purely physical effect caused by high temperature.

Leaf Spot (Cercaspara carotae and Macrosporium carotae). The leaves are spotted, blighted, and more or less completely killed. The disease works from the outer leaves inward. In shipping the leaves of affected plants become decayed and "slimed." Dust with copper-lime for control of this disease which also is called blight.

Scab (Phytomonas carotae). Rough pits, rings and other irregularities of the root are characteristic of scab. Organisms are seed borne and can persist in the soil. Suggested control is crop rotation for about 3 years and the use of clean seed.

Soft Rot (Erwinia carotovora). Roots of affected plants decay with a soft, slimy, bacterial rot. This usually follows some injury and may occur in field or storage. Somewhat serious in roots planted for seed since wet weather favors the disease. Only sound, healthy carrots, free from injuries should be used for seed growing.

Fig. 66. Typical heat injury on young carrot plants.

References

1. Baur, Karl, Loyd L. Stitt, and John F. Moore: Carrot production in Western Washington. *W. Wash. Exp. Sta. Cir. 93,* 3 p., (Mimeo.) 1950.
2. Davis, G. B. and D. Curtis Mumford: Cost of producing carrots in the Willamette Valley, Oregon, *Ore. Agr. Exp. Sta. Bull. 467,* 20 p., 1949.
3. Enzie, J. W.: Experiments in the production of carrot seed, *N.M. Agr. Exp. Sta. Bull. 308,* 11 p., 1943.
4. MacGillivray, John H., *et al:* Labor and material requirements of California vegetables, *Cal. Agr. Exp. Sta. Litho. Leaflet,* 15 p., 1944.
5. Whitaker, T. W. *et al.:* Carrot production in the West and Southwest, *U.S.D.A. Cir. 750,* 32 p., 1946.
6. Woodbury, George W.: Carrot seed production, *Idaho Food Prod. for War Cir. 16,* 4 p.

GROUP B. MINOR CROPS

Chinese Cabbage. This crop (*Brassica pekinensis*) must be grown in a moderately cool climate, with a short to medium length of day to discourage premature bolting. Temperatures at 50° to 60° F., and medium day length produce the best quality. Temperatures around 45° will cause bolting, particularly if followed by long days. The crop is grown like head lettuce, and the leaves form a head 4 inches wide and 18 inches long in the Chihli variety (Fig. 67), while in Wong Bok it is short and thick. The heads should be almost as hard as cabbage when harvested. The crop may be stored 2 months. It is eaten raw as salad, cooked as a green, or is fermented and stored in a salt brine for winter use.

Reference

Kraus, J. E.: Chinese cabbage varieties, their classification, description and culture in the Central Great Plains, *U.S.D.A. Cir. 571,* 20 p., 1940.

Cardoon. The cardoon (*Cynara Cardunculus*) is closely related to globe artichoke, but is grown for its blanched leaf petioles instead of unopened buds. It is marketed about November to January. The crop is produced like globe artichoke except that the seed is used for propagation. Climatically, the plants are similar; but cardoon also is grown in a slightly warmer climate. After the plant is grown, the leaves are brought together and the plant is wrapped with burlap sacks to blanch the petioles. Blanching requires 3 to 4 weeks and is started on some plants before November. The leaves of the globe artichoke sometimes are eaten as a substitute for cardoon.

Celeriac. Celeriac also is called turnip-rooted celery (*Apium graveolens* var. *rapaceum*). The edible part is a swollen root and appears on the market

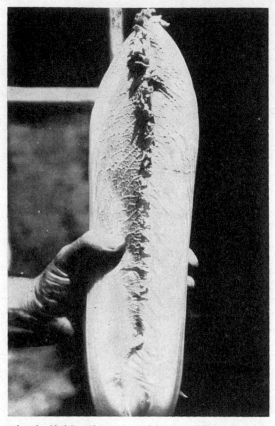

Fig. 67. A head of Chihli Chinese cabbage. (Courtesy, Associated Seed Growers, Inc.)

in bunches like other root crops. Large Smooth Prague is a common variety. Culture and climatic requirements are similar to those of celery. The crop may be transplanted or direct-seeded. Since there is no need for blanching, the crop may be grown with 2 rows per bed, or otherwise 30 inches between rows. The roots are harvested as soon as they have reached marketable size, or 2 to 4 inches in diameter. Like other root crops it stores well. The vegetable is used in flavoring soups, or is creamed, or used in salads.

Chicory. This plant (*Cichorium Intybus*) is grown for greens, and frequently both the leaves and small roots (one-half inch in diameter) are cooked. Another variety is called Witloof Chicory and the roots are forced to produce a salad crop. Common chicory is planted either in rows or sown broadcast, and grown in the cool spring or fall. Plants are harvested when the root is small, and bunched for market. Sometimes it is called radichetta or asparagus chicory.

Witloof Chicory or French Endive is grown for a salad crop, and is produced by forcing special strains of chicory. It is more commonly grown and forced in Belgium and France than in this country, and these countries sometimes export the blanched heads to eastern and even western United States. Seeds are sown in early summer and require 5 months to produce the roots, which are grown like parsnips. The roots are dug in the fall and the tops are cut off 2 inches above the crown to prevent injury to crown buds. The roots are stored in a cool place and subsequently are forced at a temperature of 60° to 70° F. The tip of the root is cut so it is uniform of length, about 6 to 9 inches, and graded according to diameter. They are set in an upright position in a trench or box with the crown up. The space between the roots is filled with soil. After thoroughly wetting the soil, the crown of the roots is covered with sand to a depth of 6 to 8 inches. The soil around the roots should be kept moist, and the slightly moist sand keeps the heads compact as well as excludes light, to cause blanching. Three to four weeks are required to produce good heads weighing 2 to 3 ounces and 4 to 6 inches tall. Medium-sized roots (one to one and three-fourths inches in diameter) produce the largest yield. Small roots produce low yields and large roots produce compound heads which are not marketable. This crop usually is listed under the variety name of Witloof or French Endive.

Reference

Beattie, W. R.: Production of chicory and endive, *U.S.D.A. Leaflet No. 133,* 6 p., 1937.

Endive. Endive (*Cichorium Endivia*) is of about the same size as lettuce, and is grown like that crop, but does not produce a head. Usually the center leaves are blanched either by crowding the plants in the row or by tying the tips of the leaves together. Two rows are grown per bed and the plants are spaced about 8 to 12 inches apart in the row if tied for blanching; or slightly closer if allowed to grow to market size with natural blanching. The blanching procedure tends to decrease the bitterness of the leaves. There are two general types: The Full Heart Batavian has broad leaves and also is called "escarole". The finer-leaved, curled, or fringe-leaved types are represented by varieties such as Green Curled, Ruffec and Pancalier (pink ribbed).

Reference

Beattie, W. R.: Production of chicory and endive, *U.S.D.A. Leaflet 133,* 6 p., 1937.

Florence Fennel. Florence fennel (*Foeniculum vulgare* var. *dulce*) is somewhat similar to late celery in culture and is grown with 2 rows per bed;

or otherwise about 30 inches between rows and 4 inches between plants. The enlarged bottom section of the leaf petiole is eaten raw, like celery, or is cooked with other food to impart flavor. The sweet anise-like flavor is characteristic. The plants are harvested when the bulb or "apple" is of sufficient size; usually about 2 inches in diameter. The crop is known as sweet anise to shippers and others call it "finnochio."

Mustard. Mustard is a cool season crop of several species (*Brassica* spp.) grown for greens either in the spring or fall. Long days and warm weather are likely to result in seeding. Under irrigated conditions 2 rows are planted per bed and the plants thinned to 4 to 8 inches apart in the row. Culture is similar to that of spinach. Southern Giant Curled is a good variety. When grown in a cool climate more than one harvest may be made from one planting. The leaves are cut and tied in bunches for market.

Parsley. Parsley (*Petroselinum crispum*) is grown for its foliage and is used in garnishing or for flavoring soups and stews. There is also a root type —Hamburg or turnip-rooted parsley. Foliage types include both plain and a moss, or double-curled leaf. Moss Curled is a desirable variety for garnishing but the Plain or Single leaf variety is preferred for flavoring food. A cool season crop, the seed is planted in the spring about the time of carrot planting. Plants are spaced 8 inches by 2 feet. The older leaves are harvested for garnishing and the younger leaves are left to manufacture food for growth. This procedure provides a continuous supply which, in a mild climate, furnishes leaves until the following spring. The crop is a biennial; hence, it goes to seed the second spring.

Reference

Beattie, J. H.: Production of parsley, *U.S.D.A. Leaflet 136,* 5 p., 1937.

Pak-choi. This crop (*Brassica chinensis*) is grown largely by Oriental people for greens. Its culture and climate requirements are similar to Chinese cabbage. The plant is nonheading, with a large leaf tapering towards the stem into a thick, bare petiole. The petioles frequently have a whitish cast while the leaf blades are green. The root of some types is tuberous.

Swiss Chard. Swiss Chard (*Beta vulgaris* var *Cicla*) is similar to beets, but is grown for the leaves, and not the root. Chard requires wider spacing (3 feet by 1 foot) but otherwise is grown like beets. This plant is very popular as a green because of good eating quality as well as the fact that it will furnish a continuous supply of food in a mild climate almost throughout the year. The seed is planted in the spring at the same time as beets, and the young plants which are thinned may be used for greens. Lucullus and Fordhook are common varieties. Two or three plants will supply the average family. Individual leaves are harvested for market and tied in bunches of about a pound.

Chapter 17

Group C. Cool Season Crops Which Thrive Over a Wide Range of Temperature and Are Tolerant of Frost

Group C. Adapted to 55° to 75° F. Tolerant of frost

ONION

Botany. Members of the Liliaceae are found throughout the world. Onions and asparagus are two important food plants in this family, with garlic, chives, and shallot of minor importance. Many of this group, such as lilies and tulips, are grown for their showy flowers. In the onion, the flowers occur in a group called an umbel. The fruit of this family is either a capsule or a berry. In the onion the capsule contains three pairs of seeds, black in color and angular. The fruit of asparagus is a red, round berry.

The onion (*Allium cepa*) is characterized by a pungent, alliaceous compound. The bulb is made up of thickened bases of leaves attached to a small conical stem. The many roots extend only to shallow depths. The leaf is round and hollow. Flowers are insect pollinated and there is probably frequent interpollination among the flowers of the same umbel.

Origin and History. The onion is one of our oldest vegetables and originally seems to have come from Palestine to India. This plant was mentioned in the Bible. Hippocrates speaks of onions being eaten commonly in 430 B.C. As early as 60 A.D. onion types were classified as "long or round, yellow or white." They were eaten either cooked or raw by the people belonging to all classes. By 1570 there were available receipts for cooking onion, discussions of methods of culture as well as descriptions of the different types. Onions were grown in America as early as 1629, and in 1806 some 6 varieties were listed by seedsmen.

Producing Areas. Early maturing onions are produced in the southern states and southwest, and the late maturing varieties in the cool northern states. The 1940–1951 statistical data for market onions are given on p. 270.

The most active harvest season for some of the important market states as well as those in the West is: New York, August and September; Texas, April

Onions for Market

	Acreage	Sacks* Per Acre	Production Sacks	Price Per Sack Dollars	Farm Value Dollars
United States	128,313	301	38,617,000	1.24	47,929,000
New York	14,358	471	6,766,000	1.32	8,989,000
Texas	51,808	90	4,667,000	1.65	7,713,000
California	10,208	483	4,927,000	1.25	6,162,000
Colorado	10,358	478	4,954,000	0.98	4,879,000
Michigan	9,067	398	3,612,000	1.29	4,677,000

(Farm value, other Western states: Oregon, $2,746,000; Idaho, $1,432,000; Washington, $801,000; Arizona, $776,000; Utah, $763,000; New Mexico, $402,000; Nevada, $291,000.)
* Approximately 50 pounds.

5 to May 20, also June; California, May to September; Colorado, August and September; Michigan, August and September; Oregon, August and September; Idaho, August and September; Washington, July to September; Utah, August and September; Arizona, May 10 to June 20, also September and October; New Mexico, July; Nevada, August and September.

Food Values. Onions are used as much for flavoring material as for their food value. They are placed in group 2 on general food efficiency. The flavoring compound of onions and garlic is allyl-propyl-disulphide ($C_6H_{12}S_2$). Usually late varieties of onions contain more of the compound than the early varieties. An over supply of onions does not increase greatly the consumption of this vegetable, but when they are scarce and expensive people continue to use them in moderate amounts. Evidently, onion flavor is essential in many of our cooked foods. Onions contain 87.5 per cent water and the food value per 100 gm. of edible portion is energy, 49 calories; protein, 1.4 gm.; calcium, 32 mg.; vitamin A, 20 I.U.; ascorbic acid, 12 mg.; thiamine, 0.03 mg.; riboflavin, 0.12 mg.; and niacin, 0.1 mg. The following data give the relative rank of late onions in comparison with other vegetables on a pound, acre, and man-hour basis as well as those nutrients where this crop ranks in the highest ten.

Pound, rank 16: Energy, 4½; calcium, 7½; riboflavin, 7½.
    Acre, rank 3: Riboflavin, 1; energy, 2; protein, 2; calcium, 4; iron, 7; thiamine, 9; ascorbic acid, 10.
Man-hour, rank 6: Riboflavin, 1; energy, 3; protein, 3; calcium, 3; iron, 8; thiamine, 9.

Varieties. Onions vary as to color, time of maturity, shape, and keeping quality. The bulb color may be white, yellow or red. In the case of the colored varieties, the color is located in the epidermal cells of each scale-leaf and the rest of the scales may be white or clear. By the use of male-sterile lines of onions, it has been possible to develop hybrid varieties. Growers are finding that many hybrid varieties are being made available by the seed companies.

Australian Brown. Standard variety noted for long-keeping qualities. Bulbs, light yellow, flattened globe shape; they bulb in about 15 or more hours of daylight (photoperiodism). Used for export to Cuba, late spring storage, and as sets.

Excel. Used in Texas and West for early shipment; early flat onion, straw-colored; small tops; flesh mild and white; bulbs in about 12 hours or more of daylight.

Hybrid Onions. Several varieties (Fig. 68) are being offered by seedsmen adapted to certain growing conditions. Care should be used to select a hybrid for the conditions under which it is to be grown. Benefits include better yield, desirable size, and uniform maturity.

San Joaquin. Intermediate maturity; bulbs yellow, intermediate in shape between full globe and top-shape of Grano bulbs; flesh white, mild; non-bolting type; bulbs in about 14 hours or more of daylight.

Fig. 68. The bulb of a hybrid onion is shown in front with bulbs of the two parents in the background. (Courtesy, Associated Seed Growers, Inc.)

Southport Globe. Available in white, yellow, and red scale color. Standard late variety; bulbs medium large, globular; flesh white and mild; keeps well; bulbs in about 15 or more hours of daylight. The white globe type is used greatly by dehydrators and it is also the most important bunching onion.

Sweet Spanish. Best of the large, mild types; amber orange, small neck, globular; bulbs in about 16 hours of daylight. There are both white and yellow strains. The Utah strains are popular in the West.

Texas Grano (Babosa). Early-maturing variety used in Texas and the Southwest; bulbs large, top-shaped, light yellow, mild flavor; early but poor keeper, nonbolting type, bulbs in about 14 or more hours of daylight.

Yellow Globe Danvers. Popular late globe type; hardy, yields well; bulbs round, yellow, with small neck; flesh white with yellow cast; bulbs in about 15 hours of daylight.

Climatic Requirements. Onions may be grown almost anywhere in the United States at some season of the year, but fairly cool temperatures (55° to 75° F.) are needed during the early stages of growth before bulbing. During bulbing, harvesting, and curing, fairly high temperatures are desirable as well as low humidity during curing. The time an onion will begin to bulb is determined primarily by length of day and not by age (Fig. 69). The bulbing photoperiod differs with variety. This period ranges from 12 hours for

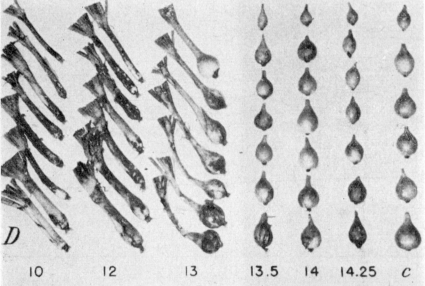

EXPOSURE PER DAY TO NORMAL LIGHT (HOURS)

Fig. 69. The Southport Yellow Globe variety forms bulbs at 13.5 or more hours of light each day. If days are too short, the onions fail to form bulbs. (Courtesy, *Journal of Agricultural Research.*)

extra early varieties to about 15 hours for late types. Thus, it is impossible to obtain an early crop with late varieties in the South because the days are too short early in the season and too warm later. Low temperature may tend to prevent bulbing but this is rarely a field factor. Warm and dry weather may result in serious attacks from thrips. Onion smut seems more prevalent below 80° F. and almost absent above 85° F. Downy mildew thrives under moderate temperature and high humidity. Onion seed germinates best near 65°, but with good germination from 45° to 85° F.

Soil. The most desirable type of soil is one retentive enough under cultivation to keep sufficient moisture about the roots, and at the same time is friable enough to be cultivated easily and to allow proper expansion of the bulbs. It should be fertile, well supplied with humus, and relatively free of weed seeds. The onion crop is grown mainly on sandy loams, silty loams, and peat. Heavy clay and coarse sand should be avoided.

Fertilizer. The onion is an intensive crop and should yield large quantities of marketable bulbs for the area planted. The plant is shallow-rooted, and a fairly high concentration of nutrients must be maintained in the upper foot of soil. The grower is justified in using rather heavy applications of fertilizer.

California growers use 60 to 100 pounds of nitrogen on the early and intermediate crops and about 40 pounds on the late crop. In the San Joaquin Valley the fertilizers also should contain 60 pounds of phosphoric acid per acre. Onions grown during the cooler parts of the year respond well to fertilizer, which should be applied at the time of field transplanting. For the direct-seeded crop the fertilizer should be applied at seeding time or soon after the emergence of the seedlings. Fertilizer placement is important and should be as close to the plant as possible without causing burning. One inch to the side, and three inches below the plant, is best for transplanted onions; while for direct seeding the fertilizer should be placed farther away to eliminate possible burning. Bed grown onions have given much better response from fertilizer placed under the row than by placing it in the center of the bed. Oregon growers use commercial fertilizers to supplement stable manure or covercrops. On peat land several analyses are used such as 0-10-10, 2-8-10, 3-10-10, or 3-10-20. On soils with less organic matter a 1-2-2 or 1-3-3 ratio is used. About 750 to 1000 pounds of fertilizer are applied broadcast before seeding. Some growers side-dress with 300 pounds of fertilizer when seedlings appear. New Mexico fertilizer experiments at Mesilla Park show the largest return from fertilizer by using 400 pounds of ammonium sulfate and 10 tons of manure. Eastern Washington growers on irrigated soils use 15 tons of manure plus 60 pounds of nitrogen or 100 pounds of nitrogen and 60 pounds of phosphoric acid without manure. In Western Washington 1000 to 1200 pounds of a 5-10-10 is used without manure or 800 to 1000 pounds of 3-10-10 is used with 15 tons of manure.

Planting and Spacing. Planting periods for commercial acreage are:

Arizona: Salt River Valley, November and December; September and October.

California: Kern to Riverside counties, November to January; San Joaquin Valley, December to February; late onions, February to April.

Colorado: March.

Idaho: March.

Nevada: March 15 to April.

New Mexico: Dona Ana County, October 1–15 and February 1–15.

Oregon: March 25 to April 15.

Utah: East of Salt Lake and Sevier County, March 15 to April.

Washington: Walla Walla and Benton counties, February 15 to March 15; Clark, King and Yakima counties, March 15 to April 15.

Two methods of planting are used in growing the commercial onion crop. Some growers plant the seed and later transplant the seedlings to the production field. Onions are raised by direct seeding in the field, but in this case the grower needs to control his seeding rate very accurately. The transplanting method is used more commonly for early or intermediate varieties and most of the late onions are produced by direct seeding.

For the transplant crop, seeds are planted on beds in rows 2 to 10 inches apart about 6 to 10 weeks before time to transplant. About 2 pounds of seed will produce enough plants to transplant one acre. The plants are removed to the field from November to March, according to the climatic conditions. Transplanting is by hand on beds or on the flat, according to local practises. Since transplanting requires 40 hours of labor per acre compared to 2 hours for direct seeding, there is a trend away from this practise.

Most of the onion crop for late market or storage is seeded directly into the field as early in the spring as possible. Seed usually is sown at the rate of 2 to 4 pounds per acre at a depth of one-half to one inch, according to soil type. The deeper plantings are made on lighter soils. Various types of garden seeders are used, run singly or in gangs. For planting on previously prepared beds, two rows are drilled on top of each bed. For plantings on the flat, the rows are spaced 12 to 18 inches apart; the distance depends on the method of cultivation to be used.

Irrigation. The onion is a very shallow-rooted crop, most of the roots being limited to the upper foot of soil. As a result most onions benefit from irrigation. In the absence of rainfall the soil should be irrigated thoroughly before planting. Once the plants have started to grow they should never suffer from lack of water. Irrigation experiments performed at Davis, California gave greater increases in yield with late than with early onions because more of the growth was made during the dry months. Irrigation greatly increases yield, primarily through increased size of bulb. Irrigation decreases slightly the percentage of dry matter in the onion. Early onions need 5 to 7 applications, and the late crop, 7 to 9. Fifteen inches of water are required for the early and intermediate crops, and 24 inches for the late crop. Maximum yields were obtained in New Mexico irrigation experiments[2] by the use of 30 inches of water.

When the plants have started to mature, irrigation should be discontinued and the soil allowed to dry out as much as possible; otherwise a second root growth may start—one that is difficult to stop. Digging will stop root growth.

Harvesting and Curing. When onions ripen properly the leaves weaken in the region just above the bulb and the top falls over while the leaves are still green. Onions do not mature uniformly. Under warm weather conditions where onions are subject to sunburn, they are harvested when 25 per cent of the tops have broken over. Under normal conditions harvest is delayed until 90–95 per cent of the tops have broken over.

Onions usually are loosened in the soil by running some type of blade or cutter below the bulbs (Fig. 70, p. 284). They are then pulled by hand and thrown in windrows to dry before topping. In the warm interior valleys 4 to 7 days usually are sufficient for drying; more time is necessary in regions of cooler climate and higher humidity. Where the sun is hot the tops are laid so as to protect the bulbs from sunburn. When properly dry the tops are removed by hand either by twisting or by cutting with a knife, shears, or by power-driven mechanical toppers. After topping, the bulbs are placed in sacks or slat crates and allowed to cure for a few days before being transported to market or placed in storage.

Machine versus Hand Harvesting. Labor is an important factor in vegetable production both from the standpoint of cost per hour of labor and having an adequate supply of workers available. There have been two points of view in attacking this problem. In the West and particularly California emphasis has been placed upon the development of labor saving machinery with a reduction in the amount of labor needed but with an increase in capital invested in equipment. Such labor saving equipment has been developed for harvesting onions[7]. Labor saving equipment needs large acreages to be harvested, in order to reduce costs, as well as a crop that can be harvested at one time. In some vegetable crops all the marketable product is not ready to be harvested at one time as in the case of cantaloupes. Here is a crop which requires human judgment to harvest each fruit at the proper stage of maturity. In some crops plant breeders are trying to develop varieties which are more determinate in maturity time so machines may be used to harvest the crop.

Another point of view is to train workers to use the least possible movements in harvesting and thus increase their efficiency and reduce the cost of harvesting. Considerable advancement has been made on this procedure both in the East and Colorado. A publication[9] is available from the latter state which lists suggestions for easier and faster topping of onions as follows:

"1. Lift the onions with a machine if they are hard to pull.
2. Pile onions evenly with tops all in one direction.
3. Keep close to onions—to save back and arms.
4. Always move onions TOWARD the basket.
5. Keep tools sharp—carry a whetstone.
6. Keep basket close to work and dispose of onions by a 'twist of the wrist.'
7. Check frequently to see if you are always using the easiest method.
8. Try to develop easier methods of topping onions."

The grower needs to give thought to the use of less labor in producing a crop. Efficient use of labor is applicable to small acreages as well as to crops that do not lend themselves to machine harvesting.

Storage. Onion varieties differ as to their suitability for storing. After onions are harvested they lose considerable water for several weeks. Varieties which lose large amounts tend to keep poorly, while those resistant to water loss are good storage onions. Early varieties are high in moisture, have a high water loss, and are classified as poor-keeping types.

Onions may be stored in bulk, in 50- to 100-pound sacks, or in shallow slat crates which hold about a bushel. The bulk method, being seldom satisfactory, should not be practised if any alternative is possible. If stored in bags these are best piled in pairs laid crosswise in stacks 5 or 6 sacks high. The stacks should be set a few inches off the floor on wooden strips and the individual stacks separated by a few inches to permit air circulation.

While cold storage, by artificial refrigeration, is a very satisfactory method of keeping onions over long periods, the common storage houses can be constructed so that they are also well suited for storing this crop. In some sections of the West, the warehouses have forced ventilation under the stacks of onions and the air is sucked off above the onions. In this way the onion bulbs are kept dry and it is possible to store the crop from harvest time in the fall until March or April. Only well cured onions should be placed in storage. Recommended storage conditions are 32° F., 75 per cent relative humidity, and the storage period is not longer than 6 to 8 months for late onions.

Quality Characteristics for the Retail Buyer. Bright, clean, hard, well-shaped mature onions with dry skins are usually of good quality. Onions possessing a seed stem are undesirable. Usually the neck of such onions is thick with a tough, woody condition of the stem. This tough stem extends to the base of the bulb causing much waste. Decay generally appears as a rot attacking either the outer scales or the scales in the center of the bulb. It may penetrate the bulb from the neck to the base. Moisture at the neck is an indication of decay. Misshapen onions sometimes are found on the markets. The most common of these forms are known as "splits" or "doubles" and "bottle necks"—terms which refer to shape only. Misshapen onions are objectionable mainly because of the possible waste in their preparation for table use.

Production of Dry Onion Sets. Onion sets are small bulbs (one-half to one inch in diameter) produced by growing plants under crowded conditions in the field, and are used to produce green or ripe onions. The sets mature when small in size due to crowding or other conditions limiting growth. For the small home gardens, sets are more satisfactory than raising the crop from seed. Onion sets are used for growing green onions or the plants are allowed to mature to be harvested as ripe onions.

For set production on rich soil, 80 to 100 pounds of seed are sown to the acre; on poorer soil 60 to 80 pounds. Seed may be sown by hand seed drills, by special seeders that distribute the seed thickly in rows about 1 inch wide, or by using a special funnel shaped spreader or wide shoe which will distribute the seed in a band 3 or 4 inches wide. Cultural requirements other than planting procedure are about the same for sets as for large bulbs.

When mature, sets are loosened by running a U-shaped knife under the row. They are then gathered and placed in shallow trays with lath bottoms. Topping seldom is necessary since the small tops shrivel up and generally are broken loose by handling and grading. The trays are left scattered a few days to dry, then stacked in the field until stored.

Green Bunching Onions. Green bunching onions generally are limited to small plantings grown for local market. Bunching onions may be produced from multiplier onions, dry sets, or seeds. The multiplier onion does not produce bulbs, but multiplies by giving rise to a number of side shoots at the base of the original plants. If sets or seed are planted, a white variety should be selected, since such plants make a more attractive package than a colored variety.

In marketing this type of onion, the young plants are pulled, the roots trimmed and the outside leaf scale pulled off, leaving the stem white and clean and several inches in length. They are then tied in small bunches, with tops trimmed slightly, and are packed in crates or baskets for transport to market.

Insects: *Onion Maggot (Hylemya antiqua).* In spring, particularly in wet seasons, small, white maggots attack onions. Clean culture and destruction of onion refuse after harvest are important in keeping down the infestation. Chlordane as a 5 per cent dust or chlordane sprays may prove effective if applied properly. Mercuric chloride or calomel also is used mixed 1 ounce to 8 gallons of water. The solution is applied with a watering can—about one-half pint per plant.

Onion Thrips (Thrips tabaci). The life cycle is similar to that of bean thrips; a complete generation takes only 2 weeks. The eggs, laid on the tender tissues, hatch in 5 days and the larvae feed on the epidermis, extracting the cell contents. The pupal stage lasts 4 days. The silvering of the leaves and premature drying up of the leaves are characteristic of onion thrip injury. Spanish types are more resistant to thrips. DDT as a 10 per cent dust or DDT-oil emulsion sprays give good control, usually 2 to 3 applications are necessary.

Red Spider. In dry years red spiders often attack late onions. Good control is obtained by dusting with commercial dinitro dusts, 30 to 40 pounds per acre.

Stem Nematode. This pest is severe on garlic and may affect onions. Use seed from noninfested fields. No other control is known.

Diseases: *Black Mold (Aspergillus niger).* A black, powdery fungus sometimes develops in spots and streaks between the outer bulb scales, usually on onions in storage. Appearance and keeping quality are injured. Discard affected bulbs and store at 32° to 35° F.

Downy mildew (Peronspora destructor) is serious when it affects the seed crop. The plants turn yellow, with down curling and narrowing of leaves. Large, oval, slightly chlorotic lesions on leaves and seedstalks result from secondary infection. The grayish-violet downy growth of conidiophores on the surface of infected tissues is the most characteristic sign of the disease. A combination of methods must be employed to hold mildew in check: (1) Development of mildew resistant varieties; (2) avoid disease by using clean bulbs, isolation from other fields, and an unfavorable climate for disease; and (3) spraying with 2-2-100 rosin-soap lime sulfur spray.

Leaf Mold (Macrosporium porri). Leaves damaged by mildew and other causes are subject to invasion by several fungi, which cause the leaves to appear blackened and moldy. Usually not important when mildew is controlled.

Neck Rot (Botrytis sp.). A gray, felt-like growth of fungus mold appears at the neck of affected onions and softens, and rots the tissue. White varieties are more susceptible than colored. Proper curing of bulbs after harvest will reduce losses.

Pink root (Phoma terrestris) causes roots to shrivel and die and to become pink. A diseased plant may send out new roots which become diseased. Control by a long rotation to avoid planting on infected soil.

Smudge (Colletotrichum circinans). Attacks most white varieties and makes circles or concentric rings of dark-colored dots, the spore pustules of the fungus. Injury to bulbs is not great but gives them a dirty appearance. Proper curing is the best preventive.

White rot (Sclerotium cepirorum) usually appears during cool, moist weather in spring and autumn. The first signs are yellowing and wilting of the leaves, followed later by a total collapse of the top. Roots usually rot and bulb is covered with a white fluffy mass of mycelium. Avoid diseased bulbs and replanting on infested soil.

Yellow Dwarf. Leaves and stems twisted, flattened and changed from their normal green to various degrees of yellowing, extending from a few streaks to almost complete yellowing. Such plants are stunted severely, caused by a virus which lives over in bulbs. Disease is spread by aphids. Symptoms may be masked by high temperatures.

References

1. Bouquet, A. G. B.: Production and marketing of onions, *Ore. Agr. Ext. Cir. 419*, 9 p., (Mimeo.) 1943.
2. Curry, A. S.: Effect of irrigation practices on the growth and yield of White Grano onions, *New Mexico Agr. Exp. Sta. Bull. 281*, 34 p., 1941.
3. Davis, G. N.: Onion production in California. *Cal. Agr. Exp. Sta. Cir. 357*, 19 p., 1943.
4. Fite, A. B.: Onion fertilizer experiments, *New Mexico Agr. Exp. Sta. Bull. 233*, 22 p., 1935.
5. Garcia, Fabian, and A. B. Fite: Early Grano onion culture, *New Mexico Agr. Exp. Sta. Bull. 193*, 15 p., 1931.
6. Jones, H. A., *et al.*: Growing the transplant onion crop, *U.S.D.A. Farmers' Bull. 1956*, 26 p., 1949.
7. Lorenzen, Coby: Onion harvester, *Calif. Agr. 3:* (No. 2) 9, 12, 1949.
8. Moore, John F., Loyd L. Stitt, Leo Campbell, and Karl Baur: Growing onions in Western Washington, *W. Wash. Exp. Sta. Cir. 95*, 3 p., (Mimeo.) 1950.
9. Paschal, J. L. and R. W. Roskelley: Suggestions on how to top more onions, *Col. Agr. Exp. Sta. Press Bull. 100*, 4 p., 1945.
10. Walker, J. C., *et al.*: Onion-set production, *U.S.D.A. Farmers' Bull. 1955*, 21 p., 1946.
11. Woodbury, George W. and Carl F. Dietz: Onion seed production in Idaho, *Ida. Agr. Exp. Sta. Bull. 247*, 14 p., 1942.

ASPARAGUS

Botany. The genus *Asparagus* has 150 species spread throughout the world in temperate as well as tropical regions. All are perennials and many species are grown for ornamental purposes. The roots of cultivated asparagus (*Asparagus officinalis*) are numerous and fleshy, they occur horizontally in the soil and serve as a storage organ. The spear production is primarily at the expense of the sugars stored in the fleshy roots. The crown is made up of roots and rhizomes which are underground stems. The harvested spear is an aerial stem and arises from a bud on the rhizome. The crown of the roots grows closer to the surface of the soil each year and the older and fibrous roots die and rot away. The first stems produced in spring are cut for eating, but later stems are allowed to grow and form a fernlike foliage. Plants usually are either staminate or pistillate. Flowers are insect-pollinated; and produce 6 black angular seeds which are contained in a fleshy berry. Asparagus is a perennial, grown normally for 10 to 15 years, with beds known to be 35 years old.

Origin and History. Asparagus has been used for 20 centuries both as a food and for medicinal purposes. The native home was Europe, and the plant is found wild in southern Russia, Poland, and Greece. About 200 B.C., Cato developed a set of cultural directions for growing asparagus which were very similar to those we use at the present time. However, he recommended the use of seed from wild plants indicating that there were some differences between wild and cultivated asparagus. Some early writers even praise the wild plants because they were sweeter in taste. As early as the first century, writers recommended the transplanting of young roots from the seedbed— a practise we still use.

Producing Areas. California is the most important state in value of asparagus produced. The crop is cut green until about April 15, and shipped east. Then the beds are ridged high for the production of white asparagus for the canneries or without ridging for green cannery asparagus. For many years the production of canned asparagus was confined almost entirely to California and was of the blanched type. In recent years there has been more demand for green asparagus, which is being produced in eastern states as well as in the West. The 1940–1951 statistical data are given on p. 281.

The most active harvest season for some of the important market states as well as those in the West is: California, March and April; New Jersey, May and June; Washington, April and May; Pennsylvania, May and June; Illinois, May and June; Oregon, April and May.

Food Value. The vitamin A content of green asparagus is higher than that of white or blanched asparagus. Both are relatively low in food value and fall in group 3. Green asparagus contains 93 per cent water and the food value per 100 gm. of edible portion is energy, 26 calories; protein, 22 gm.; calcium, 21 mg.; vitamin A, 700 I.U.; ascorbic acid, 30 mg.; thiamine, 0.20 mg.; riboflavin, 0.16 mg.; and niacin, 1.0 mg. Vitamin A content of white asparagus is about 20 I.U. The following data give the relative nutrient rank of green asparagus.

Pound, rank 7: Thiamine, $1\frac{1}{2}$; riboflavin, $5\frac{1}{2}$; niacin, $6\frac{1}{2}$; ascorbic acid, $9\frac{1}{2}$; protein, $9\frac{1}{2}$; vitamin A, 10 (green only).
Acre, rank 29: Nutrient rank is 11 or lower.
Man-hour, rank 26: Nutrient rank is 11 or lower.

Asparagus for Market

	Acreage	Crates* Per Acre	Production Crates	Price Per Crate Dollars	Farm Value Dollars
United States	51,187	85	4,345,000	3.24	14,100,000
California	24,068	78	1,875,000	3.30	6,195,000
New Jersey	10,067	111	1,114,000	3.27	3,643,000
Washington	2,925	155	453,000	2.47	1,119,000
Pennsylvania	2,046	82	168,000	3.97	667,000
Illinois	2,192	77	169,000	3.44	581,800

(Farm value, other Western states: Oregon, $126,000; Arizona, $12,000.)
* Approximately 30 pounds.

Asparagus for Processing

	Acreage	Tons Per Acre	Production Tons	Price Per Ton Dollars	Farm Value Dollars
United States	77,242	1.17	90,969	167.79	15,264,000
California	45,799	1.13	52,047	161.64	8,413,000
New Jersey	12,808	1.26	16,175	193.81	3,135,000
Washington	5,166	1.44	7,484	164.08	1,228,000
Illinois	6,050	1.18	7,180	157.93	1,134,000
Michigan	3,691	1.25	4,614	167.75	774,000

(Farm value, other Western states: Oregon, $16,000.)

Varieties. The variety differences in this crop are not distinct. Most of the production at the present time is classified as Mary Washington, a rust-resistant type. This variety was the result of breeding work done by Dr. J. B. Norton of the United States Department of Agriculture. Palmetto also is grown to a minor degree. Seed needs to be obtained from plants which produce good yields and quality. Yield can be determined roughly by the spread of the crown at 3 to 5 years as compared to surrounding plants. Desirable spears have tight heads, are round in cross section, and have good green color without purple pigment. About 1945, new strains of Mary Washington asparagus were introduced by the University of California and given the names of 499 and 500. The spear size of both strains average from medium to large in size with 500 averaging slightly larger as well as being consistently earlier. Both have tight heads, possess a uniform green color, and are uniform in appearance. Considerable Western acreage has been planted to these strains and 500 has been most popular. Some new varieties also have been developed by processing companies.

Climatic Requirements. Asparagus is not grown successfully in areas near the Gulf of Mexico, Imperial Valley, or Alaska. These areas give poor yields probably because there is insufficient food stored in the roots. In Alaska, the growing season is short and in the warmer areas of the South the food is used for new fern growth rather than storage. Areas with monthly average temperatures of 60° to 75° F. and a winter dormant period produce good crops. Daily average temperature affects rate of growth of spears; thus, at 53° F., five and three-tenths days are required to grow 6 inches of spear, and at 78° F. only one and nine-tenths days are required. Branching, an undesirable characteristic, is increased by high temperatures. Shoots at 100° F. branch at 2 to 3 inches above the ground, and at 59° F. they branch at 30 to 40 inches. Strong drying winds are objectionable because they retard the growth on one side of the spear causing the production of crooked, unmarketable spears. Most asparagus areas have a dormant season of 3 to 5 months which is the result of frosty, freezing weather. Dormant asparagus rarely is harmed by freezing weather. Flooding of dormant beds in California a month or two before normal harvest period has resulted in producing spears 10 to 14 days earlier. This response was discovered through the flooding of beds to control the garden centipede.

Plants. Planting of asparagus involves either the raising or purchasing of plants. Since asparagus varieties are not pure lines, great care should be used to obtain seed or plants of good productive capacity.

Seed should be obtained from high-yielding plants which are producing good quality spears. Frequently seed is saved from poor plants because they produce more seed and consequently the seed may be saved at less expense. One pound of seed is sufficient to raise the plants for 2 or 3 acres. Since the field lasts from 12 to 15 years, the cost of good seed per yearly crop is negligible. Asparagus seed is slow to germinate. Rate of seed sprouting may be increased by soaking the seed for 3 to 5 days in water at 85° to 95° F. The surface of the seed is then dried on a canvas for a few hours, so it will feed through a seeder uniformly. The seed in the nursery is planted in early spring, one to one and one-half inches deep, with rows about 2 feet apart. Seed is planted thinly so the crowns will be about 3 to 4 inches apart in the row. The seedlings need to receive good care as to cultivation and irrigation, to ensure large crowns for planting. A preëmergence spray of Stoddard solvent oil may be used at the rate of 60 to 100 gallons per acre.

Soil. A crop which is to be grown on the same soil for 10 to 15 years should be planted only on good soil. Lighter soils are desirable from the standpoint of producing straight spears, therefore loams or organic soils are used. Considerable asparagus production is found in or near the delta of the Sacramento and San Joaquin rivers where the soils are referred to as peat-sediment. In this area growers have not been successful in planting new fields of asparagus in the same ground where old beds have been plowed under.

Fertilizer. Soils needing complete fertilizer for maximum yields should be fertilized generously with phosphoric acid and potash before planting the crowns. This practise places the fertilizer deep in the soil where it will be available for several years. Fertilizer usually is applied in the spring before cutting, although part of the nitrogen may be applied after the cutting season. Experiments in the Delta region of California have failed to give commercial increases in yield with the usual types of fertilizer alone or in combination. Oregon recommends increasing the organic matter of the soil through the addition of rotted manure and the growing of green manure crops. Broadcasting a 6-8-6 fertilizer also has increased yields. Cyanamid at the rate of 500 pounds per acre will help to kill weeds and add to the supply of available nitrogen. Eastern Washington growers on irrigated soil use 100 pounds of nitrogen and 30 pounds of phosphoric acid. In Western Washington 15 tons of manure are used plus 500 pounds of superphosphate or 800 to 1200 pounds of a 5-10-10 without manure.

Planting Crowns. The young plants seeded the previous year are called crowns and should be dug in the spring before growth starts and planted in the field within a few hours. Commonly the planting time in Arizona and California is January to March; and in Oregon and Washington, March and April. The crowns are planted in trenches made with a double mold-board plow with extension wings (Fig. 70). On sandy loam or organic soils the crowns should be planted deeper than on heavier types of soil. In the Delta on organic soils an average depth of 10 inches is most common. On slightly heavier mineral soils the best depth is 8 inches. The crowns are covered with 2 inches of soil, and the trench gradually filled with soil the first season. Several shoots a foot or more in height should be in evidence before the crowns are covered too deeply.

Spacing of the rows depends upon whether green or white (blanched) asparagus is to be grown. The rows need to be farther apart if soil is to be thrown up over the row to a depth of 8 to 12 inches for the production of white "grass". California growers favor the wider spacing so the asparagus may be harvested either green or white. For blanching, the rows should be seven and one-half to eight feet apart, and for green asparagus 5 to 6 feet. The distance between the plants in the row is usually 18 to 24 inches, while 12 inches have been found most productive in California.

Green versus White Asparagus. In an 8-year comparison[2] made between harvesting the crop white or green, there was found to be little difference in yield. The white spears average larger in size but fewer spears are produced

Fig. 70. (*Top*) Equipment used for loosing and lifting onion or garlic bulbs previous to drying the crop in windrows.

(*Bottom*) Making a trench for the planting of asparagus crowns.

per crown. Many Western growers prefer to produce white spears because there is less breakage in handling and less expense in harvesting.

Male versus Female Plants. In young asparagus plants there is usually a 1:1 sex ratio. As early as 1890, Green in Ohio noted that male plants produced larger yields; this yield was proportionally greater during the early part of the cutting season. Several other workers have confirmed this same result, but also found that the male plants produced a larger number of small spears. A seven year test made at Davis[5] gave the following average data: Male plants produced an average of 5856 pounds per acre, 20 spears per plant, and with an average weight of 22 grams per spear; female plants produced 4901 pounds, 12 spears per plant, and with an average weight of 31 grams per spear. Very similar results were obtained in the Delta area of California. Thus, male plants produce more weight and the female plants produce large spears which grade higher. The economic advantage is not great enough to justify discarding half of the plants belonging to one sex.

Irrigation. In the organic soils of the Sacramento-San Joaquin Delta the crop is watered by sub-irrigation. The main ditches which carry the water are called "buckeyes"; they are about 800 feet apart, 6 to 8 feet wide and deep. In the case of asparagus nurseries for plants, the water is conveyed across the field by so-called "spud" ditches, which are about 60 feet apart, 9 inches wide, and 15 to 18 inches deep. Ditches are filled with water which is held there until the water from one ditch penetrates laterally far enough to meet the moisture from neighboring ditches. Two to three applications are made each season. On sediment soils, surface irrigation is used with sufficient water to penetrate 6 feet. Irrigation experiments made at Davis on sediment soil indicate that it requires several years for the nonirrigated plots to give any indication of insufficient moisture. Although the above field had a water table at 10 feet, probably irrigation is not so essential for asparagus as for some of our shallow-rooted crops. Growers in northern California use about 20 inches of water besides the usual winter rains. In the Yakima Valley of Washington, the heavier types of soil receive 3 to 5 irrigations and the shallow, sandy soils may require 5 to 8 irrigations.

Other Operations. Cultivation is practised as in other crops in order to keep the soil free of weeds. In the late fall when the frost has killed the top growth or it has matured because of cold weather, the fern should be cut off at the surface of the soil. It may be disposed of by cutting into small pieces, and turning under, or by raking and burning. Adding of the tops to the soil is to be preferred particularly on mineral soils to add organic matter. In peat soil burning is dangerous from the standpoint of fire in the peat. The land is then disked and left slightly rough over winter. This general procedure is followed in caring for the field in future years.

Physiology of Production. Asparagus is one of the few perennial vegetables. The spring production of spears is at the expense of food stored in the roots the previous year. The cutting season should be limited in duration, so the plants have ample time to manufacture and store food for the succeeding year's crop. In the fall the leafy growth (fern) should not be cut until there has been ample opportunity for the food to be translocated to the roots. Carbohydrates seem to be exhausted more quickly from the roots than are other constituents. Climatic conditions affect the amount of carbohydrates manufactured by the plant, and exhaustion of sugars is indicated by the production of spears small in diameter. Interval between cuttings is related directly to the temperature, as there is usually ample moisture in the spring. Cutting is more frequent during warm weather.

Harvesting. The age for making the first harvest on a young field, as well as the length of the cutting season, will depend upon the vigor of the past year's plants or the amount of stored food. Cutting period will vary with climate. In California, with a long growing season, the plants are cut 3 to 4 weeks the year after transplanting and 2 years after setting, the beds are cut the full season. In Oregon and Washington the first full year of harvest is the second year after crown planting. Eight to 10 weeks are used for the regular harvesting season in the North, while about 12 weeks are used in California. Too severe harvesting will result in reduced yields.

During cool spring weather the bed will need to be cut every 2 to 4 days, but as the temperature increases the beds should be cut every day and sometimes oftener than once each day. Green market asparagus is cut so the spears are 10 to 12 inches in length, and the cannery crop is trimmed to a 7 inch length. In the West the green asparagus should have at least 4 inches of green. The cutter considers both the length and compactness of head, since in warm weather the head branches closer to the ground.

The stalks are cut with an asparagus knife, which has a wide, chisel-like blade. This knife is pushed down at about a 45° angle to the spear, to cut it off below the surface of the ground (Fig. 71). The distance below the ground depends upon whether white or green asparagus is being produced. This operation should be performed carefully so that new shoots which have not appeared above the ground will not be injured. Cutting injury to younger spears below the surface frequently reduces yield 15 to 25 per cent. The stalks may be carried to the end of the row in baskets or grasped by the tops and laid on the bed when a handful has been harvested. The spears are picked up by a one horse cart.

Crooked spears are a source of culls. They are caused frequently by injury to the cells on one side of the stalk, resulting from carelessness. Rubbish, stones, insects, and winds also contribute to this defect.

Preparation for Market. Asparagus is hauled to a shed for grading, bunching, trimming, washing, and packing in crates. In grading, all crooked, poorly formed, and branched spears are discarded. In California, spears are divided into 6 grades according to the number of spears per two and

Fig. 71. Cutting a green asparagus spear. Cut spears are carried in the left hand by the tip of the spear. They are left in bunches on the bed to be collected by a worker using a two-wheeled cart.

one-half pound bunch; large sized spears are 14 per bunch, and the small are 68 to 100. The spears are placed in a buncher and clamped tight so the bunch may be fastened with cloth tape, or rubber bands. The bunch is trimmed to proper length and placed upright in a pan of water to await packing. After wrapping in oil paper they are placed in a "pyramid" two-compartment crate. There are one dozen bunches per crate, with wet sphagnum moss on the bottom. In other areas, the bunches vary in weight from 1 to 2 pounds. Some asparagus is packed loose in the crate.

The cannery crop is placed on a rack and trimmed to a 7 inch length, washed and placed in a 50 pound lug box for delivery. A sample of this asparagus is graded at the factory to determine the payment to be made the grower.

Storage. Recommended storage conditions are 32° F., 90 per cent humidity, and for a period not to exceed 3 to 4 weeks. Asparagus deteriorates rapidly so usually this vegetable is stored only a few days unless good conditions are available. At room temperature the spears become tougher if stored for a short time. It is desirable to keep the cut end of the spear wet either by placing in a pan of water or a pad of wet moss as in the case of the packing crate. Asparagus to be shipped should be precooled and shipped in cars with bunker ice. After arrival at Eastern markets their storage life is not more than 3 to 6 days.

Quality Characteristics for the Retail Buyer. Asparagus ages rapidly after it is cut; the tips spread and the stalks become tough and woody. The purchase of fresh asparagus lessens the risk of buying tough spears. Asparagus to be its best must be fresh, tender, and firm, with close compact tips. A tender stalk is brittle and is punctured easily. A wilted appearance or a spreading tip is often an indication that considerable time has elapsed since cutting. Such stalks may or may not be freshened by placing in water; usually there is wastage, only the tips being edible. Angular stalks are likely to be tough and stringy. The whole stalk, with the exception of an inch or two of the base should be tender.

Insects: *Asparagus Beetle* (*Crioceris asparagi*). It is about one-fourth inch long, of a steel-blue color with a red thorax and with yellowish spots on the wings. The mature larvae are about one-third inch long, soft, fleshy, much wrinkled, and smoky gray. They drop to earth from the plants and form small, earth-covered cocoons. The mature beetles attack both the spears and the stalks. Early in the spring the adults feed upon the growing spears and cause distorted growth. After the cutting season, both the adults and the larvae feed upon the top growth of the plants. Severe infestations often kill the tops, especially the upper portion. Most of the damage is confined to young asparagus fields. Over-wintering adult beetles have a chance thus to deposit eggs on the young fern growth. The larvae appear in 3 to 8 days; the life cycle is completed in 3 to 4 weeks. There are many overlapping generations. On young fields the population increases rapidly, and serious injury may result if control measures are not taken.

The asparagus beetle has many natural enemies. Several species of ladybird beetles feed upon the eggs, while the numerous soldier bugs and dragonflies prey upon the larvae. Sometimes blackbirds feed upon both larvae and adults. The seedlings and fern often are damaged, and can be protected by dusting with DDT or BHC dusts. No poisonous materials should be applied to the developing stalks.

Garden Centipede (*Scutigerella immaculata*). Though small, these animals are very destructive when they occur in large numbers. When mature they are about one-fourth inch long with delicate soft bodies. In feeding they make a large number of small, round holes in the underground portion of the spear. When the centipedes are abundant in the soil, practically all the spears in the infested area will be injured. The top growth of such fields is reduced, and often the plants are killed. Green asparagus may be cut from badly infested fields, as the green portion growing above the ground is not injured.

When infestations are scattered throughout the field, flooding is the only practical means of control. A sufficiently high levee is made around the field to hold water a foot or more in depth on the entire field for 3 or 4 weeks during December and January. No adequate chemical control on these highly organic soils is known, but DDT may have some value on mineral soils.

Disease: *Asparagus Rust (Puccinia asparagi)*. Asparagus rust is recognized readily by brown, rusty spots on the stems and branches of the fern. In severe infestations the whole field takes on a brown, rusty color. As this disease is prevalent only where summer rains or dews are encountered, it does little damage in the interior valleys, although in some years the rust has been rather severe. Good control has been obtained from 25 to 30 pounds per acre of finely ground sulfur, applied as a dust about 3 weeks after the cutting season and followed by another application a month later. Fair control has been obtained by cutting, raking, and burning the tops in mid-summer, the second top growth being relatively free of the disease. The introduction of the rust-resistant Mary Washington asparagus has reduced the rust hazard.

Phytophthora Rot. Soft, watery spots appear on the asparagus shoots in market or transit and cause a foul-smelling decay. This condition is caused by a species of *Phytophthora* which lives in the soil. The spears are infected by spores either by direct contact or when being washed. The fungus flourishes under conditions of high soil moisture. The prevalence of the disease is correlated with high water table, poor drainage, and similar conditions.

Rusty Discoloration. Another disease generally known as rust causes a rusty discoloration on white asparagus. It is due to soil organisms, principally *Rhizoctonia* species. In advanced cases there are sunken areas on the spears, but usually the spear is cut before the disease advances very far, so that only the rust-colored spots are present. This disease is most prevalent in fields that have a high water table or recently have received a heavy irrigation. To prevent the condition, the soil should be kept from becoming too moist above the crowns. Good drainage is essential at all times.

References

1. Bouquet, A. G. B.: Asparagus growing and management, *Ore. Agr. Ext. Cir. 465*, 7 p., (Mimeo.) 1945.
2. Hanna, G. C.: A comparison of performance of green and white asparagus, *Amer. Soc. for Hort. Sci. Proc. 37:* 770–772, 1940.
3. Hanna, G. C.: Asparagus production in California, *Calif. Agr. Exp. Sta. Cir. 91*, 23 p., 1947.
4. Hanna, G. C.: New asparagus, *Calif. Agr. 3:* (No. 3) 15, 1949.

5. Jones, H. A.: Spacing studies with male and female asparagus plants, *Die Gartenbauwissenschaft 6:* 465–477, 1932.

GROUP C. MINOR CROPS

Chives (*Allium schoenoprasum*) are small, bushy and onion-like, and are grown for the leaves which are used in salads, garnishing, or for flavoring stews and soups. It is propagated either from seed or by the division of a cluster of plants. The plants grow about 1 foot high, and, though perennial, the clumps should be replanted every 3 or 4 years. Climatic requirements are similar to other crops in the onion group. Enough chives for home use require only a couple of square feet of space, and usually are grown near the kitchen in a border or flower bed.

Garlic (*Allium sativum*) is propagated vegetatively by dividing the bulb into separate cloves, each of which will produce a bulb. No seed is formed. Most of the garlic is produced near Hollister, California, with production also in Texas and Louisiana. Climatic requirements are similar to those for onions, or a little cooler. Limited demand and slightly specialized practises, mostly cultural, tend to limit areas growing the crop. There are early (White or Mexican) and late (Pink or Italian) garlic varieties.

One of the handicaps in growing garlic is the fact that the cloves usually are hand planted, requiring 55 hours of labor per acre after the cloves have been separated. Machine planting is used; but by this procedure the cloves are not spaced evenly, and those that fall on their side do not make well-shaped bulbs. The cloves in an irrigated area are planted 2 rows per bed and about 4 inches apart in the row. Early garlic is planted in November to December, and late garlic about a month later. Culture of garlic is similar to onions as is the harvesting. Maturity is determined by the tops falling over. The bulbs are dried in windrows. A small portion of the crop is plaited in braids, leaving the tops on the plants with about 50 bulbs per string. With the bulk of the crop the tops are removed, as in the case of onions, and the crop is sold in sacks. Usually the bulb is broken into cloves before it is sold at retail. This operation may be facilitated by the use of compressed air as is the case in getting the bulbs separated into cloves for planting. The edible part is an enlarged leaf petiole.

References

1. Beattie, J. H.: Production of garlic, *U.S.D.A. Leaflet No. 138,* 5 p., 1937.
2. McCallum, R. D., and J. E. Knott: Growing and handling garlic in California, *Calif. Agr. Ext. Cir. 84,* 18 p., 1942.
3. Bouquet, A. G. B.: Garlic culture and marketing, *Ore. Agr. Ext. Cir. 399,* 3 p., (Mimeo.) 1943.

Leek (*Allium porrum*) produces a sheath of leaves an inch or more in thickness, is mild in flavor, and does not form a bulb like the onion. The leaves are flat and solid. The lower part of the leaves are blanched with earth and are eaten raw or used for flavoring in cooked foods. The blanched portion should be 4 to 6 inches long. Culture is similar to that of onions and requires 5 months. Large American Flag is a common variety. Leek is usually a fall crop and may be stored.

Perennial onions (*Allium cepa*) include Egyptian or tree onion; multiplier, or potato onion; and shallots. They are propagated vegetatively. All of these are grown for bunch onions and differ mainly as to the part of the plant used in propagation. Egyptian Tree onion plants divide at the base and also produce small bulbs on the stems in the fall. Either may be used for propagation. Both multiplier and shallots produce mother bulbs which divide into segments and may be planted to produce bunch onions. These frequently are grown as annuals in the cool season; their culture is similar to that of onions, except that dirt may be used to blanch the leaves near the stem.

Reference

Montelaro, Joseph and E. C. Tims: Louisiana shallots, *La. Agr. Ext. Ser. Pub. 1051*, 12 p., 1950.

Chapter 18

Group D.   Warm Season Crops
Intolerant of Frost

Group D. Adapted to 65° to 80° F. Intolerant of frost

SWEET CORN

Botany. The Gramineae or grass family furnishes us with many food plants, particularly the grains. Sweet corn (*Zea mays*) is a member of this family and the fruit or grain is eaten when immature. The roots are usually shallow and fibrous in nature, particularly in early varieties of sweet corn. There are also brace roots which arise along the stem above the ground. The stems grow rapidly and also there are produced secondary stems from the lower nodes, called "suckers". The leaves have a long, flat blade; are parallel-veined; and typically monocotyledonous in nature. The plant is monoecious, with stamens (tassel) and pistils (ear) borne in separate flowers on the same plant. This characteristic makes possible the economical production of hybrid seed corn. The pollen is spread by the wind as well as gravity, thus cross-pollination most commonly occurs. Self-pollination may be as low as 1 per cent. Pollen is produced in large amounts, so there are many thousand pollen grains for each kernel on the ear of corn.

Origin and History. Both field and sweet corn were first used by the American Indians. Eighth century records from Guatemala indicate that corn was being used at that time and both white and yellow corn were known. Corn was used for bread making in 1250 A.D. Columbus was the first European to see corn in 1492 when he visited Cuba. There are many Indian legends about the origin of corn.

In 1779 General Sullivan conducted an expedition against the Indians along the Susquehanna River and some of his soldiers found fields of sweet corn. Ears for seed were brought home by the soldiers and by 1832 sweet corn was being grown in many gardens. Soon after the middle of the 19th century sweet corn was grown commonly and in 1866 a seedsman listed 12 varieties.

Producing Areas and Value. Due to sweet corn's perishable nature it is generally grown close to consuming areas or preserved by canning. However, in the last few years some sweet corn has been shipped considerable distances by the use of adequate icing. In recent years, corn has been preserved by freezing both on the cob and the cut kernels. The 1940–1951 statistical data are given below:

Sweet Corn for Market

	Acreage	Ears Per Acre	Production 1000 Ears	Price Per 1000 Ears Dollars	Farm Value Dollars
United States	61,708	5,070	312,874	$23.53	$7,365,000
New York	28,900	5,225	151,029	22.13	3,343,000
New Jersey	21,833	4,904	107,075	26.43	2,831,000
Pennsylvania	10,975	4,990	54,770	21.72	1,190,000

Sweet Corn for Processing

	Acreage	Tons Per Acre	Production Tons	Price Per Ton Dollars	Farm Value Dollars
United States	451,413	2.52	1,140,683	$18.23	$20,801,000
Wisconsin	79,500	2.44	194,475	17.80	3,463,000
Minnesota	74,508	2.86	213,225	15.78	3,365,000
Illinois	64,966	2.64	171,941	18.37	3,160,000
Iowa	37,083	2.44	90,525	16.50	1,494,000
Maryland	38,200	2.14	81,950	17.81	1,460,000

(Farm value, other Western states: Oregon, $863,000; Washington, $859,000; Idaho, $505,000; Utah, $270,000.)

The most active harvest season for some of the important market states is: New York, July to September; New Jersey, July and August; Pennsylvania, August and September.

Food Value. Sweet corn is found in group 4—the least efficient on a food-production basis. As corn matures it becomes higher in energy and poorer in quality because of increased starch content and tougher kernels. The edible portion of corn as purchased is the lowest of any of our vegetables, or 38 per cent. Sweet corn's popularity is due to its appetizing taste. Sweet corn contains 73.9 per cent water and the food value per 100 gm. of edible portion is energy, 108 calories; protein, 3.7 gm.; calcium, 9 mg.; vitamin A, 100 I.U.; ascorbic acid, 9 mg.; thiamine, 0.17 mg.; riboflavin, 0.06 mg.; and niacin, 1.7 mg. The following data give the relative nutrient rank of sweet corn.

Pound, rank 22: Energy, 8; niacin, 10.
Acre, rank 26: Nutrient rank is 11 or lower.
Man-hour, rank 16: Energy, 6; niacin, 6; thiamine, 7; protein, 8.

Varieties. Types of sweet corn for human food include those with yellow, white and purplish-black (Black Mexican) kernels at the immature stage. The number of kernel rows in most varieties is even, but a few have a zigzag arrangement of the kernels (Country Gentleman). Some flint corns are used for early production because the seed will germinate at a lower soil temperature (Trucker's Favorite). Most of our present sweet corn is grown from hybrid seed in spite of the higher cost of the seed. New sweet corn varieties are being introduced so the following varieties are only typical of those being used at the present time. Varieties are arranged according to time of maturity with the earliest varieties given first.

Spancross. Hybrid, yellow, stalks 5½ feet; ears 6½ inches; 10 to 12 rows; resistant to wilt.

Marcross. Popular early yellow hybrid; stalks 5 feet; ears 7½ inches; 10 to 14 rows; ears long, plump, tapered at tips.

Carmelcross. Hybrid, yellow, stalks 5½ feet; ears 7 inches; 12 to 14 rows.

Golden Bantam. Old favorite, open-pollinated variety; yellow; stalks 4½ to 5 feet; ears 6 to 7 inches; 8-rowed; good quality. There are several improved strains listed by seedsmen and sometimes the modern types have more than eight rows of kernels.

Golden Cross Bantam. Hybrid; yellow; stalks 6½ to 7 ft.; ears 8 inches, 12 to 14 rows; resistant to wilt. Most of the acreage is planted to this variety. The first hybrid sweet corn was introduced about 1933. There are many strains of this variety including the T strain as well as the F-M Cross which is slightly earlier, shorter ear, and has 2 more rows of corn.

Seneca Chief. High quality hybrid for freezing and market; stalks 6½ feet; ears 9 inches; 12 rows; with deep narrow kernels.

Ioana. Hybrid, yellow; stalks 6½ feet; ears 8 inches; 12 to 14 rows; resistant to wilt. This variety seems to yield better than Golden Cross Bantam in a cool climate.

Climatic Requirements. Temperature, moisture, light and length of day conditions for optimum growth of sweet corn are similar to those of field corn. Best yields are obtained with average monthly temperatures of 68° to 72° F. Varieties differ as to temperature requirements; some field corn varieties produce ears at 60° F. and some even near 50° F. Growth of the plant is favored by warm temperatures which is desirable until a week before harvest. Cool weather during harvest greatly increases the period of picking good-quality corn. High temperatures cause rapid change of sugar to starch, with impaired quality. Sweet corn is not tolerant of frost or prolonged exposure near freezing.

Corn is grown under a wide range of climatic conditions and is grown below sea level[8] and at elevations of 12,000 feet. This crop is grown as far north as a latitude of 58° and south to a latitude of 40° in the Southern Hemisphere. Corn is variable in its adaptation to different climates and success depends upon having the proper variety. This characteristic is not important when areas are compared within a few degrees of latitude, but are important when corn is to be grown in a distant area. Hybrid seed corn varieties of the Middle West do not produce satisfactorily in Central America. A variety of field corn in an extreme northern climate may be 2 feet tall and mature in 70 days while another variety grown in the Gulf states may be 10 to 12 feet tall and require 190 days to mature. Corn is affected by length of day, but the response is not so pronounced as with some other plants. Part of the above climatic adaptations may be explained by the effect of length of day. The period of emergence to flowering is reduced by short days and increased by long days.

Soil. Sweet corn is grown on most soil types—sandy loams are favored for an early crop and heavier types of soil for the main or canning crop. Corn makes a very rapid growth beginning with the appearance of the tassels. Under such conditions the plant needs an ample supply of water and nutrients. Corn also is sensitive to poor soil aeration.

Fertilizer. Sweet corn responds to fertilization in many areas of the West. California growers use 160 pounds of nitrogen for the early crop. The late crop needs a smaller amount or 80 to 100 pounds. In some areas like Coachella Valley, the Delta, some soil types in Kern and Tulare Counties as well as the coastal area of Los Angeles County, the use of 100 pounds of phosphoric acid is desirable particularly on the early crop. Phosphorus should be applied in addition to the nitrogen. Ten to 12 tons of barnyard manure or 4 to 5 tons of poultry manure can be used to replace part of the above fertilizers and should be worked into the soil before planting. Oregon growers should use either green manure crop or animal manures plus 300 to 500 pounds of 4-12-4 or 4-16-4. The commercial fertilizer should be put in bands two and one-half inches from the row and below the seed level. Utah recommends the use of 30 to 50 pounds of nitrogen and 60 to 100 pounds of phosphoric acid per acre along with ample soil moisture. In the Walla Walla area of Washington the use of 80 pounds of nitrogen was found desirable. Western Washington growers should use 400 to 500 pounds of 5-15-10 without manure and 125 to 150 pounds of treble superphosphate with 6 to 10 tons of manure. Buckley loams and soils of the Chehalis, Newberg, and Wapato series need 400 to 600 pounds of a 5-10-10.

Planting and Spacing. The crop is planted soon after the last average frost date in spring. Planting dates for some western states are:

California: Coachella Valley, January to March; interior valleys, March and April also June and July; south coast, March to July; north coast, April to July.

Idaho: Late April to June 15.

New Mexico: May and June, and in April in early areas.

Oregon: Late April to June 15.

Washington: Western, May; eastern, after killing frosts.

Utah: Late April to June 15.

Rows are two and one-half to three feet apart with plants 10 to 14 inches apart in the row. With hill planting there are 3 to 4 plants per hill, and they are spaced the same distance as the rows. On poor soils or those lacking in soil moisture the plants should be spaced farther apart. Early, small varieties are planted closer together than late varieties. Seed is planted one and one-half to two inches deep. Some 8 to 15 pounds are used per acre.

Protection against both soil and seed-borne organisms can be secured by treating sweet corn seed with Semesan Jr., at three and one-half ounces per 100 pounds of seed. Disease-free seed usually will give a satisfactory stand without treatment except in heavily infested soil, or in soil excessively wet after planting. Arason and Spergon sometimes are preferred for home garden use.

Better pollination is obtained when the corn is planted in 4 or more parallel rows rather than 1 long, single row. Canning sweet corn seed sometimes is graded for size and the different sizes are planted separately. This procedure increases the evenness of maturity and thus gives greater yields. Large-sized seed tends to produce slightly greater yields.

Irrigation. Sweet corn makes very rapid growth during the time of maturing the crop. There is usually insufficient water stored in 2 feet of soil to mature a maximum crop. In experiments performed at Davis, California, large increases in yield were obtained from irrigation. A lack of sufficient soil moisture is shown by a "rolling" (Fig. 72) of the leaves and this is sometimes evident on moist plots at noon or soon after. The nonirrigated plots produced smaller plants on which the ears were short and poorly filled out, as well as producing some plants without ears. Eighteen inches of water are used in most areas in California. Irrigation may start with applications every 3 weeks and become more frequent until there is 1 each week, just before harvest. Late varieties are deeper-rooted and thus obtain water from more soil.

Suckering. There arise, from the lower nodes of the plant near the soil surface, secondary stems called suckers. Growers have felt that if these are removed by pulling 2 or 3 times ("suckering"), yield, size of ear, and earliness would be improved. Data obtained in the East, and in California[9], indicate that little or no benefit is obtained from this practise which requires

Fig. 72. Rolling of sweet corn leaves—an indication of wilting from insufficient soil moisture.

35 hours of labor per acre. In a test made in 1942, the nonsuckered plants produced 1.3 pounds per plant with the ears averaging 0.46 of a pound. Plants suckered weekly produced 1.0 pound per plant, and the ears averaged 0.44 pound. Suckering is an exceptional case where a common farm practise cannot be justified by experimental results.

Chemical and Other Changes in the Ear. As an ear of sweet corn matures, there occur several chemical and other changes. The outer covering of the kernel, or pericarp, becomes tougher as it matures. The contents of the kernel are referred to as in the premilk, milk, early-dough, and dough stages. The earliest stage, or premilk[3], is highest (6.3 per cent) in sugar and lowest in starch (3.3 per cent). The dough or more mature stage contains 3.2 per cent sugar, and 21.6 per cent starch. Sweet corn should be harvested at the milk stage to obtain a product which is sweet, with tender kernels. Temperature[4] affects the length of time corn is in good edible condition—thus at 60° F. the corn will be in good eating maturity for 5 days, and at 85° for only one and one-half days.

Harvesting. The determination of the proper stage for harvesting individual ears of corn is difficult when the husks must be left intact. The milk stage can be determined by the slight drying of the silk, and the plumpness of the ear when grasped with the hand. The husks may be pulled back on a few ears to test the accuracy of the picker's judgment (Fig. 73). When the husks are pulled from the ear, maturity may be told from the color of the kernels and by pushing the thumbnail into the kernel. The stage of maturity is determined by whether the exudate is milky or doughy and with yellow

Fig. 73. The appearance of sweet corn at different maturities. Immature on the left and overmature on the right.

varieties of corn there is a change towards a more yellow color at maturity. The ear is removed by a downward pull and twist. The harvest season may be prolonged by planting corn several times during the season at two-week intervals.

Storage. Sweet corn deteriorates in storage slightly at 31° to 32° F. and very rapidly at higher temperatures. Humidity should be 90 per cent and sweet corn rarely will keep in a marketable condition for more than 3 to 5 days. Some growers ship corn and resort to precooling to prevent the rapid loss of sugars. Ears should be cooled to below 35° F. Both the use of package and top ice are recommended in order to keep the corn temperature as near to 32° F. as possible. The demand in the cities for fresh sweet corn causes growers to ship or market corn from distant areas even though the good qualities of the vegetable rarely are preserved. Sweet corn stored at 32° F. for 24 hours loses 8 per cent[2] of its sugar, while corn stored at 86° F. for the same length of time loses 50 per cent of its sugar.

Quality Characteristics for the Retail Buyer. Quality can be determined best by pulling back the husk and examining the kernels. A good ear of corn is one that has a cob well filled with bright, plump, milky kernels that are just firm enough to offer slight resistance to pressure. The husk should be fresh and green.

Dry, yellowed, or straw-colored husks are an indication of age or damage. Corn heats rapidly when packed for shipment. Heating causes the yellowing and drying-out of the husk as well as the toughening, discoloration, loss of flavor, and shriveling of the kernels. Immature corn is unsatisfactory. The kernels on cobs of immature corn are very small and very soft, and when cooked they lack flavor. Worm injury is not serious when confined to the tips, since the injured portion usually can be removed with little waste, but it is more objectionable if it occurs along the side of the ear.

Insects: *Seed-corn Maggot* (*Hylemya cilicrara*). Might be controlled by BHC seed treatment.

Corn Aphid (*Aphis maidis*). A dark green aphid sometimes occurs abundantly on the leaves and tassels. This pest seldom is damaging enough to require attention on sweet corn. Nicotine or tetraethylpyrophosphate dusts could be applied for very serious outbreaks.

Corn Earworm (*Heliothis armigera*). The corn earworm is a very destructive pest attacking the ears of sweet corn. The worms may be abundant on any planting, though usually they are more serious late in the season than early. The night flying moths normally lay the eggs on the silks. The eggs hatch in 3 to 5 days and the young worms work their way down the silk channel. Sometimes before the silks appear, the eggs are laid on the tassels from where the worms later migrate to the ears, entering through the side. In areas where these side worms are a problem, 1 or 2 dustings with 10 per cent DDT starting when the tassels first appear usually will give control. Apply 25 to 30 pounds of dust per acre.

For worms that enter through the silk channel (Fig. 74), 75 to 90 per cent control can be obtained by careful injection of a highly refined mineral oil into the silk channel at the time the silks begin to dry and change color. This is usually between 5 and 7 days after the silks appear. An oil mixture containing 0.2 per cent pyrethrins is more effective than oil alone. In recent years a mixture of oil and DDT (1 per cent) has been proved to be more effective and less expensive than the pyrethrum mixture. The oil should have viscosity of 100 to 150 and an unsulfonated residue of about 99 per cent. A plunger type oil-can commonly is used for injecting the oil. The injector should be adjusted to deliver about 1 cubic centimeter (cc) (one-fourth teaspoon) of oil per ear with pyrethrum or six-tenths cc to seven-tenths cc with DDT. Only one application per ear is required, but usually it is necessary to go through a field 2 or 3 times at 5 to 7 day intervals in order to treat the majority of the ears at the proper stage. On the first trip the ears treated should be marked with lamp-black or paint to distinguish them on the second time through the field. Applications made too early result in poor pollination of the kernels near the tip of the ear and those made too late may not prevent worm damage. From 2 to 4 gallons of oil are required per acre. One worker can treat one-fourth to one-half acre of corn per day.

Fig. 74. The corn earworm not only likes corn, but also will attack tomatoes.

General field dusting with DDT or similar insecticides for the control of worms that enter the silk channel has given variable results. Sometimes 2 to 3 applications of a 10 per cent dust at the rate of 25 pounds per acre starting when the silks first appear and repeated at intervals of 5 to 7 days will give fair control when the worm population is low.

Removing the silks after fertilization of the ear is complete will give some degree of worm control when the worm population is low.

Wireworms. See page 163 for discussion.

Diseases: *Bacterial Wilt, Stewart's Disease (Phytomonas stewartii).* The plant gradually wilts, beginning with the lower leaves. A cross section of the stem shows a yellow slime oozing from the fibrous vessels. Golden Cross Bantam is resistant to this disease. To control, destroy infected plants and do not grow on infected land.

Ear Mold, Pink Rot (Diplodia zeae, Fusarium moniliforme, and Others).

Several fungi, particularly *Fusarium moniliforme,* may develop on ears in the field. The ears become moldy and the kernels may split open and turn a pinkish color which ruins the corn for market. This trouble usually develops only in heavily irrigated fields during periods of high temperatures. Regulation of planting schedules, avoiding over irrigation, and prompt harvesting constitute the main control measures.

Smut. Two fungus diseases called smut attack sweet corn. Boil smut (*Ustilago maydis*), the most common, causes large, fleshy, irregular swellings on the stems, ears or tassels. Head smut (*Spacelotheca reiliana*) stunts the plant and transforms the tassels and ears into masses of dusty spores. The spores live over in the soil. Seed treatment is not effective for either disease. It is advisable to remove diseased plants or parts from the field and destroy them, preferably by burning.

Virus Diseases. Two virus diseases have caused losses on sweet corn in the San Joaquin Valley. Stunt, which is spread by leaf hoppers, causes stunting and bending of the plants. Western Cucumber Mosaic spread by aphids, causes purple blotches on the leaf sheaths, leaves, and husks. Sometimes both virus diseases occur on the same plant.

References

1. Andersen, E. Milton, Ethelwyn B. Wilcox, Delbert A. Greenwood, and L. H. Pollard: Sweet corn varieties for commercial processing, *Utah Agr. Exp. Sta. Mimeo. Series No. 343,* 5 p., 1948.
2. Appleman, C. O., and J. M. Arthur: Carbohydrate metabolism in green sweet corn during storage at different temperatures, *Jour. Agr. Res. 17:* 137–152, 1919.
3. Appleman, C. O.: Reliability of the nail test for predicting the chemical composition of green sweet corn, *Jour. Agr. Res. 21:* 817–820, 1921.
4. Appleman, C. O.: Forecasting the date and duration of best canning stage for sweet corn, *Md. Agr. Exp. Sta. Bull. 254:* 47–56, 1923.
5. Baur, Karl, John F. Moore, and Loyd L. Stitt: Growing sweet corn in Western Washington, *W. Wash. Agr. Exp. Sta. Cir. 96,* 5 p., (Mimeo.) 1950.
6. Bouquet, A. G. B.: Growing sweet corn for market and manufacture, *Ore. Agr. Ext. Bull. 706,* 11 p., 1950.
7. Davis, G. B. and D. Curtis Mumford: Cost of producing sweet corn in the Willamette Valley, Oregon, *Ore. Agr. Exp. Sta. Bull. 465,* 23 p., 1949.
8. Jenkins, Merle T.: Influence of climate and weather on growth of corn, *U.S.D.A. Yrbk. Climate and Man,* p. 308–321, 1941.
9. MacGillivray, John H., P. A. Minges, Bernarr J. Hall, Hilton B. Rich-

ardson, and D. N. Wright: California sweet-corn suckering studies, *Amer. Soc. Hort. Sci. Proc. 47:* 378–382, 1946.

10. MacGillivray, John H., P. A. Minges, H. B. Richardson: Sweet corn production in California, *Calif. Agr. Ext. Multolith,* 10 p., 1949.

SNAP BEAN

Botany. Snap beans (*Phaseolus vulgaris*) and peas are both members of Leguminosae Family. The beans climb by means of twining stems, but some are bush types like many of our garden varieties. The edible part of the plant are the immature beans and the fleshy pod which encloses them. Snap beans differ from field beans by possessing a thicker walled pod which is relatively free of bast fibres in the earlier stages of development. The roots penetrate to a depth of 3 or 4 feet and may have nodules in which live nitrogen fixing bacteria. The leaves are three-lobed. The flower has 10 stamens and these and the pistil are so arranged that the flowers are pollinated rarely by insects. The pods vary in color but green or wax (yellow) snap beans are grown most commonly as a vegetable. The seed color of beans varies a great deal and some varieties may be identified by this characteristic.

Origin and History. Early explorers in America found beans being grown over most of the new world. The Indians were growing beans of many colors and frequently planted them among the corn so the vines could twine around the corn stalks. Most early explorers reported on the types of beans they found, and the crop was grown generally in all the countries from Canada to Chile. Some of the early explorers referred to this crop as Indian beans and they are still a staple food among these people from Mexico south. Other species of legumes were grown in the Old World, but soon after the discovery of America kidney beans were grown generally in many areas of the Old World.

Producing Areas. Snap beans are marketed in important volume both as a fresh and canned product. The 1940–1951 statistical data are given on p. 303.

The most important harvest season for some of the important market states as well as those in the West are: Florida, January 20 to March 15, also April, also November and December; New York, July to September; California, May and June, also September 15 to November 15; North Carolina, June, also August, also October; New Jersey, June to August, also September 15 to October 15; Colorado, July 20 to September 10.

Food Value. Snap beans, sometimes called string beans, are placed in group 3 on food-production efficiency. The crop is used as food at various stages; the beans may be just appearing in the pod or they may be almost mature. Beans form an important food particularly the dry seed. This is also true of other legume seeds. The high protein content of the dry legume seed makes them essential for diets where meat is available in limited quantities.

Snap Beans for Market

	Acreage	Bushels* Per Acre	Production Bushels	Price Per Bushel Dollars	Farm Value Dollars
United States	174,541	98	17,087,000	$2.04	$34,924,000
Florida	65,391	96	6,272,000	2.24	14,084,000
New York	14,500	147	2,137,000	1.95	4,182,000
California	8,000	190	1,521,000	2.39	3,646,000
North Carolina	12,412	84	1,043,000	1.62	1,699,000
New Jersey	9,283	97	905,000	1.66	1,510,000

(Farm value, other Western states: Colorado, $274,000.)
* Approximately 30 pounds.

Snap Beans for Processing

	Acreage	Tons Per Acre	Production Tons	Price Per Ton Dollars	Farm Value Dollars
United States	118,273	1.79	211,860	$97.36	$20,627,000
Oregon	4,825	6.86	33,125	109.40	3,624,000
New York	18,541	1.65	30,700	112.18	3,444,000
Wisconsin	10,775	1.44	15,516	93.70	1,454,000
Florida	9,875	1.53	15,159	93.67	1,420,000
Maryland	11,116	1.42	15,858	87.08	1,381,000

(Farm value, other Western states: Washington, $903,000; California, $723,000; Colorado, $305,000; Utah, $177,000.)

Snap beans contain 88.9 per cent water and food value per 100 gm. of edible portion is energy, 42 calories; protein, 2.4 gm.; calcium, 65 mg.; vitamin A, 500 I.U.; ascorbic acid, 12 mg.; thiamine, 0.09 mg.; riboflavin, 0.11 mg.; and niacin, 0.64 mg. The following data give the relative nutrient rank of snap beans.

Pound, rank 5: Calcium, 2; protein, 5; energy, 9; thiamine, 10; riboflavin, 10.

Acre, rank 19: Calcium, 10.

Man-hour, rank 30: Nutrient rank is 11 or lower.

Varieties. There are both pole and bush types of snap beans. Varieties may be selected which have green, yellow (wax), and green-splashed with red, pods (horticultural variety). The last is used primarily as a shelled bean with bush and pole types available. Scarlet runner (*Phaseolus coccineus*) also is used as a snap bean. The most common market types are the green bush and pole beans.

Blue Lake. Widely used in the West for processing both freezing and canning; pole type; pods 5½ to 6½ inches long, ⅜ to ½ inch wide, round to oval, medium green, stringless when young; seed oval, white. There are several strains available such as, Early Blue Lake, Blue Lake No. 65, and Stringless Blue Lake B-5.

Black Valentine. Used for shipping and local market. Plant bush type but large, and prolific; pods 6¾ inches long, ⅜ inch wide, oval, nearly straight, dark green; seeds oval, solid black.

Kentucky Wonder. Popular pole bean; available as either green or wax pod, white or brown seed; strong climber, hardy, prolific; large pods, 9 inches long, ⅜ inch wide, occur in clusters, curved and indented; has a pleasing flavor. Morse's 191 is a white seeded type and rust resistant.

Pencil Pod Wax. Used in home gardens; plant large, of bush type; prolific; pods yellow, round, slightly curved, 6 inches long and ⅜ inch wide; excellent quality; seed oblong, solid black.

Stringless Greenpod (Tendergreen). Of general use; plant large of bush type; prolific; pods 5¾ inches long, ⅜ inch in width, round, meaty, and stringless; color dark green; seed oblong, purple mottling on buff with brownish cast (Fig. 75).

Climatic Requirements. Snap beans are similar to dry beans as to climatic conditions, but the bush types require a shorter growing season. Snap beans are not concentrated in a few areas but due to the short growing season required for immature beans they are grown generally throughout the United States. Because of the competitive and speculative character of some plantings, beans sometimes are grown part of the season below the optimum range of 60° to 70° F. Hot, dry winds damage the flowers and warm wet weather encourages destructive diseases. Optimum seed germination occurs in soil temperatures of 65° to 85° F.

Soil. Beans are grown on the entire range of soils. Lighter soils usually lack fertility, but through their ability to encourage the fixing of nitrogen, beans may be profitable on lighter soils. Soils close to sandy loam and with good drainage are the most desirable. The cotyledons of the seed must push through the soil during germination, hence a friable soil is desirable. Organic soils are used in the South and the West.

Fertilizer. This crop also is sensitive to fertilizer placed with the seed, so it should be applied 3 inches on either side and 3 inches below the seed. California recommends the use of 300 to 500 pounds of ammonium sulfate on the lighter soils with about half this amount on the heavier soils along the coast. Fertilizer may be applied in bands or broadcast before seeding. If

Fig. 75. The Stringless Greenpod variety of snap bean is a bush type. (Courtesy, Associated Seed Growers, Inc.)

growth is slow and the foliage is yellow a side-dressing with nitrates during the growing season may be beneficial. Oregon growers supplement manure and green manures with fertilizers having a 1-3-1 or 1-4-2 ratio. The fertilizer is applied in bands 2 inches or more from the seed row at planting time at the rate of 250 to 300 pounds. Sometimes Ammo-phos 16–20 is broadcast prior to planting. In Western Washington 500 to 600 pounds of 5-15-10 is applied on mineral soils and the same amounts of a 5-15-20 fertilizer is used on muck soils. In Eastern Washington on irrigated soils 40 pounds of nitrogen are added where 10 tons of manure are used or 60 pounds of nitrogen and 40 pounds of phosporic acid are used without manure.

Nitrogen Fixation. This crop is a legume, and bacteria forming nodules on the roots will fix nitrogen from the air. The evidence, that the presence of these bacteria will increase yields, is not as good as with peas. The bean group of bacteria (Culture VI) should be used for inoculation.

Planting and Spacing. Commercial areas are planted as follows:

California: South coast, February to August; central coast, March to July; San Joaquin Valley, April and August; Coachella and Imperial valleys, February to March and August.

Colorado: Denver and Pueblo areas, May 15 to June.

Idaho: May to June 15 (bush).

Oregon: May to June 15, (bush types) to July 15.

Utah: May 15 to June 15 (bush) and May 15 to June 1 (pole).

Washington: Western, May (pole types mostly); eastern, after danger from frost, and in July to escape curly-top disease.

The beans are planted 2 inches deep. Bush beans are planted in rows 28 to 36 inches apart and sometimes may be planted 2 rows per bed. Plants are spaced 2 to 4 inches apart with 60 pounds of seed used per acre. Pole bean rows are 4 to 5 feet apart. The seed may be planted in hills or in a single row. The seed requirement is 25 pounds per acre. Pole beans are supported on a trellis or individual poles per hill.

Some garden varieties of beans are benefited by seed treatment with Spergon or Arasan, especially when they are planted in wet soils or under low temperatures. Spergon is used at the rate of 50 ounces per 100 pounds of seed, and Arasan at 3 ounces per 100 pounds of seed. Spergon is preferred if bacterial inoculation is to be used.

Irrigation. Snap bean roots are usually in the top 4 feet of soil which provides a fairly good sized soil moisture reservoir. They are a rapid growing plant; therefore care should be used to keep plants growing without any darkening of the foliage, which indicates a slowing down of growth. Irrigation treatments at Davis, California increased yields about 200 per cent and also increased the size of individual bean pods. The spring crop receives some rain but needs a supplementary 12 inches of water which may be applied in about 3 applications. The fall crop and pole beans should receive a minimum of 18 inches of water. Oregon growers use 12 to 15 inches of water during the growing season.

Supporting and Training Pole Beans. The plants are supported on a trellis made with posts, wire, and string; or in some cases with individual poles at each hill, which are 1 inch square and 6 to 8 feet long. In the case of the trellis method posts which are at least 3 inches square and 9 feet long are driven into the ground at the end of the rows. Similar posts or slightly smaller ones are placed about 10 feet apart in the row. A wire is stretched between the posts at the top (No. 12) and another wire is placed near the bottom of the post (No. 14). Sometimes No. 8 crosswire is used for support instead of stakes. A string is tied to the top wire at the beginning of the row, and passed under the bottom wire and back over the top wire, continuing the full length of the row. The string should be spaced 12 inches apart and No. 4 ply cotton twine is used. Every 5 feet or so a half hitch is taken with string to prevent the row from falling if the string breaks. Sometimes the string is fastened to the bean plant rather than the bottom wire. The vines grow counter clockwise and attach themselves to the string and the few plants which do not should be moved to the support by hand.

Cost of Production. Oregon grows a considerable acreage of Blue Lake snap beans for processing.[7] These beans are of excellent quality and it is not common in all states to use a pole bean for this purpose. Table 36 reports a study made in 1946 of the cost of producing this crop. During this year most growers were paid the following prices for their crop: No. 1 grade, $150.00 per ton; No. 2, $135.00; No. 3, $90.00; and no payment was made for culls. During this study the cost of production varied from $80.00 per ton for the grower with the lowest cost to $200.00 per ton for the high cost producer. The average cost for 67 growers was $104.60 per ton, and the average yield was 7.9 tons per acre. There were 3 factors largely responsible for the variation in per acre cost which were as follows: "(a) Tons of beans produced per acre; (b) the hours of labor used per acre, excluding picking; and (c) the acres per bean yard (field)." Picking labor was an important item and absorbed 53 per cent of the total cost or $434.00. The total labor require-

Table 36*

COST OF PRODUCING POLE BEANS IN WILLAMETTE VALLEY, OREGON.
(67 GROWERS, 9.3 ACRES PER FIELD, AVERAGE YIELD 7.9 TONS)

Item	Cost Per Acre	Cost Per Ton	Per Cent of Total
Operator and family labor†	$102.10	$13.00	12.4
Hired labor (excluding picking)	115.20	14.60	14.0
Picking labor (all hired)	434.00	55.20	52.7
TOTAL LABOR COST	$651.30	$82.80	79.1
Irrigation (excluding labor)	32.20	4.00	3.9
Tractor	7.00	.90	0.9
Truck and automobile	22.80	2.90	2.8
Other equipment	7.70	1.00	0.9
Horse work	2.30	.30	0.3
TOTAL EQUIPMENT AND HORSE COST	$72.00	$9.10	8.8
Bean seed	4.90	.60	0.6
String and nails	10.70	1.40	1.3
Fertilizer and manure	21.60	2.70	2.5
Dust	3.20	.40	0.4
Cover crop seed	2.30	.30	0.3
Bean tickets, etc.	2.10	.30	0.3
TOTAL SUPPLY COST	$44.80	5.70	5.4
Yard equipment (depreciation and interest)	20.90	2.70	2.5
Buildings (repairs, depreciation and interest)	4.70	.60	0.6
Liability insurance and office expense	8.70	1.10	1.1
Taxes	3.20	.40	0.4
Interest on land at 4 per cent	17.30	2.20	2.1
TOTAL COSTS	$822.90	$104.60	100.0

* Courtesy, Oregon State College, 1948.
† Includes overhead labor of operator.

ment was 824 hours or 19 pounds were produced with 1 hour of labor. Picking of the snap beans required almost 595 hours. Growing of pole snap beans gives a poor seasonal use of labor with 60 per cent required during August and 83 per cent during July, August, and September. The labor study made in California during 1943 indicated that processed pole beans were produced with 1 hour of labor per 20 pounds of beans. In the case of market bush beans the production per hour was only 15 pounds. The lower rate for the bush beans can be accounted for by the lower yield per acre. The Colorado Extension Service[3] has made a study of the most efficient methods of picking snap beans.

Harvesting. Absence of strings is an important factor in the quality of snap beans. Picking the beans at an immature stage insures tenderness but also decreases total yield. Snap beans are usable at various degrees of maturity. Most frequently the stage used for picking is when the beans are one-third to one-half grown. In canning they are hand-picked when the beans are small. This gives a more uniformly shaped pod, but requires more frequent and careful picking. Some people enjoy beans shelled, after they have reached full size but are still succulent.

During good weather the pods will be ready for picking in 2 to 3 weeks after blooming. Bush beans are picked 2 to 3 times and pole beans 5 to 7 times. The individual pods are picked by hand, so excessive vine growth slows down the pickers. Intervals between pickings should be 3 to 4 days in the summer and 7 to 10 days in the cooler part of the year. The best yields are obtained from the late spring and summer plantings.

Processing contracts usually specify sizes of pods for the Blue Lake or similar varieties. A premium is paid for the smaller pods. Pod size[1] is expressed in sixty-fourths of an inch. No. 1 pods are $14/_{64}$ to $21/_{64}$; No. 2 from $21/_{64}$ to $23/_{64}$; No. 3 from $24/_{64}$ to $26/_{64}$; and No. 4 $27/_{64}$ or more in diameter (Fig. 76). A general rule is to pick the vines clean of all beans the size of a lead pencil or larger. Picking should be performed carefully to prevent injury to the bean pod, vine, or adjacent blossoms. An experienced picker should average about 25 pounds per hour with an average for all age groups of 18 pounds. Pods in which there are only 1 or 2 seeds, hence are misshapen, sometimes are referred to as "polliwogs."

Storage. Snap beans are stored for relatively short periods of 1 to 2 weeks at 34° to 40° F. and humidity should not be lower than 85 per cent to prevent wilting. Beans should be stored in containers which will facilitate ventilation or air circulation. When beans and containers are packed close together the temperature may rise because of the heat given off by the crop. This condition encourages damage and lowering quality by decay.

Quality Characteristics for the Retail Buyer. Pods should be clean, fresh in appearance, firm, crisp, tender, free from blemish; and all in a lot should be of the same stage of maturity so that they will cook uniformly. Firm, crisp,

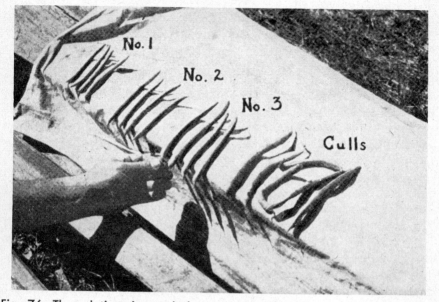

Fig. 76. The relative size and shape of snap bean grades for processing. (Courtesy, Oregon Agricultural Experiment Station.)

tender beans will snap readily when broken. Pods in which the seeds are very immature are the most desirable. Generally, length is unimportant if the beans meet the other requirements for quality.

If the seeds are half grown or larger, the pods are likely to be tough, woody, and stringy. Stringiness is very undesirable. This characteristic can be detected by breaking the pod. Beans age rapidly on the plant and develop toughness as rapidly as they age. A dull, dead, or wilted appearance may indicate that the beans were picked several days before and no longer are of the best quality. Decay is shown by mold or a soft, watery condition.

Insects: *Aphid (Aphis fabae).* For aphid infestations dust with a 10 per cent nicotine dust at the rate of 15 to 30 pounds per acre. The free alkaloid form of nicotine is more effective in cool weather.

Diabrotica (Diabrotica undecimpunctata). The Diabrotica or spotted cucumber beetle often feeds on the leaves or pods. Injury can be prevented by dusting with cryolite, DDT or rotenone.

Red Spider. Red Spider is often a serious pest in late spring and summer especially in the interior valleys. Sulfur dusts are partly successful. Parathion and TEPP are used in certain areas. Of the newer acaricides, Aramite (88-R) is one of the more promising.

Thrip (Thrips tabaci and *Hercothrips fasciatus).* Thrips can be checked with nicotine or rotenone dusts or oil-rotenone sprays. DDT is very effective on thrips, but should not be used after the pods begin to set. Also after DDT has been used serious infestations of red spider and aphid may develop. For bean thrips the control of prickly or wild lettuce and other weed hosts has given excellent control.

White Fly (Trialeurodes glacialis). White Fly may be troublesome in late summer especially in the central coastal district. Oil-rotenone sprays are fairly effective if thoroughly applied to the undersides of the leaves.

Good weed control in and around the fields helps to reduce red spider, white fly and thrip infestations by eliminating the host plants. Inadequate irrigation encourages the red spider. Irrigation by sprinkling or flooding may help to control thrips.

Diseases: *Anthracnose (Colletotrichum lindemuthianum)* causes circular sunken spots up to 0.4 inches in diameter, usually with a black border and with pinkish spore masses in the center, on the pods. Leaf and stem lesions inconspicuous. Use disease-free seed.

Bacterial Blight (Phytomonas medicaginis var. *phaseolicola* also *P. phaseoli)*. A water spread fungus. Small water-soaked spots appear on the underside of the leaves of affected plants. These gradually increase and form large, dead areas. In the center may be seen a dried incrustation surrounded by a yellowish zone. Dead sunken, red spots develop on the stems and pods. The plants may become defoliated. Disease may be seed carried but being spread by water the disease is rare in the Southwest.

Curly Top. Plants are stunted and the leaves are deformed and curled in a peculiar manner. Disease caused by virus which is carried by beet leaf hopper.

Mosaic. Clean seed and aphid control will hold mosaic in check.

Powdery Mildew (Erysiphe polygoni). Mildew sometimes develops on the foliage in coastal districts. Sulfur dust put on at the rate of about 20 pounds per acre helps prevent its development.

Rust (Uromyces phaseoli var. *typica)*. Bean rust is controlled best by the use of resistant varieties. The winter crop in the relatively frostless areas of the Southwest is more likely to be attacked by this disease than are plantings during warmer weather.

Stem Blight, Charcoal Rot (Sclerotium bataticola). This disease causes the death of seedlings that germinate during hot weather and also attacks older plants. Dark-brown cankers are formed on the stems of the seedlings, which usually are killed soon after emergence from the soil. On the stems of older plants the fungus produces light-gray cankers, speckled with numerous minute black dots.

Stem Rot (Rhizoctonia and *Fusarium)*. Dark red or brick red, dead areas or cankers develop on the lower part of the stem and kill or stunt the plant. No good control available but crop rotation, cover crop during winter, good soil preparation and proper irrigation and cultivation will keep plants growing vigorously.

References

1. Bouquet, A. G. B.: Growing snap beans for market and for manufacture, *Ore. Agr. Ext. Ser. Bull. 705,* 12 p., 1950.
2. Davis, G. B., and D. Curtis Mumford: Cost of producing pole beans in the Willamette Valley, Oregon, *Ore. Agr. Exp. Sta. Bull. 452,* 28 p., 1948.
3. Drage, Chas. M., R. W. Roskelley, and J. L. Paschal: Instructions for snapping beans, *Colo. Agr. Ext. Ser. Cir. 137-A,* 2 p., 1945.
4. Knott, J. E., and P. A. Minges: Snap bean production in California, *Calif. Agr. Ext. Multo.,* 6 p., 1948.
5. Randall, T. E., and C. D. Schwartze: Growing pole beans in Western Washington, *W. Wash. Exp. Sta. Mimeo. Cir. 120,* 7 p., 1943.
6. Wade, B. L.: Snap beans for marketing, canning, and freezing, *U.S.D.A. Farmers' Bull. 1915,* 14 p., 1942.
7. Wilcox, Margaret Tiffany, and D. Curtis Mumford: Man labor requirements for harvesting pole snap beans in Oregon, *Ore. Agr. Exp. Sta. Cir. 166,* 43 p., 1946.

LIMA BEANS

Botany. There are two types of lima beans (*Phaseolus lunatus*). The Sieva, Baby, or sometimes called Carolina lima, has small flat seeds. The so-called true lima or large seeded type has much larger seeds as well as larger plant. Both types have bush and climbing varieties as well as being used immature and as dry beans. The Sieva is an annual, early maturity, and the pods are numerous, small, papery, and split open at maturity. The pods are curved and have a well defined point. The large lima produces a larger plant, is a perennial in warm climates and is much more sensitive to cold temperatures. The pods are larger, fleshy, and are less likely to shatter upon maturity. Both types are used as a vegetable when the bean is fully grown as to size, but still high in water content, and green in color.

Origin and History. The lima bean is of American origin and has been found growing wild in Brazil, seeds also have been found in several mummy pits in Peru. Lima beans were cultivated in the American tropics in prehistoric times. The Sieva type was introduced into the United States about 1700 and the large lima about 1824. There is a report that a few hundred pounds of bean seed were purchased from a tramp steamer in Santa Barbara about 1865 by Henry Lewis. These beans had been purchased in Peru by the captain of the vessel. Within a few years this seed was being grown generally in the Carpinteria and Ventura areas and formed the basis of the dry lima bean industry which still flourishes in Southern California. For many years it was believed that lima beans came from Peru. It would seem logical that they were called Lima beans after the capital of that country.

A recent study by Mackie cites evidence that lima beans were native to the highlands of Guatemala. The beans were taken from this area to North America, Cuba, and Florida as well as to Peru in South America. Since these Central American beans bloom only when days and nights are of equal length, the movement of the types north and south must have been over a period of years.

Producing Areas. Baby lima beans are produced generally throughout the United States. Most of the large seeded dry lima beans are produced along the ocean from Santa Ana, California north to Santa Barbara. This same area also produces the highest yield per acre of large green lima beans. Large seeded lima beans are produced in several areas including California and eastern states. In the following statistics for 1940–1951 the 2 types of lima beans are not separated.

Lima Beans for Market

	Acreage	Bushels* Per Acre	Production Bushels	Price Per Bushel Dollars	Farm Value Dollars
United States	17,400	78	1,356,000	$2.37	$3,222,000
Florida	4,625	72	335,000	2.89	971,000
New York	3,433	117	401,000	2.25	905,000
New Jersey	2,833	82	232,000	2.29	532,000
South Carolina	2,200	50	110,000	2.15	237,000
Maryland	1,283	76	98,000	2.17	213,000

* Approximately 32 pounds in the shell.

Lima Beans for Processing

	Acreage	Pounds Per Acre	Production Tons	Price Per Ton Dollars	Farm Value Dollars
United States	74,871	1398	52,397	$129.22	$6,771,000
California	10,925	2356	12,876	156.33	2,013,000
Delaware	14,950	1326	9,912	115.51	1,145,000
New Jersey	12,754	1208	7,716	139.96	1,080,000
Wisconsin	3,966	1298	2,576	118.01	304,000
Maryland	3,941	1224	2,415	108.90	263,000

(Farm value, other Western states: Washington, $128,000.)

Food Value. Lima beans are found in group 3 on a food efficiency basis along with snap beans and peas. The pods represent more than half of the total weight purchased or 60 per cent. This and the labor required to hand pick the pods reduces the rating of market lima beans. Lima beans contain a glucoside, linamarin, which upon being acted on by the proper enzyme forms cyanide. Most cultivated lima beans contain only small amounts of this glucoside and are not dangerous, but some wild types contain large amounts that may cause the death of animals. Linamarin is thought to give lima beans their characteristic flavor. This vegetable contains 66.5 per cent water and the food value per 100 gm. of edible portion is energy, 131 calories; protein, 7.5 gm.; calcium, 31 mg.; vitamin A, 270 I.U.; ascorbic acid, 38 mg.; thiamine, 0.18 mg.; riboflavin, 0.36 mg.; and niacin, 0.29 mg. The following data give the relative nutrient rank of unshelled lima beans.

Pound, rank 10: Riboflavin, 4; energy, 3; protein, 3.
Acre, rank 22: Nutrients rank 11 or lower.
Man-hour, rank 27: Nutrients rank 11 or lower.

Varieties. Baby and large seeded types have been mentioned previously. Both kinds have both plump seeded varieties as well as the flat seeded type (Fig. 77). Henderson and Fordhook types are used most commonly. Henderson is a flat baby type and Fordhook is a plump large seeded variety sometimes referred to as a potato lima. The plump baby type and the flat large

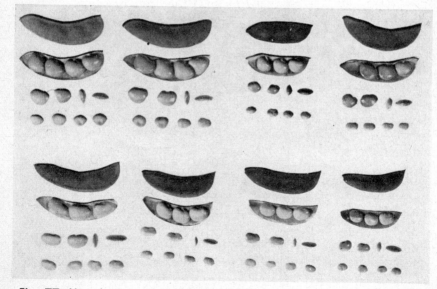

Fig. 77. Lima bean varieties. Left to right (*Top row*)—Concentrated Fordhook, 242, Triumph, Peerless. (*Bottom row*)—Early Market, Clark's Bush, Henderson, Early Baby Potato. (Courtesy, Associated Seed Growers, Inc.)

seeded type are not used commonly. Some of the common varieties are described below.

Henderson. Flat, baby type; plant small, dark green, erect, and early. Pods flat with 3 to 4 seeds; dry beans creamy white.

Clark's Bush. Similar to Henderson in plant type but the seed retains its green color even when mature. Dry seeds are pale green. Other similar varieties are Thorogreen, and Cangreen.

Sieva (Carolina). A small flat, baby type with long climbing vines.

Fordhook. Plump large seeded type or a potato lima type slightly later than the baby types. An old variety with a large, upright plant, very sensitive to environment, and highly productive. Pods large, thick walls, containing 3 or 4 seeds. Dry seeds white with a tinge of green. Similar variety types are Concentrated Fordhook which seems adapted to cool coastal areas and 242 which produces somewhat better than other Fordhook types in a warm climate.

Burpee's Improved Bush. Plant is similar to Fordhook in size, pods produced in clusters of 5 or 6 averaging 4 seeds each.

King of the Garden. Large seeded, flat, pole type. Plant is vigorous and productive. Pods flat, with 4 to 5 large, greenish white beans.

Climatic Requirements. Lima beans require somewhat warmer weather for production than snap beans. The large seeded types are very particular as to their climatic requirements and the baby varieties can be produced in hotter and drier climate. When temperature is too high or humidity too low the large seeded types fail to set fruit. Areas close to the ocean have been used successfully because of moderate temperatures and higher humidity. Average monthly temperatures of 59° to 75° F. and the absence of frost are desirable for the production of large seeded limas.

Planting and Spacing. Baby limas are planted about the same time as snap beans or slightly later. Large seeded limas need a warmer soil for germination and usually are planted 2 or 3 weeks later. Soil temperatures should be about 60° to 65° F. for good germination of Fordhook beans. The seed is planted 2 inches deep. For market, rows are about 30 inches apart for the bush types with 3 plants per foot of row. Growers of processed beans prefer a spacing of 28 to 30 inches. Pole beans should have rows 3 to 4 feet apart and the plants in hills 3 feet apart or 6 inches apart in the row. Both for green beans and dry beans some vine varieties are grown without staking and with about the same planting distance as the bush types. Since baby seed is smaller in size, 50 to 60 pounds is sufficient to plant 1 acre. With large seeded types like Fordhook 100 to 125 pounds are used to produce maximum yields. Large seeded limas grown on poles would require only about 40 to 50 pounds. Seed treatment tends to reduce seed decay and preëmergence damping-off, particularly in a cold, wet soil. Spergon has been used at the rate of 4 ounces per 100 pounds of seed or Arasan at the rate of 2 ounces. Seeds also are treated sometimes with Lindane to prevent wire worm damage to the young plants. About one-third ounce of 75 per cent Lindane is added per 100 pounds of seed. These materials are applied as a semiwet treatment and have been very beneficial to bean growers.

Fertilizer and Irrigation. Most of the information on these practises must be based on grower experience. Nitrogen fertilizer should be applied carefully as to amount or time of application. Some believe an excess of nitrogen will reduce productivity of plants. If a soil is moderately or severely deficient in nitrogen, the fertilizer should be applied to increase the growth of plants up to the time of blooming. Excesses of phosphoric acid or potash are not so likely to be detrimental to growth.

Some of the best yields are obtained by following a crop of celery in Orange County. On other fields ammonia gas and other forms of nitrogen are used heavily before planting with the belief that this practise permits more of the beans to reach adequate size for freezing. Many of our beans for processing are irrigated. A furrow is placed between each row for this purpose. Plants should be supplied with sufficient water to maintain a uniform growth. Two or possibly three irrigations will supply sufficient water, particularly if winter rains or a preirrigation has wet the soil to the depth of 6 feet. Either an excess or deficiency of water should be avoided.

Ratio of Green to Dry Beans. In some areas growers may harvest their fields for processing or harvest them as dry beans. Since some dry types sometimes are processed in the mature green stage, this consideration is important for both garden and dry varieties. If beans are harvested immature they are higher in water content so yield should be increased. However, some pods and beans are small and too immature while others may be waste due to overmaturity. With garden varieties of lima beans, the yield of green beans could be greater than dry beans. More green beans than dry beans are produced usually the ratio falling between 1.5 and 2.0. Sometimes less green beans are produced than dry beans and ratios have been as high as 3 to 1. Weather conditions affect the concentration of set of flowers and experience is required to harvest a field at its maximum production of green beans.

Harvesting. All pods on a plant do not reach the correct stage for immature harvest at the same time. Fields for processing are harvested when most of the beans have reached maximum size and the beans are green. Overmaturity is indicated by white beans and a yellow pod. One procedure is to go through a field and pull 30 plants or more and then shell the beans in the pod. By this procedure the relative abundance of small green, fully grown green, and white mature beans may be determined. For maximum yield there should not be more than 10 per cent white beans. Growers prefer varieties and a climate which cause a concentration of the set of flowers and consequently a large number of pods to reach processing maturity at the same time.

For market, beans are harvested by hand and are shipped to market un-shelled. Two or three hand pickings are required and care should be used to harvest the correct maturity. Processed beans are shelled by means of a pea viner which has screens with larger holes than used for peas. In some cases the vines are cut and hauled to the viner located near the field or at the processing plant. In other cases the plants are cut and windrowed. A self-propelled viner (Fig. 3) moves through the field, picks up the plants and shells out the beans. The vines are left in the field and the shelled beans are taken to the processing plant. This latter type of equipment requires con-siderably less labor. Sometimes a field may be hand picked for the early ma-turing pods to be sold on the fresh market with the remaining crop being harvested for processing.

As lima bean pods grow there is an increase in the weight per bean fol-lowed by a decrease in weight as the beans become dry. The period of great-est bean weight is after maximum quality for freezing is reached. As the beans grow from immature to dry beans there is a great increase in percent-age of dry weight and to a somewhat lesser extent of starch. Sugar content is never large and decreases slowly with maturity.

Storage. Shelled lima beans do not store as long as do the beans in the pod. The shelled beans may be stored near 32° F. for 2 weeks but they will main-tain in an edible condition only 4 days at 40° F. If stored too long, the beans tend to fade to a light color and become sticky. Unshelled beans may be stored 1 to 3 weeks at 34° to 40° F. and 90 per cent humidity. Although good quality lima beans are an excellent vegetable, their shipment has been in limited quantities. The frozen lima bean industry has increased rapidly because of a high quality product and the difficulty of shipping fresh lima beans.

Quality Characteristics for the Retail Buyer. The pods of unshelled lima beans should be well filled, clean, bright, fresh, and of dark-green color. The shelled lima bean should be plump, with tender skin, and the skin should be of good green or greenish-white color. Dried, shriveled, spotted, yellowed, or flabby pods of unshelled lima beans may be old or may be affected by dis-ease. Usually beans contained in such pods are of poor quality; they may be tough and of poor flavor. Decay may appear on the pods in the form of irregular sunken areas in which mold may appear.

Shelled lima beans are very perishable. They heat quickly and if kept under ordinary conditions soon become moldy or slimy. Shelled limas should be examined closely for damage and tested for tenderness by puncturing the skin. Those with hard, tough skins are overmature and usually lack flavor.

Insects: *Bean Pod Borer* (*Etilla zinckenella*). The larvae of this small gray moth borrow into the immature lima beans. Their damage to the beans is very noticeable. The corn earworm and the Velvet bean larvae also attack the bean pods as well as punctures being made by the Lygus bug. Control of these insects is difficult and expensive. A 5 per cent dust of DDT applied before or after blooming and when the pods are 2 inches long are the best control measures. After the larvae have entered the pod it is difficult to reach them with insecticides.

References

1. Cory, W. M. *et al.:* Green lima bean variety trials in California in 1947, *Truck Crops Mimeo. No. 43,* 7 p., 1948.
2. Mackie, W. W.: Origin, dispersal, and variability of the lima bean, *Phaseolus lunatus. Hilgardia 15:* 1–29, 1943.
3. Osterli, V. P. *et al.:* Spacing trials with green lima beans, *Truck Crops Mimeo. 48,* 2 p., 1949.

TOMATO

Botany. *Tomatoes (Lycopersicon esculentum)* are perennials which usually are grown as annuals since they are killed by frost before completing the first year's growth in most areas of the United States. They are normally prostrate in growth although some varieties are more upright than others. The tomato has a very extensive root system and with some of the larger varieties may extend to 6 feet and even to the depth of 10 to 12 feet. Adventitious roots are produced from the stem if it is set deeper at transplanting time. If the plant is not pruned numerous lateral branches develop from the axils of the leaves on the main stem resulting in a bushy plant. Numerous hairs and oil glands occur on the stem and are ruptured when the plant is handled. This produces a characteristic odor and the hands are stained. Leaves are alternate and compound. On garden varieties there are 4 to 8 flowers per cluster or raceme, but with small fruited types the number may be 30 to 50. Usually the style elongates beyond the stamens before the pollen is shed so the style is exposed to cross pollination. Wind pollination is rare, but bumble bees sometimes visit the flowers. Cross pollination is very small and may vary from 4 to 0 per cent. Some varieties produce several flower clusters and then the stem ends with a flower cluster. Such varieties are referred to as determinate types. The fruit is a fleshy berry and the number of locules varies from 2 to 18 with most garden varieties having from 4 to 8 locules. The period from blooming to a ripe fruit is frequently about 45 to 50 days.

Origin and History. The tomato came from tropical America and was used by the Indians as food long before the time of Columbus. Indians of Mexico referred to this vegetable by using the word "tomati" and the crop was grown sometimes among maize plants. Tomatoes were taken to Europe from Mexico previous to 1554. At first it was grown for decorative effect and considered poisonous. By 1812 tomatoes were grown extensively in fields in Italy and particularly Sicily. Jefferson grew tomatoes in 1781 and the fruit did not appear on our markets until about 1829. Tomatoes were a popular food by 1844 and were available on most markets. Thornburn offers one tomato variety in his catalogue of 1828, and 31 varieties in 1881.

Producing Areas. The tomato, sometimes called the "Poor Man's Orange" is produced extensively both for fresh market and canning. The 1940–1951 statistical data, for marketing and processing of tomatoes, follow.

Tomatoes for Market

	Acreage	Bushels* Per Acre	Production Bushels	Price Per Bushel Dollars	Farm Value Dollars
United States	237,735	125	29,687,000	2.79	83,099,000
California	31,783	194	6,163, 000	3.52	21,732,000
Florida	31,591	140	4,433,000	4.80	21,293,000
Texas	75,683	69	5,253,000	2.28	12,004,000
New Jersey	10,666	172	1,837,000	2.24	4,122,000
New York	9,041	215	1,944,000	1.63	3,177,000

(Farm value, other Western states: Washington, $892,000; Colorado, $883,000; Oregon, $666,000; Utah, $88,000.)
* Approximately 53 pounds.

Tomatoes for Processing

	Acreage	Tons Per Acre	Production Tons	Price Per Ton Dollars	Farm Value Dollars
United States	483,120	6.2	3,012,729	25.22	76,001,000
California	109,376	9.7	1,056,591	25.30	26,733,000
Indiana	87,108	5.4	469,375	22.93	10,765,000
New Jersey	33,191	6.7	223,158	30.12	6,723,000
Maryland	45,791	4.9	224,416	28.25	6,341,000
Pennsylvania	26,150	6.1	159,133	27.73	4,414,000

(Farm value, other Western states: Utah, $1,534,000; Colorado, $549,000.)

The most important harvest season for some of the important market states as well as those in the West are: California, April and May, also June and July, also October and November; Florida, February and March, also May, also December; Texas, May and June, also November; New Jersey,

July and August; New York, August and September; Colorado, September; Washington, July 15 to August; Oregon, August and September; Utah, September.

Food Value. Tomatoes are found in group 2 on food production efficiency. Only 2 fruits, winter squash and tomatoes, are found in the groups 1 and 2. Tomatoes are an appetizing vegetable and are used in many ways. They are available every month of the year, fresh and canned. Tomato contains 94.1 per cent water and the food value per 100 gm. of edible portion is energy, 23 calories; protein, 1.0 gm.; calcium, 7 mg.; vitamin A, 1000 I.U.; ascorbic acid, 22 mg.; thiamine, 0.09 mg.; riboflavin, 0.03 mg.; and niacin, 0.8 mg. The following data give the relative nutrient rank of tomatoes:

Pound, rank 13: Niacin, 5; vitamin A, 8; thiamine, 9.
Acre, rank 15: Thiamine, 7; vitamin A, 8; niacin, 8.
Man-hour, rank 17: Vitamin A, 8; niacin, 10.

Varieties. Tomato fruits may be globe-shaped or almost round, oval or flattened, and pear shaped. While most of the varieties of commercial importance are red or scarlet, a few are pink. The flesh of both types is similar, but red or scarlet tomatoes have yellow skin whereas the pink varieties have a transparent skin. Yellow-fleshed types also are available, but rarely are used except in home gardens. In California, the San Marzano, a pear-shaped type is used by the canning industry for the making of tomato paste. Tomato varieties are needed for different types of production: canning and fresh market. The latter tomatoes are grown either in greenhouses, in the open, supported by stakes ("sticks"), or grown without support. Canning and greenhouse tomatoes are picked red ripe, and the others as "green wraps" up to and including the partially colored stage or "breakers." Partially red and completely red tomatoes are sold on local markets. Many tomato varieties are available. Some are used for considerable acreage and others find considerable value because they are adapted to certain conditions or a special market. Some of the important types are listed below together with other varieties or strains of similar characteristics which are used in the West.

Bonny Best. Standard second early for market; plant medium size, fruits flattened globe, medium size, bright red. John Baer similar but slightly earlier. Other varieties which mature about the same period are Break o'day, Chalk's Early Jewel, Grothen's Globe, Stokesdale, and Valiant.

Earliana Strains. Standard, first early variety; widely adapted, used in areas of short seasons; plant open, spreading, with fine foliage; fruits flattened, medium size, and bright red. Used in the West for early market and shipping. Strains of Earliana are First Early, Morse's Special 498, and Earliana. June Pink is similar to Earliana but the outside color is pink. Other early varieties are Bounty, Chatham, Firesteel, Victor, and Pearl Harbor. The latter is resistant to spotted wilt and nailhead rust.

Marglobe. General purpose variety which has decreased in importance in recent years. Plant vigorous, heavy foliage, resistant to fusarium wilt and nailhead rust; fruits medium large, nearly globular, deep red, thick walls, some tendency to crack.

Moscow. Canning variety used in California and mountain states. Fruits red, moderately large, short globe, with thick walls.

Pearson. Used for canning and shipping in California; vigorous, self-topping plants with ample foliage for fruit protection; fruits semiglobe, medium large, of good red color with tough skin.

Pennheart. A second early used for shipping and market in southern desert areas. Fruits are scarlet red, large, flattened globe.

Pritchard. Used some as staked tomato for market; plant self-topping; resistant to fusarium wilt and nailhead rust; fruits globular, with thick walls; color light scarlet.

Stone. Plants large, of dense foliage, and productive; fruits large, slightly flattened, smooth, scarlet-red color. Norton is a wilt resistant strain. Baltimore is similar in type but earlier.

Climatic Requirements. Tomatoes are grown where there is a frost-free season of 4 months; but a longer season of 5 to 6 months is desirable. During the winter months, tomatoes are greenhouse grown in the north central states; there is outdoor production in southern Florida and the lower Rio Grande, as well as with protection by brush and paper in the Imperial Valley. Tomatoes produce best at average monthly temperature of 70° to 75° F.; they are grown at 65° to 70° F. or 75° to 80° F. Temperatures above 80° F. are undesirable. Fruit temperatures below 30° F. damage the fruit as does chilling from 40° to 45° F. Temperature also affects set of fruit and formation of red color as discussed later. Fusarium wilt is more prevalent under warm weather conditions, and verticillium wilt under cooler conditions. Tomato seed will germinate at 55° but more rapidly and with higher germination at 65° to 85° F.

Soils. The crop is grown on most types of soils. Sandy loams are favored for early fruit even though they are usually of poor fertility and water-holding capacity. Purely organic soils usually are not used unless there is a considerable mixture of sediment soil. Other crops are more profitable on such soils and growers have experienced slow ripening on some muck and peat soils.

Fertilizers. On soils deficient in phosphorus the use of this element has increased total yield as well as the amount of tomatoes harvested the first part of the season. There is no evidence that the period of time between blossom set and picking is shortened by phosphorus fertilization, but size of plant and number of blossoms have been increased by its use. Starter solutions have been found beneficial in some areas. The fertilizer is added to water at the time of transplanting and where fertilizer gives response is likely to affect early growth of the transplants. Fertilizers such as 2 pounds of ammonium sulfate, or 2 to 3 pounds of 16-20, or 5 pounds of 6-30-0, are added per 50 gallons of water used at transplanting time.

California growers in Imperial Valley use 100 pounds of phosphoric acid, while other areas use from 25 to 80 pounds of nitrogen per acre. Colorado recommends the use of 10 to 15 tons of rotted manure plus 125 pounds of superphosphate, increased yields have been obtained also by the use of 200 pounds of 6-30-0. Oregon also suggests the use of rotted manure supplemented by superphosphate; or a fertilizer high in phosphorus such as an 11-48-0 or 4-24-4. Utah growers use 10 to 15 tons of rotted manure or legume green manure; but when manure is not available, not more than 150 pounds of ammonium sulfate. If alfalfa is plowed under, it is desirable to apply 150 to 200 pounds of superphosphate. Eastern Washington recommends 10 tons of rotted manure plowed under a few weeks before planting plus 80 pounds of nitrogen or 100 pounds of nitrogen and 50 pounds of phosphoric acid when no manure is used. Western Washington growers should use 600 to 800 pounds of a 5-15-10 fertilizer without manure or 400 to 500 pounds of 5-15-10 with 10 tons of manure.

Plant Production. In most areas the seed is planted in a hotbed, coldframe or area of warmer temperature, and the plants are put in the field after the danger of frost. However, Imperial Valley growers seed directly in the field and give the plants protection with brush and paper. Several different methods may be used to produce plants: (a) Seeding in a hotbed, transplanting to a coldframe, and then to the field (Fig. 78); (b) seeding thinly in a coldframe or sometimes in a hotbed, and then transplanting to the field; (c) growing plants outdoors in a warmer area and then transporting them to the area where they are to be field-planted; (d) direct seeding in the field with or without protection. The method selected depends upon the custom of the area and the cost of plants. Crops produced with many operations are likely to be more expensive, and handling is likely to cause infection with tobacco mosaic virus.

Canning tomatoes may be planted in a hotbed, coldframe, or directly in the field. Plants for fall "green wraps" may be started later than market or canning tomatoes with the use of a coldframe. In the East, many of the canning tomato plants are sown in the open fields in southern Georgia and shipped north at the proper time for field setting. Utah tomato growers obtain their plants from Moapa Valley in southern Nevada. Canning tomato plants have been field seeded for 25 years in the northwest section of Ohio near Lake Erie. This practise has been used in other sections near Ohio and is now being used in California. Very early plants are needed for stake tomatoes so hotbeds always are used to start these plants.

Most plants are hardened before field-setting. This can be done by keeping the covers off at night and by keeping the soil on the dry side. This will re-

Fig. 78. A tractor pulling a two-row transplanter with a fertilizer distributor on the rear of the square water tank. Each person plants a single row.

duce the amount of growth and tend to produce a hardier plant. Hardening tends to decrease early yields. This process should not be carried too far when early fruits are desired.

Planting and Spacing. The commercial planting dates of tomatoes for market are as follows:

California: Imperial Valley, November to January, also August; Orange,
   Los Angeles and Merced counties, February to April; fall crop in
   northern part, May and June; fall crop in southern part, June and July.
Colorado: May 15 to June.
Oregon: April 15 to June 15.
Utah: May 15 to June 15.
Washington: May to June 15.

Canning tomatoes are planted April 15 to May in California, and slightly later than market tomatoes in other states.

Tomato seed is treated to eliminate surface-borne organisms such as those causing bacterial canker or fusarium wilt, and to protect the young seedlings against damping-off. Protection from surface-borne organisms can be accomplished by soaking the seed in a one to 2000 solution of mercuric chloride for exactly 5 minutes. The mercuric chloride at the rate of one and nine-tenths grams of powder, or 4 large tablets or 16 small tablets per gallon of water, should be dissolved in a wooden or earthenware container. The seed is then placed in a loosely woven cloth bag not over half full and immersed in the solution (1 gallon for each pound of seed). The bag of seed should be agitated with a paddle while in the solution. At the end of 5 minutes remove the bag, and immediately wash it in running water for 15 minutes. Then dry the seed thoroughly. Use a fresh solution for each lot of seed.

After drying, the seed can be protected against damping-off by treatment with yellow copper oxide at 1.5 per cent of the seed weight (1 level teaspoonful of dust for each pound of tomato seed).

New Improved Ceresan solution sometimes is used instead of the above 2 treatment procedures. The seed is soaked in a 1 to 1200 solution of New Improved Ceresan (1 ounce in 9 gallons of water) for exactly 5 minutes. It is then drained and dried without washing. One gallon of solution is used for each pound of seed. The procedure is effective against both seed and soil-borne organisms. It may, however, be harmful to germination, especially if the seed is stored wet or in tight containers.

Spacing of plants varies with the farm equipment used and the method of growing. Stake or "stick" tomato plants may be 9 to 18 inches apart in the row, with rows 3 to 4 feet apart. Early market tomatoes like Earliana may be 3 by 4 feet, or slightly farther apart. Canning tomatoes in the Southwest frequently have rows 6 feet apart. Pearson and San Marzano may be 6 by 3, or 6 by 4 feet. In Colorado and Utah, canning tomatoes are spaced three and one-half by three and one-half to four by four feet.

Many advantages are claimed for stake tomatoes (Fig. 79) and among these are: (a) Earlier ripening, (b) larger fruits, (c) less disease, (d) larger yields, (e) cleaner fruit, and (f) convenience in harvesting. The closer planting gives more plants per acre, which in turn gives higher acre yields and more early fruits at a higher total cost of production. With closer spacing, plants usually are pruned to 1 or 2 stems. Plants are pruned 3 or 4 times

Fig. 79. Tomato plants trained to stakes supported by a wire.

during the season. It is an intensive method of culture and similar to the methods used in raising greenhouse tomatoes. Its success depends upon the type of market available for the fruit.

Irrigation. Tomatoes are a deeprooted crop; but some of the smaller and earlier types do not produce as deep roots as the late canning types. Coastal areas use about 12 inches of supplemental irrigation water, and other areas, including interior valleys of California, about 24 inches. The first irrigation occurs at the time the tomatoes are transplanted in a small furrow either side of the plant. Four or 5 subsequent irrigations are sufficient, care being used to wet completely the soil just previous to the first picking of canning tomatoes. With such a procedure there may be no need for irrigation during the picking season. Irrigation experiments in Idaho[3] indicate the need for abundant soil moisture after the fruits start to ripen. If water was withheld after August 15th there was a marked reduction in yield, while the application too often during the ripening season delayed the ripening of fruits. At Davis, California, irrigation increased yield about 50 to 60 per cent—mainly through increased size of fruit. Irrigation treatments did not affect greatly the amount of blossom-end rot in California—a condition which causes the blossom end to have a dry black rot. Idaho[3] reports losses from blossom-end rot as great as 50 per cent of the crop. Perhaps differences in the size of the soil moisture reservoir and climatic conditions may cause differences in the severity of this disease under irrigation in these 2 states.

Cost of Production. Tables 37 and 38 give the cost of producing tomatoes for a cannery and also stake tomatoes for market where the last portion of the crop is sold to the cannery. These tables illustrate that procedures are used in growing canning tomatoes which are lower in cost. Fourteen tons of cannery tomatoes were produced with a total cost of $292.79. The stake tomatoes produced 12 tons for market and 8 tons for the cannery at a cost of $1,015.13. Stake tomatoes are planted much earlier therefore plant growing costs are higher. There is the additional operation of staking, pruning, and tying the plants that requires $180.00 for labor. Stake tomatoes are irrigated more often than canning tomatoes. This can be explained by the use of more sandy soil, two and one-half times more plants per acre, as well as more intensive cultural methods. The cost of picking and packing market tomatoes is about double that for the cannery because there is need for sizing, wrapping in paper, and packing of the market fruit.

Fruit Set. Not all tomato blossoms form fruits, and the dropping of any flowers is a great source of concern. There are several causes for the blossoms to fall. Poor set may be due to unfavorable nutritional conditions such as lack of a fertilizer element or a temporary unbalanced condition of the plant's food supply. Extreme temperature also may cause the blossoms to fall. Average temperatures of either 100° or 50° F. will produce a large percentage of drop (Fig. 80), while 70° and 85° F. will give a much higher

Table 37*

LABOR REQUIREMENTS AND COST OF PRODUCING
CANNING TOMATOES IN THE STOCKTON TO WOODLAND AREA OF
CALIFORNIA (1948).

(YIELD WAS 14 TONS PER ACRE, PLANTS WERE TRANSPLANTED
3 BY 6 FEET, 2,420 PLANTS PER ACRE)

	Hours Per Acre†			Costs—Dollars	
	Man Labor	Trac-tor	Truck	Per Acre	Per Ton
Growing plants‡	10	.1	.1	8.77	....
Land preparation	4	4.0	...	11.40	....
Transplanting and replanting	5	1.0	1.0	6.95	....
Hoeing and weeding	6	...	...	5.10	....
Irrigation, 4 or 5 times	12	...	...	10.20	....
Cultivation and furrowing, 5 times	4	4.0	...	8.20	....
Fertilizing	1	.5	.1	1.60	....
Pest and disease control	2	.5	.1	2.45	....
Miscellaneous	2	.5	.1	2.45	....
Subtotal cultural labor	46	10.6	1.4	57.12	4.08
Picking, 602 boxes (usually piece rate at 17 cents)	150	...	...	127.50	9.10
Hauling boxes and fruit including loading	15	...	5.0	20.25	1.45
Total labor cost	211	10.6	6.4	204.87	14.63
Irrigation water 24 to 30 acre-inches				7.00	...
Seed and coldframe supplies (1 oz.)				2.00	...
Fertilizers, commercial 400 lbs. at $60 per ton				12.00	...
Pest and disease control materials				9.00	...
Miscellaneous materials				2.00	...
Total material costs				32.00	2.29
General expense				11.84	...
County taxes on land				6.60	...
Repairs to equipment				2.00	...
Compensation insurance				2.00	...
Total cash overhead costs				22.44	1.60
Total depreciation	...	...	6.40	6.40	.46
Total interest on investment	...	27.08	...	27.08	1.93
Total all costs	....	....	....	292.79	20.91

* Courtesy, *Calif. Agr. Ext. Ser. Cir. 167,* 1950.

† Labor costs above are based on the following hourly rates: man labor, 85 cents; tractor for land preparation, $2; cultivating tractor, $1.20; truck, $1.50.

‡ The cost of growing plants, as included above, amounts to about $14 an acre with pulling included in transplanting around $5 per 1,000.

Cultural Practices

Table 38*

COST OF PRODUCING STAKED TOMATOES FOR SHIPPING
IN MERCED COUNTY, CALIFORNIA UNDER 1948 CONDITIONS

(BASED ON RENTED LAND WITH A YIELD OF 800 30 LB. PACKED
BOXES OF SHIPPING AND EIGHT TONS OF CANNING TOMATOES PER ACRE)

	Hours Per Acre†				Costs—Dollars	
	Man Labor	Horse Work	Trac- tor Work	Truck Work	Per Acre	Per Packed Box
Growing plants	80.0	....	....	....	68.00	
Preparing land	5.5	....	5.5	....	11.28	
Planting, replant and pull plants	19.3	....	3.2	1.1	21.90	
Staking	38.0	....	....	2.0	35.30	
Pruning and suckering	80.0	....	....		68.00	
Tying	90.0	....	....		76.50	
Irrigation, 18 to 20 times	53.0	....	....		45.05	
Cultivating, hoeing, fertilizing	19.0	16.0	1.0	....	21.35	
Spraying and dusting (contract)	....			....	4.50	
Miscellaneous (heating, baiting)	11.0	1.0	1.0	2.0	13.80	
Picking–shipping (725 43-lb. field boxes or 800 30-lb. packed boxes)	280.0				238.00	
Picking–cannery, 8 tons, 380 field boxes at average of 17 cents	....	....	....	....	64.60	.
Hauling at $1.50 per ton	....	....	....	....	30.00	
Miscellaneous harvesting	8.0	....	....	2.0	11.80	
Subtotal harvesting labor	288.0	....	....	....	344.40	
Total labor cost	683.8	....	....	....	710.08	
Fertilizer (liquid, 10–10–5, and side-dressings)					36.00	
Seed (4.00), spray, dust, bait					14.00	
Miscellaneous (heating oil, tules, repoint stakes [$7])					19.00	
Total material cost					69.00	
General expense					38.95	
Repairs (3.00), county taxes (0.20), other					5.20	
Compensation insurance					7.00	
Rent (cash), landlord furnishes water					75.00	
Total labor and cash cost					905.23	
Total depreciation 98.65; interest 11.25					109.90	
Total all costs					1015.13	1.27
Deduct income from 8 tons cannery tomatoes at $25					200.00	.25
Net cost of raising 800 30-lb. boxes of shipping tomatoes					815.13	1.02

* Courtesy, *Calif. Agr. Ext. Ser. Cir. 167,* 1950.
† Labor rates per hour: man, 85 cents; horse, 25 cents; tractor, $1.20; truck, $1.50.

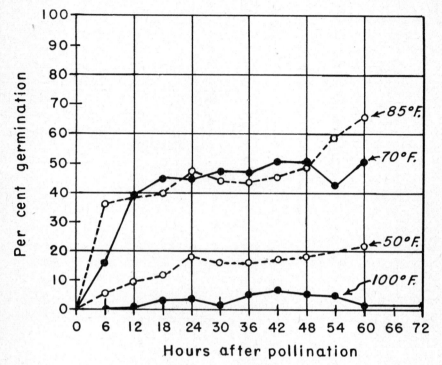

Fig. 80. Effect of temperature on the germination of tomato pollen. Poor fruit set may be due to either high (100° F.) or to low (50° F.) temperatures. (Courtesy, Cornell University.)

percentage of set. Diseases may reduce the vigor of the plants and insects may eat either the stamens or pistils. A tomato plant produces a large number of flowers—too great in number for the plant to produce good sized fruits from each one.

Fruit Ripening. As a tomato fruit grows there is an increase in size and a storage of starch. As ripening begins there is a softening of the fruit, change of starch to sugar, and the formation of red color. In red tomatoes there are two pigments—a red pigment called lycopin and a yellow pigment, carotin. Yellow tomatoes have only the yellow pigment. Carotin formation is not affected seriously by temperature but this is not true in the case of the red pigment lycopin. The red color is formed primarily between 68° and 85° F., and its development tends to be inhibited by a daily temperature above 89°. Thus, it is possible for a normally red tomato to be entirely yellow in color if ripened at temperatures above 90° F. Such an extreme case rarely occurs in the field, but this condition is indicated by tomato fruits having yellow shoulders at harvest. These yellow areas on the fruit are defects according to canning grades.

In U.S. canning grades of tomatoes there are two color descriptions. A U.S. No. 2 is "fairly well colored" or two-thirds good red color while a U.S. No. 1 is "well colored" or 90 per cent good red color. Fig. 81 illustrates these color changes with reference to age of the tomato. Color improvement is rapid as a cull, much slower as a U.S. No. 2, and there is a very gradual improvement of color at the U.S. No. 1 or "well colored" stage. In order for canning tomato growers to deliver a large percentage of "well colored" tomatoes their pickers need to be informed adequately about color standards. Skill is required to obtain the maximum percentage of "well colored" tomatoes from a field.

Harvesting. A fruit normally ripens in about 45 to 50 days from fertilization of the ovules. The immature tomatoes are green; as they mature in size they turn to a whitish green and then the red color starts to develop at the blossom end. For canning, the tomatoes are harvested at the red-ripe stage. Market tomatoes are picked at this stage or even at the mature green stage. Shipping tomatoes are picked at the whitish green stage; hence called "green wraps," since usually they are wrapped in paper before packing.

Canning tomatoes of various qualities and sizes are marketed together in

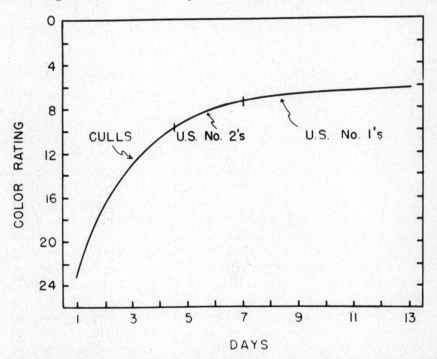

Fig. 81. Color improvement as a tomato fruit ripens. Color improves very rapidly in a cull tomato, but very slowly after the fruit becomes a U. S. No. 1. (Courtesy, Purdue University.)

lug boxes, but must comply with the grade specified in the contract. Sorting is unnecessary for the removal of fruits other than those with serious defects which are discarded in the picking operation. Market and shipping tomatoes are graded carefully as to size (Fig. 82). The pack of tomatoes usually is expressed in terms of the number of rows on top of the lug. Thus, a 4 by 4 pack is 16 tomatoes in the top layer, and 7 by 8 pack is 56 tomatoes. These are packed in a Los Angeles lug box, to a weight of 32 pounds.

Storage. Both storage temperature and desirable length of storage period varies for ripe and mature green tomatoes. Ripe tomatoes if not already soft may be stored for a week or 10 days at 40° to 50° F. and 85 per cent humidity. Lower temperatures frequently cause the fruits to break down. At a storage temperature of 55° F. or slightly higher, green tomatoes will ripen slowly and may be kept for a period of 3 to 5 weeks. If more rapid ripening is desired temperatures between 60° to 70° F. should be used even though it will also accelerate the development of decay.

The ripening of green wrap tomatoes at the terminal markets is an expensive procedure since the fruit do not ripen evenly. Chilling injury tends to accentuate uneven ripening. The ripening tomatoes must be sorted 2 or 3 times to remove those that are ready for market in order to store the re-

Fig. 82. Grading, sizing, and packing of "green wrap" tomatoes in a growers' packing shed.

mainder for further ripening. Tomato ripening operators are able by adjusting ripening temperature to maintain a uniform supply of ripe tomatoes on the market.

Quality Characteristics for the Retail Buyer. Good quality tomatoes are mature; firm, but not overripe; fairly well formed, plump, smooth, of good color, and free from blemish.

There are many defects which are serious only from the standpoint of waste in preparing for the table. "Catfaces" or scars around the blossom end are typical of these defects. Fruits that are rough or irregular in shape may not be attractive in appearance; yet for certain purposes they can be used with little waste. Worm damage is very objectionable, especially if the worm has bored deeply. A worm may make a very small hole to enter the fruit and destroy a large area in the interior. Fruits having growth cracks seldom will keep long, but are fit for immediate consumption. Puffy and watery fruit usually is of poor flavor and is wasteful. Puffy tomatoes generally are angular in shape and light in weight.

Insects: *Corn Earworm (Heliothis armigera).* A description of this insect will be found in the sweet corn section. The corn earworm attacks many crops and causes severe damage to the plant and fruit of the tomato. The worms enter the tomato fruits causing characteristic burrows. As the worm grows it may shed its skin 5 times and finally drop to the ground to pupae. Dusting or spraying gives good control. DDD or DDT as 5 per cent dusts are used at 30 pounds per acre, or these materials may be used as sprays using 3 pounds of 50 per cent wettable powder per acre. Sulfur is combined commonly with DDD and DDT dusts to control tomato mite.

Darkling Ground Beetle (Blapstinus spp. and *Metoponium abnorme).* These beetles often cut off recently transplanted tomatoes at the soil level. Baiting with arsenical-bran baits is a common practise. These baits can be placed out before planting, or can be spread by fertilizer attachments on the planters. Dusting with 10 per cent DDT often is used in severe infestations.

Flea Beetle (Epitrix cucumeris and Others). The potato flea beetle and others may damage tomatoes occasionally. DDT dusts are effective.

Hornworm (Protoparce quinquemaculata and *P. sexta).* These large worms are destructive in certain areas. The horns of the caterpillars and the handle-like proboscis of the pupae are characteristic. Calcium arsenate dust at the rate of 15 to 25 pounds per acre is an effective control.

Potato Tuber Moth (Gnorimoschema operculella). Occurs in south coastal region. Larvae enter fruit at the calyx end and make a dry burrow through the core and the fleshy portions. Infestation usually is associated with potato culture.

Tomato Pinworm (Keiferia lycopersicella). This caterpillar is a leaf-miner and leaf-folder, but during the last half of its larvae existence it also bores frequently into the fruit. The larvae will enter the fruit at any point. They make dry burrows, are small, and usually do not penetrate very far into the fruit. Since it has a number of generations per season, this insect becomes more serious as the season advances. DDT as used for tomato fruit worm will control this insect, as will 60 or 70 per cent cryolite dust.

Tomato Russet Mite (Vasates destructor). This mite is a microscopic, yellow-orange species which is capable of severely damaging tomatoes. The eggs are laid among the hairs on the stems, or on the fruit, and a complete cycle may take only a week. The mites suck out juices of individual cells, and cause a russetting of the leaves, stems or fruit. The "greasy" appearance of the leaves, and stems may indicate the presence of mites. These insects overwinter on petunias and other solanaceous plants. As a result of mite damage the leaves start to dry up, beginning with the lower leaves and the loss of leaves causes sunburn of the fruit. Sulfur dust is an effective control. Growers usually apply one dusting of 100 per cent dusting sulfur early, and follow with one later dusting, or use sulfur in combination with DDT or DDD.

Vegetable Weevil (Listroderes costirostris obliquus). The beetle has a brown or buff-colored snout that measures about three-eighths inch in length. Plants may be treated with a 50 per cent cryolite dust and be sure to cover foliage and ground about the base of the plants thoroughly with the dust.

Diseases: *Bacterial Canker (Phytomonas michiganensis).* Wilting and upward rolling of leaflet margins; usually one side of leaf is affected at first; leaves browning, withering, and drying but remaining attached to stem. Dying of leaves progressing up the stem; one side of the plant often attacked first. The softer tissues just within the bark or cortex of the stem are attacked, and the pith is then separated easily from the woody portion of the stem. As decay progresses the pith becomes yellow and mealy in appearance, and cavities form within the stem. Sometimes the fruit have small, raised, white spots, about one-fourth inch in diameter. This disease is spread by topping knife and by handling. Control consists of the use of canker-free seed and planting on canker-free soil.

Bacterial Speck (Phytomonas punctulans). Very small, dark-brown or black spots develop on the leaves and fruit. When close together on the leaves, the spots coalesce into large, irregular blotches and the surrounding tissues become yellow. Young plants in plant beds sometimes become affected severely. The disease is spread by water.

Blossom-End Rot. Small, discolored spots sometimes appear on the green fruit at the blossom end and these coalesce into a large, flattened, brown, dead area (Fig. 83). Molds and bacteria may invade the blackened area. The cause is nonparasitic and usually results from an irregular soil moisture supply.

Curly Top. Plants yellowed and stunted, with abnormally erect stems. Upward rolling of leaflets exposing under surface. Veins purple and leaves stiff

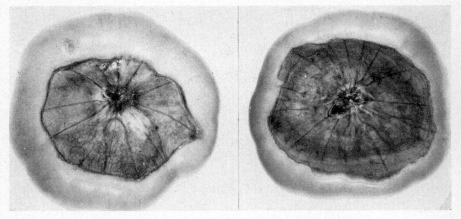

Fig. 83. Blossom-end rot on tomato fruits.

and leathery. Petioles curved downward and leaflets twisted. Plants often die prematurely. Fruits ripen prematurely with practically no fruit-set occurring after infection. Disease caused by virus spread by beet leaf hopper. The only control is to avoid infection or plant closely and thin out the infected plants after the period of infection. Russian thistle is a host plant to the leaf hopper and control has been attempted by killing these plants as well as killing the leaf hopper in the foothills where it overwinters.

Damping-Off (Species of *Pythium, Rhizoctonia,* and *Fusarium*). Emergence failure or collapse and wilting of seedling plants caused by decay of stem at ground line or rotting of roots. Control is by protective seed treatment such as soaking for 5 minutes in a 1 to 1200 solution of New Improved Ceresan, drain and dry without washing.

Early Blight (*Alternaria solani*). Small, dark-colored spots with target-board markings are found on the leaves and stems, especially on young seedlings in plant beds. The collar rot stage on the stem causes serious damage. Prolonged wet weather is likely to encourage the disease. Small, roundish spots also are produced on the fruit.

Fusarium Wilt (*Fusarium oxysporum* f. *lycopersici*). Bright yellowing of leaves, sometimes on only one branch or one side of plant is characteristic during early stages of disease. Yellowing often is followed by gradual death of the plant. Dark-brown discoloration of woody tissue occurs just below green outer cortex of the stem. For control (a) use disease free seed, (b) do not grow in infested soil, and (c) use resistant varieties when available.

Late Blight (*Phytophthora infestans*). The leaves, petioles and stems of affected plants possess rapidly enlarging, moist, brown and black blotches which cause a sudden blighting and killing of the tops. On the fruit, small, water-soaked blotches appear, spread rapidly over the surface, and cause complete rotting or spoilage. The disease is encouraged by cool, rainy weather —sometimes a delicate, whitish mold can be seen on affected parts. Spray vines with a 4-4-50 Bordeaux mixture before the disease appears, or dust with an 18-85 copper-lime dust.

Spotted Wilt. Young leaves show numerous small, dark, circular spots, and often have a bronzed appearance. Such leaves sometimes turn dark and wither. Tips of young plants show dark streaks and sometimes are killed. New growth often is stunted severely. Ripe fruits show spots about one-half inch in diameter, marked with concentric, circular bands of red and yellow. Centers of spots often are raised. Disease is caused by a virus and is carried by flower thrips. Isolate tomatoes from infected ornamental plants. Tomatoes may be seeded or planted thickly to allow the disease to thin the stand or one may remove the diseased plants at thinning.

Tobacco Mosaic. Green and yellow mottling of leaves; some curling, malformation and dwarfing of leaflets. Plants slightly to moderately stunted. Fruits mottled by some strains of the virus. The virus causing this disease is the same as that which causes mosaic of tobacco. It also affects peppers, eggplants, and other members of the Nightshade Family. The control is based on preventing the seedlings and plants from becoming infected. This is accomplished by (a) using disease free seed, (b) using uncontaminated soil or refuse in soil, (c) preventing spread from perennial weeds like ground cherry and horse nettle, and (d) preventing workers from spreading the disease by using tobacco and having the virus on their fingers. Direct field-seeded plants usually are free of this disease. Shoe string mosaic or cucumber virus is spread by aphids in the plant bed.

Verticillium Wilt. Gradual death of foliage confined largely to base of shoots. In early stages plants may wilt during middle of day. All branches usually are affected. Affected plants are stunted but usually remain alive. Discoloration of stem generally confined to basal portions and occurs as a brown patchy spotting over entire stem area instead of in the outer woody portions as in fusarium wilt disease. Avoid soil with verticillium wilt which requires planting nonsusceptible crops for 6 to 7 years. The Pearson variety is somewhat resistant.

References

1. Binkley, A. M.: Growing tomatoes in Colorado, *Colo. Agr. Ext. Ser. D-46,* 21 p., 1944.
2. Bouquet, A. G. B.: Growing tomatoes in the garden, *Ore. Agr. Ext. Bull. 621,* 8 p., 1944.
3. Kraus, James E.: Tomato yield and grade as affected by variety, irrigation and fertilizer, *Ida. Agr. Exp. Sta. Bull. 277,* 14 p., 1949.
4. MacGillivray, John H., A. E. Michelbacher, and C. Emlen Scott:

Tomato production in California, *Calif. Agr. Ext. Ser. Cir. 167,* 60 p., 1950.

5. Moore, John F., Karl Baur, Leo Campbell, and Loyd L. Stitt: Growing tomatoes in the Puget Sound region of Western Washington, *W. Wash. Agr. Exp. Sta. Cir. 92,* 4 p., (Mimeo.) 1950.

6. Pollard, L. H., H. B. Peterson, H. L. Blood, and W. E. Peay: Tomato production in Utah, *Utah Agr. Exp. Sta. Cir. 120,* 31 p., 1944.

PEPPER

Botany. The pepper plant is slightly woody and grows upright from 2 to 4 feet tall. This vegetable is a perennial which is cultivated as an annual. The fruit, a podlike berry, is less juicy than the tomato. The fruit frequently is two-celled and in the mild types three- or four-celled. The pungent compound of peppers is called capsaicin ($C_9H_{14}O_2$). This material does not seem to be present in sweet or bell peppers (*Capsicum frutescens*). In the hot types (tabasco, chili, and cayenne) capsaicin occurs in the cross or septa walls and generally is considered to be present in the placenta. Outside walls and seed are not pungent. Unless care is used in sampling peppers, the seed and outer walls are easily contaminated with capsaicin from other regions of the fruit. Most pepper flowers are self-pollinated, but there is enough cross-pollination to require the separation of varieties for seed.

Origin and History. Peppers are of tropical America origin, and were taken to Europe by Columbus about 1493. There were numerous types available in the Americas which had been eaten for centuries before the coming of the white man. Pepper seed was sent to many countries the first part of the 16th century and so has been used widely. Peppers are grown widely in Spain, Greece, and Hungary. Paprika is grown in Hungary where the product is pungent while the type grown in Spain is mild. Some pepper seed is ground with the pods since the oil in the seeds improves the color of the product. McMahon (1806) lists 4 varieties of peppers and Thorburn in 1826 offered Long or Cayenne, Tomato-shaped or Squash, Bell or Ox-heart, the Cherry, and Bird or West Indian.

Producing Areas. Several types of peppers are grown in the United States. The most important crops are the green or bell peppers and pimientos for processing. There are no statistics for chili, hot peppers, and paprika, all of which, however, are grown. The 1940–1951 statistical data for bell and pimiento peppers are given on p. 335.

The most active harvest season for some of the important market states are: Florida, February and March, also May and June, also November and December; New Jersey, August to October; California, August to October; Texas, November and December; North Carolina, July.

Food Value. Bell or sweet peppers are used most commonly and are found

Peppers for Market

	Acreage	Bushels* Per Acre	Production Bushels	Price Per Bushel Dollars	Farm Value Dollars
United States	24,966	263	6,554,000	$1.74	$11,415,000
Florida	9,341	273	2,550,000	2.26	5,773,000
New Jersey	8,575	210	1,799,000	1.05	1,896,000
California	2,358	344	811,000	1.80	1,463,000
Texas	2,791	164	459,000	1.86	855,000
North Carolina	3,066	141	433,000	1.38	599,000

Pimiento peppers for processing: Georgia, $986,000.
Chili and paprika peppers for drying: California, $1,782,000.
* Approximately 25 pounds.

in group 4 on food production efficiency. Bell peppers are high in ascorbic acid, and 1 pound of raw pepper contains enough ascorbic acid to supply the daily requirements of nine men for this nutrient. Bell pepper contains 92.4 per cent water and the food value per 100 gm. of edible portion is energy, 29 calories; protein, 1.2 gm; calcium, 11 mg.; vitamin A, 870 I.U.; ascorbic acid, 175 mg.; thiamine, 0.06 mg.; riboflavin, 0.03 mg.; and niacin, 0.55 mg. The following data give the relative nutrient rank of bell peppers:

Pound, rank 19: Ascorbic acid, 1; vitamin A, 9.
Acre, rank 20: Ascorbic acid, 2; vitamin A, 9.
Man-hour, rank 19: Ascorbic acid, 3; vitamin A, 9.

Varieties. Most areas grow only the bell or sweet type of pepper, but the Southwest grows a few pimientos for canning, and considerable chili peppers for drying. Areas with short growing season use Harris' Early Giant, World Beater, and Chinese Giant. California Wonder is grown primarily in areas with a long growing season (Fig. 84).

Anaheim Chili (California Long Red). All purpose, hot variety used both for drying and fresh market; long, smooth, tapering deep green fruits, 1 by 7 inches changing to bright scarlet at maturity.

California Wonder. Used for market gardening and shipping; plant vigorous, upright, and prolific; fruits 4-lobed, three and three-fourths by four and one-half inches, upright, attractive, smooth, uniform, with thick sweet flesh. An earlier strain is Early Calwonder and a yellow fleshed strain is Golden California Wonder.

Harris' Early Giant. An early sweet variety for local market; plant small, productive; fruits pendent, 3 lobed, tapered, three and one-half by four and one-fourth inches.

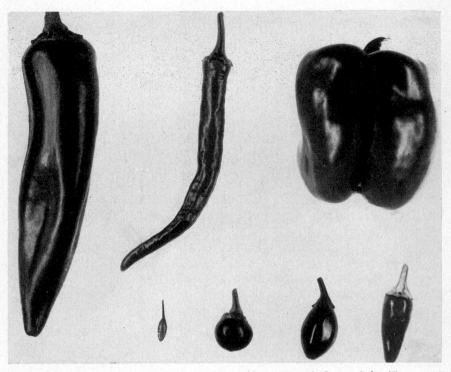

Fig. 84. Various types and varieties of peppers. Left to right (*Top row*)
—Anaheim Chili, Long Red Cayenne, and California Wonder (only nonhot
type). (*Bottom row*)—Chili (wild type), Paprika, Mirasol, and Floral Gem.

Mexican Chili. Hot type, dried for Chili powder in Southwest. Plants tall,
vigorous; fruits 5 inches long with diameter 2 inches at the shoulder, sloping
to a point, dark green when immature, and ripens to a red color.

Pimiento (Perfection). Canning variety; plant large; fruit heart shaped
two and one-half by three and one-half inches, pendent, smooth, with excep-
tionally thick flesh and sweet flavor.

World Beater. Used by market gardeners and shippers; plant upright,
productive; fruits 4 lobed, five by three and three-fourths inches; flesh red,
thick, mild, and sweet.

Climatic Requirements. Most of the commercial production is in the
warmer areas with a few grown in the New England states during the
summer months. The temperature requirement of sweet (bell) peppers is
slightly higher than for tomatoes. They are more sensitive to cool, wet
weather in spring and more tolerant of high summer temperatures. The hot
types of peppers, such as tabasco and strains of chilis, appear to be even more

tolerant of high temperatures than are the sweet varieties. Such peppers should be classed with sweet potato and watermelon as to temperature requirements. Tabascos are grown in Louisiana and the chilis in the Southwest. Air temperature at the time the flowers bloom affects the set of fruit as discussed later. Good seed germination occurs at soil temperatures of 65° to 85° F.

Culture. The general procedures used are very similar to those for tomatoes. Peppers stand erect without support. Soil and fertilizer requirements are similar to those for tomatoes.

Planting and Spacing. Plants usually are produced for field planting by procedures similar to those used for tomatoes. Seed is planted in the coldframe or hotbed about February for different sections of California, and about March 15 in Oregon. Plants are put into the field slightly later than tomatoes. In Coachella and Imperial Valleys, the seed is planted directly in the field. Rows are spaced two and one-half to three feet apart, with plants 18 inches apart in the row. For seed treatment see the description given for tomatoes.

Irrigation. Most of the roots occur in the top 4 feet of soil, but insufficient soil moisture greatly affects yield. At Davis, an irrigation experiment indicated that watering would increase yield several hundred per cent over nonirrigated plots. The plants in the nonirrigated plot made poor growth and showed visible signs of insufficient water. The water is applied in furrows between the rows as in tomatoes, with approximately 18 inches of water being needed.

Fruit Set. Temperature affects the set of peppers just as it does tomatoes. Research studies[3] indicate that the maximum set of Bell peppers occurs at constant temperatures of 60° to 70° F. with temperatures below 60° and above 90° preventing fruit set. As previously noted, hot types appear to be more tolerant of high temperatures.

Harvesting. Sweet peppers usually are harvested as green fruit, but also may be sold partially red or entirely red. The other types are harvested ripe, or when fully red, because color is an important item of quality. Stems of the fruit are woody, but the crop may be snapped off by hand with few damaged fruits. If many are damaged, the stem may be cut with a knife.

Several types of packages are used in marketing such as Los Angeles lugs (15 pounds) ; standard vegetable crates (50 to 60 pounds) ; and the processing crop frequently is transported in sacks.

Storage. Fresh sweet or bell peppers may be kept in fresh storage for 3 to 4 weeks at a temperature range of 40° to 45° F. and a 90 per cent humidity. Some of the hot types are dried for storage or made into pickles.

Paprika and chili peppers are dried and ground into a powder. The chili types are dried in gas-heated ovens maintained at 130° to 160° F. Formerly, the equipment was not very efficient and required 3 to 5 days with some blackening of the fruit. More modern and better equipment now is used by the large driers. The fruit is dried until brittle and ground almost immediately, to prevent the fruit becoming tough with the absorption of moisture. Some chili peppers are strung on cord and dried in the sun in the open air. There is some sale of hot or mildly hot peppers as pickles. These may be fermented in a similar manner to cucumbers and some are preserved by means of strong vinegar with some added salt.

Quality Characteristics for the Retail Buyer. Peppers to be of good quality must be mature, firm, well-shaped, thick-fleshed, and of good color and fresh appearance. Immature peppers are usually soft, pliable, thin-fleshed, and pale in color. Peppers in which the seeds are undeveloped are immature; in mature peppers the seeds are hard. A firm pepper may yield to slight pressure, but it should not be shriveled, limp, or pliable. Shriveling or softness may indicate either age or immaturity. Peppers that have been kept too long are usually in this condition and are often of poor color.

Insects: *Aphid (Aphis gossypii* and *Myzus persicae).* The Spinach or Green Peach aphid on peppers can be controlled by a 10 per cent nicotine dust or a 3 per cent tetraethyl pyrophosphate dust applied at the rate of 15 to 20 pounds per acre.

Darkling Ground Beetle (Blapstinus spp. and *Metoponium abnorme).* These small dark brown beetles girdle the stems near the ground level immediately following transplanting. To protect the plants, dust the ground around the stem with hydrated lime or 10 per cent DDT. The DDT also will give protection against cut worms.

Pepper Weevil (Anthonomus eugenii).. The weevil is a serious pest in the Southwest. The small white grubs feed inside the buds and young pods, causing them to drop. The fields should be watched carefully for the first appearance of the weevils and then a weekly dusting program should be started using 50 per cent cryolite at the rate of 15 to 20 pounds per acre at each dusting. DDT and calcium arsenate also give control but aphids may build up rapidly after these materials are used.

Diseases: *Blossom-end Rot.* Sunken light brown spots on the end or sides of the fruit may be due to a physiological disorder caused by a deficiency of moisture in the plant while the fruit is growing. The moisture deficiency could result from a shortage of soil moisture or from excessive loss of water from the leaves during periods of hot weather or hot drying winds.

Mosaic. The leaves are mottled and dwarfed and the plants may become stunted. Sources of infection include smoking or chewing tobacco and overwintering host plants. The disease is spread by aphids and by handling plants. The virus seldom is as prevalent in field-seeded plantings as in fields grown from transplants.

Root Rot (Phytophthora capsici). The plant wilts and dies from a rotting of the stem and root just below the surface of the ground. This effect is worst in wet soil and at high temperatures. May be prevented partially by having land well leveled and avoiding overirrigation.

Spotted Wilt. This virus disease, which is spread by thrips, is characterized by a defoliation and die-back of the branches from the growing tip and sometimes by orange-yellow rings on the red fruit. Many ornamentals and weeds harbor the virus as well as the thrips and these are the principal sources of infection. There is no satisfactory control program.

Verticillium Wilt. This soil-borne fungus disease causes a brown discoloration in the stem. The whole plant wilts and later may die. The only control is to avoid planting for several years on land where this disease has caused damage, and to avoid following other crops such as potatoes, tomatoes, or strawberries that have been affected by the disease.

References

1. Beattie, J. H. *et al.:* Production of peppers, *U.S.D.A. Leaflet 140,* 7 p., 1944.
2. Bouquet, A. G. B.: Growing garden peppers, *Ore. Agr. Ext. Cir. 500,* 3 p., (Mimeo.) 1948.
3. Cochran, H. L.: Some factors influencing growth and fruit setting in the pepper, *Cornell Univ. Mem. 190,* 39 p., 1936.
4. Cockerill, P. W.: Economics of the production and marketing of Chili in New Mexico, *N.M. Agr. Exp. Sta. Bull. 314,* 18 p., 1944.
5. Irwin, A. T.: The peppers, *Iowa Agr. Exp. Sta. Bull. 293:* 120–152, 1932.
6. Smith, P. G. and P. A. Minges: Pepper production in California, *Calif. Agr. Ext. Multolith,* 8 p., 1948.

SUMMER AND WINTER SQUASH

Botany. The gourd family (*Cucurbitaceae*) contains important vegetable crops, such as cucumber, melon, summer and winter squash, pumpkin, and watermelon. The vegetables of this family are referred to as cucurbits, and are usually climbing or trailing plants, with tendrils with the exception of summer squash. The flowers are frequently yellow and large. The staminate and pistillate flowers usually are borne in separate flowers, that is, they are monoecious. Staminate flowers are the first to bloom, and occur in greater numbers than the pistillate flowers. The ratio of pistillate to staminate flowers varies from $1:4$ to as high as $1:10$. Flowers of the gourd family are visited by insects and bees that pollinate the blossoms. This family is characterized by a fruit called a pepo. Squash and pumpkins have the typical characteristics of the cucurbits, and are all characterized by a mature fruit with the seed in a definite cavity. Summer squash are harvested as immature fruit, usually 4 to 7 days after blossoming, and sometimes even the pistillate flowers are sold for food. The summer squash is a bush crop without vines in contrast to the other cucurbits to be studied, which produce running vines.

Summer squash, winter squash, and pumpkins all belong to the genus *Cucurbita*. Most of these crops belong to 3 species as follows, *Pepo, moschata*, and *maxima*. The terms squash and pumpkin do not have the same meaning for all people, but the above species may be described accurately. Castetter and Erwin[2] list the following characteristics for the leaves, fruit stalks, and seed.

A. Leaves
    1. Prickly, deep sinuses between lobes . . . .   *C. Pepo*
    2. Not prickly, sinuses indistinct or absent
        a. Lobes pointed; with rare exceptions, leaves soft hairy, with white spots at the intersections of veins . . . .   *C. moschata*
        b. Lobes rounded; rough hairy, kidney shaped, white spots never present . . . .   *C. maxima*

B. Fruit Stalks
    1. Cylindrical, soft and spongy, yielding readily to thumbnail . . . .   *C. maxima*
    2. Distinctly 5 sided, regularly grooved, hard
        a. Flaring at attachment to fruit . . . .   *C. moschata*
        b. Not noticeably flaring or enlarged at attachment to fruit . . . .   *C. Pepo*
    3. Roughly cylindrical, not definitely 5 sided, irregular grooved, not flaring or noticeably enlarged at attachment to fruit; hard . . . .   *C. moschata*

C. Seeds
    1. Color, grayish white to tan; margin thickened, deeper in color and different in texture from body of seed; seed scar slanting, rounded or horizontal . . . .   *C. moschata*
    2. Margin, when present, identical in color and texture with body of seed
        a. White, or brown to bronze—seed scar slanting . . . .   *C. maxima*
        b. Tan colored. Seed scar horizontal or rounded . . . .   *C. Pepo*

Summer squash are the immature fruits of *C. Pepo* var. *Melopepo,* but the immature fruits of other *Cucurbita* may be used. Summer squash are either stewed, boiled, or fried. Winter squash are usually varieties of *C. maxima* and are baked, boiled and used for pies. The flesh is fine-grained and mild in flavor. Pumpkins most frequently are varieties of *C. Pepo* and *C. moschata* and the flesh is coarse and perhaps of strong flavor. Some varieties of the last 2 species also are used in the same manner as *C. maxima.*

Origin and History. There is good evidence that the species *Pepo* and *moschata* are of American origin, but the evidence about the *maxima* species is not as conclusive. There is some confusion because of the general use of the word pumpkin to include some melons, by the early writers. There is evidence that the word squash came from the Indians along the northeast Atlantic coast.

There are several early records indicating the use of pumpkin and squash in the Americas. In 1535, Cartier found pumpkins growing in the region of Montreal. There are records of their use in Virginia in 1586. Summer squash was described from the New Netherlands in 1642. Some of this type were called "crooked neck" or "crane-necks", probably indicating the origin of the variety name of Summer Crookneck. The Indians in the Northeast as well as the Seminole Indians of Florida made use of these vegetables. The Turban squash probably came from Chile about 1856, and the Hubbard squash is reported to have been brought to Massachusetts from the Indies by a sea captain.

Food Value. Mature pumpkins are used primarily for pies. Their food value is probably very similar to that of winter squash. Summer squash is found in group four on food production efficiency, while winter squash is the only fruit crop to be found in group one. Since winter squash is harvested only once, the labor needed to harvest this crop is not great so the crop rates high in nutrients per man-hour. Summer squash contains 95.0 per cent water and the food value per 100 gm. of edible portion is energy, 19 calories; protein, 0.6 gm.; calcium, 15 mg.; vitamin A, 200 I.U.; ascorbic acid, 26 mg.; thiamine, 0.045 mg.; riboflavin, 0.052 mg.; and niacin, 0.96 mg. Winter squash contains 88.6 per cent water and the food value per 100 gm. of edible portion is energy, 44 calories; protein, 1.5 gm.; calcium, 19 mg.; vitamin A, 4000 I.U.; ascorbic acid, 5 mg.; thiamine, 0.048 mg.; riboflavin, 0.046 mg.; and niacin, 0.96 mg. The following data give the relative nutrient rank of summer and winter squash:

Summer squash:
    Pound, rank 18: Niacin, 4; ascorbic acid, 8.
      Acre, rank 16: Niacin, 4; ascorbic acid, 9.
Man-hour, rank 20: Niacin, 7.
    Winter squash:
    Pound, rank 15: Vitamin A, 1; niacin, 8.
      Acre, rank 11: Vitamin A, 1; niacin, 2; energy, 7.
Man-hour, rank 1: Protein, 1; vitamin A, 1; niacin, 1; energy, 2; thiamine,
                2; calcium, 4; riboflavin, 5.

Producing Areas. Summer squash is grown widely in the United States but primarily for nearby markets. Some of this crop is shipped north from the southern states. Winter squash is grown to a considerable extent in the northern tier of states for fall use and stored for use during winter. Statistical data of acreage, yield, and value are not reported for pumpkin and squash.

Varieties. Most important types of summer squash varieties are described here. Some of these varieties have several strains and in the case of the Zucchini there are types with different-colored fruits. Yellow Straightneck and Yellow Summer Crookneck are similar except for shape of fruit and are popular (Fig. 85). Among the winter squash there are several types of Hubbard and Banana squash.

BUSH OR SUMMER SQUASH
(*Cucurbita Pepo* var. *Melopepo*)

Cocozelle. Bush type similar to Zucchini except there are light green stripes on the immature fruits, changing to yellow when ripe.

Straightneck. Similar to yellow crookneck except in shape; bush type; fruits straight, smooth, and light-yellow color; edible when 4 to 5 inches long up to 12 to 14 inches; used for home garden and shipment.

White Bush Scallop. Bush type; plants large and productive; fruits have scalloped edges; strains vary in color, white, green, and yellow; in the southwest harvested when 2 to 3 inches in diameter.

Zucchini. Bush type; fruits straight and cylindrical; color varies with

Fig. 85. Four varieties of summer squash. (*Left to right*) Gray Zucchini, Yellow Straightneck, Yellow Crookneck, and Scallop.

strain from dark to grayish-green; popular in West and South for local markets. Black Zucchini is more popular than the grayish-green type.

VINING OR WINTER SQUASH
(*C. maxima*)

Banana. Vine type of plant; fruit cylindrical and pointed at blossom end, 20 inches long, with thin pink rind; flesh yellowish orange; there is also a strain with gray skin.

Boston Marrow. Canning type. Similar to Hubbard in size and shape but with orange skin; fruits weigh 6 to 8 pounds, 9 inches in diameter and 12 inches long, skin rough and hard.

Buttercup. Small turban-shaped squash, 7 inches in diameter with golden, pleasing flavor when cooked. Desirable as a small family-size squash.

Golden Delicious. Canning type important because of high starch content. Combined with Boston Marrow in Northwest to produce a thick canned pumpkin. Fruits top-shaped about 7 pounds, color reddish orange with green tip at blossom end; flesh orange, and fruits keep well.

Hubbard. There are 3 strains of Hubbard squash, golden, green, and warted, of which the green or blue green is the most popular. Vine type of plant; fruits 10 to 12 pounds, pointed at both ends, slightly warted, rind hard and tough, flesh thick, orange-yellow color; dry and sweet.

Table Queen (C. Pepo). Used as winter squash; vine type; fruits oval, pointed at blossom end, ribbed, thin-shelled, and dark green in color but changes to yellow upon storage; flesh yellow, bakes well with good flavor. Also called Danish, Des Moines and Acorn. There are several strains available.

Climatic Requirements. All of these crops are found in the same group of vegetables and are adapted to monthly means of 65° to 80° F., but are not tolerant to frost or prolonged exposure near freezing. This group of plants should not be planted until the monthly means have reached 60° to 65° F., or until the average frost-free date of the locality has been reached. Summer squash and pumpkin are grown more generally throughout the United States than is winter squash. *Cucurbita maxima* is produced more generally in the northern states. In canning, starch is important to produce a thick canned product. There is some evidence that Golden Delicious squash will store or accumulate more starch in an area like Wisconsin than further south in Indiana. The effect of temperature on seed germination is probably very similar to cucumbers which germinate satisfactorily at a soil temperature from 65° to 85° F.

Soil. These crops are grown successfully on most soil types, but will do better on soils that are fertile, have good drainage, and warm up early in the spring. Yields are higher if the soil is in the range of slightly acid to

slightly alkaline. These crops are of medium value and consequently sometimes are grown on medium-rated soils.

Fertilizers. These crops do not receive large amounts of fertilizer. Imperial
Valley uses 40 pounds of nitrogen per acre and a smaller amount of phosphoric acid for summer squash. Other areas use only nitrogen. Winter
squash is grown during warmer weather, when nitrification is greater, and
receives only half as much nitrogen. Oregon growers use well-rotted manure
for these crops; but if not available, about 300 pounds per acre of a 4-12-8,
4-12-6, or 4-10-6 fertilizer. Eastern Washington growers on irrigated soils
use 100 pounds of nitrogen and 50 pounds of phosphoric acid without
manure or 10 tons of manure and 80 pounds of nitrogen.

Planting and Spacing. Summer squash is planted in much the same way as
cantaloupes. Seed is planted in hills about 3 by 5 feet apart. Several plantings may be made about a month apart to insure a supply for market from
spring until late fall. Vining types of squash are produced at wider spacing,
varying from 6 by 8 feet to 9 by 9 feet according to local practise. After
plants are up they should be thinned to 2 plants per hill. About 3 to 4 pounds
of seed per acre are required for planting.

Plants are killed by frost. Planting dates for squash correspond to those
given for cantaloupes. Where earliness is desired and plants are started
before danger of frost is past, it is a common practise to protect the plants
at night by covering with empty packing boxes after the leaf and vine growth
have exceeded the capacity of ordinary hotcaps. The use of brush protectors,
as for cantaloupes, is a common practise in the Imperial Valley.

Seeds of most cucurbits are very susceptible to decay in cold, wet soil
but usually escape infection when planted in a warm, moist soil. Treatment
with Semesan at 5 ounces per 100 pounds of seed, Spergon at 8 ounces, red
copper oxide at 8 ounces, or yellow copper oxide at 5 ounces, usually will
provide good protection against soil fungi. Seed that has already been
soaked in water to hasten germination may be dipped just before planting in
a suspension of yellow copper oxide at 2 pounds per 10 gallons, or Semesan
at one-fifth of a pound per 10 gallons, or Semesan Bel at one and one-third
pounds per 10 gallons. One gallon of suspension should be used for each
pound of seed to be treated. In soil heavily infested by Rhizoctonia the
organic mercury compounds listed above give better control than copper
oxide.

Irrigation. The roots of summer squash plants are found primarily in the
top 4 feet of soil while those of winter squash and pumpkins extend to a
depth of 6 feet. There has been one irrigation experiment at Davis with
summer squash and another with pumpkins. These tests indicated a small
increase in yield from irrigation over the nonirrigated plots. The general
recommendation is for not more than 18 inches of water for all of these
crops. Summer squash needs a greater amount of water because of a

shallower root system and the need for maintaining growth. In many areas winter squash could be raised with less than 18 inches of water. Four to 6 applications would be desirable.

Harvesting. The fruits of the summer squash types are harvested while very immature. Southwestern markets favor small fruits, so they are harvested 2 to 4 days after the flowers open. Other markets favor larger fruits about 7 days old. Table 39 shows the effect of harvesting the fruits at various ages and sizes. If the fruit is harvested when fairly large, the yield is increased. Growers harvesting their crop when the fruits are 3 to 4 inches long in the case of Zucchini should receive a higher price than growers who allow the fruits to become larger before harvest. Easy indentation with the thumbnail is the common test for tenderness of the fruit. No fruits should be allowed to mature on the vines as this tends to reduce the number of fruits set and retards the production of later fruits.

Table 39*

RELATION BETWEEN FREQUENCY OF HARVESTING
ZUCCHINI SQUASH AND NUMBER OF
FRUITS AS WELL AS THEIR WEIGHT

Harvesting Interval	*Average Number of Fruits Per Plant*	*Average Weight Per Fruit Grams*	*Average Weight of Fruits Per Plant Kilos*
Daily	46	41	1.9
Three times weekly	31	86	2.7
Twice weekly	26	293	7.5
Weekly	16	300	4.9
Bi-weekly	10	481	4.7
Termination of experiment	6	3,024	18.2

* Courtesy, *Amer. Soc. Hort. Sci. Proc. 30:* 520–525, 1934.

The fruits of winter squash are harvested after the fruits have matured but before the vines have been killed by frost; the sugar content and keeping quality of the fruit improve with maturity. In harvesting, the stem should be cut so as to leave a short stub attached to the fruit. Care should be used not to scratch or bruise the fruit. Yields of from 10 to 20 tons per acre are to be expected under favorable growing conditions.

Storage. Well-matured fruit of winter squash or pumpkins can be kept until early spring by storing in a well-ventilated, warm, dry room. Abrasions in the shell allow the entrance of disease organisms and therefore bruised fruits will not keep well in storage and should be used soon after harvest. Optimum storage temperatures are from 50° to 55° F. and the humidity should be kept low (75 per cent). Accumulation of moisture on the surface of the fruit is conducive to invasion by soft-rot organisms. In the case of slightly immature fruits a curing treatment at 80° to 85° F. for 2 weeks is helpful to obtain the best storage life. Variety affects the length of storage. A Cushaw pumpkin is a poor keeper and will keep 2 or 3 months while a hard shell squash like Hubbard can be stored successfully for over 6 months. Summer squash may be stored at 50° F. 95 per cent relative humidity, and for a period not greater than two to three weeks.

Quality Characteristics for the Retail Buyer. Summer squash should be fresh, fairly heavy for the size, free from blemish, and the rind so tender that it can be punctured very easily. Winter squash should be heavy for its size and free from blemish, and the rind should be hard.

Hard-rind summer squash usually has hard or semi-hard seeds, depending on the stage of development. This condition makes summer squash undesirable, since for most table use the seeds and rind are not discarded. The flesh of hard-rind summer squash is likely to be stringy also. Soft-rind winter squash is usually immature; the flesh may be thin, watery when cooked, and lack flavor. Bruised or otherwise injured squash should be examined carefully for evidence of decay that may have penetrated the flesh. Winter squash is subject to decay, possibly because of handling and storage methods. Decay may appear as a watery or water-soaked area, sometimes covered with a mold-like growth, brown or black in color. Often the injury can be cut away without undue waste.

Insects: *Cucumber Beetle* (*Diabrotica undecimpunctata* and *Acalymma vittata*). Both the western 12-spotted cucumber beetle (or diabrotica) and the striped cucumber beetle damage cucurbits. These pests carry bacterial wilt in addition to their feeding habits. The larvae feed on the roots and the adults feed on the leaves and stems. The larvae appear like wireworms, but have a black anal plate. Dusting with 50 per cent cryolite often is effective against the adults. DDT although effective should be applied lightly to cucurbits, and mixtures with sulfur may cause damage.

Melon Aphid (*Aphis gossypii*). This insect is the most destructive aphid on cucurbits. Winged aphids fly into the field from weeds or other hosts and give birth to living young who colonize on the under sides of leaves. The infestation is spread by the winged forms. The aphids suck the plant juice causing curling and distorting of the leaves as well as spreading mosaic diseases. Large amounts of honey dew are produced which cover the fruit and allows for the growth of a sooty mold.

Natural enemies assist in aphid control. Nicotine dusts containing 2 to 4 per cent nicotine as alkaloid are effective if applied under warm conditions at the rate of 40 to 50 pounds per acre. TEPP sprays and dusts give good control if applied prior to extensive curling of the leaves. Applications of insecticides should be made prior to the build up of large populations.

Squash Bug (*Anasa tristis*). The eggs are laid on the underside of leaves and in about 12 days the nymphs appear. They reach maturity in 4 or 5 weeks. Usually 1 or 2 generations occur a year, and adults overwinter under debris, boards, loose bark, etc. The pest damages the plant by sucking out plant juices, and by injecting salivary secretions into the plant during feeding. The plants wilt and may die. The adults and nymphs often feed on the developing fruit, and after the plants die in the fall the adults cluster about the fruit. Summer squashes usually are not attacked, but winter squash and also watermelons, cantaloupes, and cucumbers frequently are damaged.

Clean culture, including the cleaning up and burning of all refuse in the fall, is of value in the control of this insect. TEPP dusts (0.66 per cent) pyrophosphate content is of value if applied at 90 pounds per acre. Lindane as a 1 per cent gamma isomer dust at 30 pounds per acre is effective. Chlordane and toxaphene may be effective, but can damage the plants.

Diseases: *Cottony Rot.* This disease may rot the stems at the surface of the ground causing the plants to wilt and die. In squash the mycelium may grow inside the seed cavity completely filling it with mycelium and sclerotia.

Curly Top. The young terminal leaves become curled, stiff, and stunted. The older leaves are yellow. This is a virus disease spread by the beet leaf hopper. Absence of leaf hoppers infected with the disease is the only control.

Damping Off. Young plants wilt and die from a rotting in the stem near the ground. The disease is more prevalent under cool weather and moist soil conditions. Seed treatment is helpful in control.

Mosaic. Cucumber mosaic virus. The young leaves of the plants are stunted, deformed and mottled with yellow and light green. The fruit may be misshapen and mottled in color. The virus is spread by aphids.

Powdery Mildew (Erysiphe cichoracearum). The leaves become covered with white mold growth and the plants are stunted and weaken. Dusting with sulfur is the best control measure.

Root Rot (Fusarium solani var. *cucurbitae).* Lower leaves turn yellow and wilt, after which the other leaves are affected and the plant dies. Near the surface of the ground on the stem there is a soft rot. Control by the use of disease free seed and rotation.

Squash Mosaic. Plant symptoms are similar to those found on other cucurbits. Disease is spread by aphids so their control is recommended to prevent decreased yields.

References

1. Bouquet, A. G. B.: Growing pumpkin and squash, *Ore. Agr. Ext. Cir. 277,* 7 p., (Mimeo.) 1938.
2. Castetter, E. F., and A. T. Erwin: A systematic study of squashes and pumpkins, *Iowa Agr. Exp. Sta. Bull. 244:* 107–135, 1927.
3. Thompson, R. C.: Production of pumpkins and squashes, *U.S.D.A. Leaflet 141,* 8 p., 1943.

4. Whitaker, Thomas W., and G. W. Bohn: The taxonomy, genetics, production and uses of the cultivated species of *Cucurbita, Economic Botany 4:* 52–81, 1950.

CUCUMBER

Botany. The cucumber (*Cucumis sativus*) has a prostrate, branching vine some 6 to 8 feet long. The fruit is oblong and tends to be three-angled. The fruits have black or white spines which may be removed by rubbing the fruit. Small cucumbers sometimes are incorrectly called gherkins. The West Indian gherkin (*Cucumis Anguria*) is about one and one-half inches long, oval with prickly spines which are longer and more permanent than those of the cucumber. The English greenhouse cucumber sets fruit without pollination.

Origin and History. The cucumber has been cultivated for many centuries and is believed to be native to the East Indies. It was introduced probably into China about 100 B.C. Early explorers introduced cucumbers to the Americas, so the Indians grew this crop from Florida to Canada in the late 16th century.

Producing Areas. Slicing cucumbers are produced by field production and in greenhouses (Fig. 2). A considerable acreage also is grown to be used in producing cucumber pickles. The 1940–1951 statistical data are given on p. 349.

The most active harvest season for some of the important market states as well as those in the West are: Florida, November to May; New York, August and September; South Carolina, June; California, May and June, also September; New Jersey, July and August.

Food Value. Cucumbers are low in food value and are found in group 4 on food production efficiency. This vegetable is used as an appetizer or mixed with other vegetables for its distinctive flavor and texture. Cucumber contains 96.1 per cent water and the food value per 100 gm. of edible portion is energy, 14 calories; protein, 0.7 gm.; calcium, 24 mg.; vitamin A. 20 I.U.; ascorbic acid, 12 mg.; thiamine, 0.024 mg.; riboflavin, 0.075 mg.; and niacin, 0.30 mg. The following data give the relative nutrient rank of cucumbers.

Pound, rank 29: Nutrient rank is 11 or lower.
Acre, rank 23: Nutrient rank is 11 or lower.
Man-hour, rank 25: Nutrient rank is 11 or lower.

Varieties. Slicing cucumbers vary in length from 6 to 12 inches and are harvested at an older stage than pickling cucumbers. Pickling types are picked from two and one-half inches up to 6 to 8 inches long, the smaller sizes selling at considerably higher prices. Most slicing types have white spines while the pickling types have black spines (Fig. 86). Special varieties are used in greenhouses. The lemon variety resembles a lemon in size and

Cucumbers for Market

	Acreage	Bushels* Per Acre	Production Bushels	Price Per Bushel Dollars	Farm Value Dollars
United States	48,856	119	5,804,000	$2.05	$11,934,000
Florida	10,883	136	1,476,000	3.05	4,509,000
New York	4,941	132	653,000	1.87	1,224,000
California	2,066	278	574,000	1.77	1,018,000
South Carolina	5,900	92	544,000	1.84	1,002,000
New Jersey	3,025	168	509,000	1.70	868,000

* Approximately 48 pounds.

Cucumbers for Processing

	Acreage	Bushels* Per Acre	Production Bushels	Price Per Bushel Dollars	Farm Value Dollars
United States	114,100	77	8,807,000	$1.23	$10,856,000
Michigan	34,158	60	2,034,000	1.28	2,614,000
Wisconsin	17,833	75	1,346,000	1.33	1,800,000
California	2,874	291	836,000	1.02	860,000
North Carolina	7,291	84	610,000	1.13	691,000
Colorado	2,125	187	398,000	1.21	480,000

(Farm value, other Western states: Oregon, $282,000; Washington, $180,000.)
* Approximately 48 pounds.

appearance and some home gardeners prefer this variety for its flavor. The Palmetto variety is resistant to Downey Mildew. There are numerous cucumber varieties, but the following are among the more important:

A and C. Introduced by Abbott and Cobb; important shipping and market variety; fruits cylindrical with white spines; dark green, tapering at ends, eight and one-half by two and one-half inches. Colorado is similar to A and C in size and other characteristics.

Cubit. New variety; fruits cylindrical with white spines; dark green; hold color well with larger size, 8 by 2 inches; shy seeder.

Marketer. Popular market type with white spines; plant is vigorous and prolific; fruits are 8 inches long and two and one-quarter inches in diameter, fruit is slightly tapered, and seed area is small.

National Pickling. Black-spines, used exclusively for pickles; fruits straight,

Fig. 86. Slicing cucumbers on the left are larger at the harvest stage than pickling cucumbers on the right. (Courtesy, Ferry-Morse Seed Co.)

symmetrical; well filled at ends, about 6 inches long when mature. Other pickling varieties are Boston Pickling and Chicago Pickling.

Straight 8. Used for market and shipping; fruit uniformly cylindrical with rounded ends and white spines; medium green, eight by two and one-quarter inches.

Climatic Requirements. Both cantaloupe and cucumber have a higher heat requirement than beans. While the latter crop can be grown without protection in Florida in the winter, this is not true of cantaloupe or cucumbers any place in the United States. Cucumbers are adapted to average monthly temperatures of 65° to 75° F. The large slicing cucumbers for market are grown mainly from New York southward and in the Gulf states to Texas. The pickling types are grown around the Great Lakes. Thus, heat is not so essential for cucumbers as for cantaloupes and they are produced in these areas even with the handicap of rather high humidity. In many of these areas, the season is likely to be shortened by disease. Cucumbers are not sensitive to day lengths in the field, but varieties show differences when grown in the greenhouse in fall and winter. The Abundance variety frequently is used in greenhouse culture. Cucumber seed germinates well in a soil temperature range of 65° to 85° F.

Attention has been called to the fact that climatic requirements of cantaloupes and cucumbers are somewhat similar; this also applies to cultural practises. Much of the pickling crop is grown on soils of fairly low value so the crop can be sold relatively cheap. The early crop of outdoor cucumbers as well as the greenhouse crop are grown under a more intensive culture.

Soil. Cucumbers may be grown on almost any good soil, but a considerable amount of the crop is grown on sandy loams. This is particularly important when earliness is desired or when the crop is grown in cooler areas of the northern states where the growing season is short. Good drainage, with high moisture-holding capacity, also is desirable.

Fertilizers. Western cucumber acreage is rather limited. Fifty pounds of nitrogen is used per acre and in addition a similar amount of phosphoric acid is used in Imperial Valley. Pickling cucumbers in central California need 100 pounds per acre of nitrogen. In Oregon, for pickles, stable manure may be applied broadcasted or if available in limited amounts, it may be put in a furrow before planting. A few hundred pounds per acre of superphosphate or complete fertilizer may be added to the furrows containing the manure. The manure should rot before planting time. Commercial fertilizer of about a 1-2-2 ratio may be applied as the seed is planted, but 2 to 3 inches from the seed row and an inch or so below the seed level. The fertilizer recommendation for Eastern Washington is the same as for squash. Gardeners favor the use of manure on vine crops and sometimes rotted manure is put in a trench below where the hill is made for the cucumbers.

Planting and Spacing. Planting distances vary with locality. Where the cucumbers are grown in hills, the hills usually are spaced 6 by 6 or 6 by 8 feet apart. When planting is in rows, the rows are placed 4 to 6 feet apart, and the plants thinned to 3 feet apart in the row. Planting times are similar to those used for other cucurbits. Seed treatments are the same as used for summer and winter squash.

Forcing Earliness. Early cucumbers may be produced through the use of hotcaps and other similar procedures which are used in producing early cantaloupes and watermelons. The hills sometimes are started in coldframes or hotbeds after an early vegetable crop for transplanting has been removed. Thus cabbage plants could be grown and shortly before they are planted in the field, cucumber seed could be planted in the coldframes. When the wooden frames are removed with the coming of warm weather, the grower has a field of early cucumbers.

Irrigation. Cucumbers are a moderately deep-rooted (4 feet) crop, but irrigation has increased greatly the yield at Davis, California in the one test that was made. The heavily irrigated plots yielded 500 per cent more than the nonirrigated plots. Irrigation increased the yields of all grades and size of the cucumbers, with some indication that bitterness may be decreased by irrigation. Four or more irrigations are desirable at Davis, California with a minimum of 15 inches of water.

Harvesting. The picking season extends over a period of a month or longer. During this period the fruits should be gathered regularly to prevent some from growing too large for market; this may require going over the vines every day during the height of the season. When picked, the fruit should be green in color although proper size will vary with variety; this variety characteristic, therefore, should be known. The fruits are cut, clipped, or broken from the vines. If the latter procedure is used, care should be taken not to harm the plant. The fruit is gathered in baskets or sometimes bags. In the picking, the vines should be handled carefully and it is customary to windrow the plants to prevent their being walked on and to make subsequent harvests easier.

Pickling cucumbers are usually smaller in size; the small sizes are paid for at a higher rate. The size of one and three-fourths to three and one-fourth inches is most desired and only those cucumbers which are missed at the previous harvest are allowed to make large size (three and one-fourth to five and one-half inches). Sometimes slightly larger fruits are used for dill pickles. A grower of pickling cucumbers must decide whether the premium paid for small cucumbers is sufficient to justify the increased picking cost and the decreased yield. The data in Table 40 show the effect of frequency of picking on the size, yield, and amount of culls harvested.

When a fruit becomes too mature there is a lighter green color and a hardening of the seeds. These are culls as are also misshapen fruits. "Nub-

Table 40*

EFFECT OF FREQUENCY OF PICKING ON CUCUMBER YIELDS 1931–1933.

Picking Interval Days	Number of Fruit Per 100 Plants of All Grades	Total Weight Pounds Per Acre	Pounds of Fruit Per Acre†			Per Cent of Total Weight		
			Small	Large	Nubs and Crooks	Small	Large	Nubs and Crooks
1	3764	4570	2366	476	1710	52	10	37
2	3020	5357	2056	1232	1881	38	24	35
3	2657	6720	1866	2059	2142	28	31	32
4	2179	8139	1476	2613	2340	18	32	29
7‡	1162	10,388	373	2166	1459	4	21	14

* Courtesy, *Mich. Agr. Exper. Sta. Spec. Bull. 259, 1935.*

† Small cucumbers are less than three and one-eighth inches long, diameter is less than one and one-eighth inches and they are shaped perfectly.

Large cucumbers are perfect in shape, more than three and one-fourth inches long and less than five and one-half inches, more than one and one-eighth inches and less than two inches in diameter.

Culls have been omitted from the above table in the last 6 columns.

‡ 1932 only.

bins" have a constriction at the blossom end and "wasps" are those which are affected similarly at the stem end. Improper pollination is one cause of poor shape in cucumbers.

Storage. Cucumbers are stored for only short periods such as 10 to 14 days. The most favorable storage temperature is 45° to 50° F. with 95 per cent humidity. If the fruit is held below 45° F. for 2 weeks they become affected by dark colored watery areas. These areas may become infected with mold. Temperatures above 50° F. cause a ripening of the fruit, with a change in color from green to yellow. Also there may be some shriveling. Waxing of market cucumbers is practised commercially which reduces weight loss and improves appearance. Pickling cucumbers are placed in a salt brine 6 to 8 hours after picking and do not receive any special storage treatment up till the time of pickling.

Pickle growers usually deliver their cucumbers to a salting station where the fruit goes through the first fermentation. The cucumbers are placed in large wooden vats and covered with a salt brine of 40° salometer or 10 per cent salt. The cucumbers are kept immersed in the brine by a heavy circular wooden head. The brine should be maintained near 10 per cent to increase the activity of lactic acid organisms and prevent the growth of unfavorable organisms. Sometimes the brine is circulated by pumping to insure a uniformity and correct concentration of the brine. This fermentation and airing process may continue for 5 to 8 weeks depending to some extent on the temperature which should be about 70° to 80° F. The cured pickles are shipped to some central factory where the salt is removed and replaced by vinegar; or vinegar, sugar, and spices depending on whether sour or sweet pickles are desired. Complete directions for making pickles will be found in circular by Joslyn and Cruess.

Quality Characteristics for the Retail Buyer. Cucumbers for slicing purposes should be firm, fresh, bright, well-shaped, and of green color. The flesh should be firm and the seeds immature.

Withered or shriveled cucumbers should be avoided. Their flesh is generally tough or rubbery and somewhat bitter. The color of overmature cucumbers is generally dull and not infrequently yellowed, the flesh is rubbery and tough, the seeds are hard, and the flesh in the seed cavity is almost jelly-like. Cucumbers in this condition are not suited for slicing but sometimes are used for certain kinds of pickles. Some varieties are of solid green color when mature enough for slicing but usually a little whitish color will be found at the tip, with a tendency to extend in lines along the seams. These lines advance from pale green to white and finally to yellow, with age. Decay when present usually appears anywhere on the surface as a dark, sunken, irregular area.

Insects and Diseases. See the discussion given for squash.

References

1. Baur, Karl, John F. Moore, Loyd L. Stitt, and Leo Campbell: Growing pickling cucumbers in Western Washington, *W. Wash. Exper. Sta. Cir. 90*, 3 p., (Mimeo.) 1950.
2. Beattie, W. R.: Cucumber growing, *U.S.D.A. Farmers' Bull. 1563*, 25 p., 1942.
3. Bouquet, A. G. B.: Growing cucumbers for pickles, *Ore. Agr. Ext. Cir. 429*, 7 p., (Mimeo.) 1944.
4. Bouquet, A. G. B.: Growing greenhouse vegetables—cucumbers, *Ore. Agr. Ext. Cir. 433*, 4 p., 1944.
5. Joslyn, M. A., and W. V. Cruess: Home and farm preparation of pickles, *Calif. Agr. Ext. Ser. Cir. 37*, 24 p., 1943.
6. Seaton, H. L.: The influence of the length of the interval between pickings on the yield and grade of pickling cucumbers. *Mich. Agr. Exp. Sta. Spec. Bull. 259*, 20 p., 1935.

CANTALOUPE

Botany. Cantaloupe (*Cucumis melo* var. *reticulatus*) plants are similar to cucumbers except that the leaves are roundish, whereas cucumber leaves are more angular or 5 pointed. Cantaloupes are an annual plant with runners 7 to 8 feet long. Secondary stems are produced from the axils of the leaves close to the crown of the plant. The stamens are borne in groups of 3 to 5 and the pistillate flowers are borne singly. Usually a stem will set about 2 fruits and the next pistillate flowers will abort so the fruits are borne in cycles. Although this family of plants is typically monoecious, in the case of most cantaloupe varieties the flowers are andromonoecious, or bear both staminate and hermaphroditic flowers. The size of fruit is intermediate between that of the watermelon and the cucumber. The Casaba and Honey Dew melons are placed in the botanical variety *inodorus*. There are several other types of melons belonging to other botanical varieties but these are of little commercial importance. The words cantaloupe and muskmelon are used loosely. Both are members of *Cucumis melo*. Some vegetable people feel that melons belonging to var. *reticulatus* should only be called muskmelons. Likewise, members of the var. *cantalupensis* should be called cantaloupe. The latter botanical variety is not grown in the United States. East of the Rocky Mountains this vegetable is called muskmelon while the term cantaloupe is used more commonly in the Southwest.

Origin and History. The cantaloupe has never been found growing wild, but is believed to be indigenous to the Old World tropics, particularly India. In spite of the confusion as to the meaning of the word melon it seems evident that cantaloupes were known in southern Europe and the area east to India, and even to China, in the early centuries. There are many records of this fruit after the 15th century and seeds were brought to America by Columbus or other earlier explorers. Within 50 years melons were being grown in Central America and Canada. Melons were reported being grown in Brazil about 1647. In Africa the seeds sometimes are pressed to obtain oil. During the Civil War many southern farmers concentrated the juice of melons for molasses and sugar.

Producing Areas. Cantaloupe production including Honey Dew and Honey Ball is centered largely in the irrigated areas of the Southwest which are able to make early shipments to eastern markets. The vegetable also is grown in other states for the late summer and early fall market. The 1940–51 statistical data for cantaloupes are given separately in the following table and the data for Honey Ball and Honey Dew melons are given below the table.

Cantaloupes for Market

	Acreage	Crates* Per Acre	Production Crates	Price Per Crate Dollars	Farm Value Dollars
United States	109,471	101	11,098,000	$2.82	$31,346,000
California	37,900	133	5,029,000	3.32	16,702,000
Arizona	22,658	119	2,693,000	3.11	8,383,000
Texas	5,266	56	294,000	3.02	888,000
Indiana	5,058	79	401,000	2.15	866,000
Maryland	5,316	83	440,000	1.95	860,000

(Farm value, other Western states: Colorado, $540,000; Washington, $482,000; New Mexico, $186,000; Oregon, $186,000; Nevada, $18,000.

Farm value of Honey Ball melons: California, $544,000; Arizona, $5,000.

Farm value of Honey Dew melons: California, $3,830,000; Arizona, $1,486,000; Kansas, $127,500; Colorado, $68,300.)

* Approximately 70 pounds.

The most active harvest season for some of the important market states as well as those in the West are: California, May to September; Arizona, June and July; Texas, July and August; Indiana, July and August; Maryland, August; Colorado, August and September; Washington, July and August; New Mexico, July and August; Oregon, September; Utah, August and September.

Food Value. Cantaloupes are found in group 4 in food production efficiency. Forty-seven per cent of the fruit is edible. Cantaloupe contain 94.0 per cent water, and food value per 100 gm. of edible portion is energy, 23 calories; protein, 0.6 gm.; calcium, 17 mg.; vitamin A, 2400 I.U.; ascorbic acid, 30 mg.; thiamine, 0.045 mg.; riboflavin, 0.065 mg.; and niacin, 1.0 mg. The following data give the relative nutrient rank of cantaloupes.

Pound, rank 28: Vitamin A, 7.
Acre, rank 24: Vitamin A, 7.
Man-hour, rank 18: Vitamin A, 6; niacin, 8.

Varieties. Varieties of this vegetable exhibit differences in size, shape, color of flesh, as well as roughness of the exterior surface. Weight varies from 2 to 7 pounds. Most varieties are roundish with some oval in shape. Most cantaloupes possess an orange flesh with the Casaba having white flesh. A few melons have green flesh. The net or roughness of the surface may be very pronounced or almost absent. Some of the common varieties are described below. Varieties like Persian, Crenshaw, Honey Ball, Honey Dew, and Casaba require a longer season and are grown more commonly in the southwestern states. Texas Resistant No. 1 is resistant to aphids and partially resistant to downy mildew.

Casaba—Golden Beauty. Keeps a month or more in storage; fruits 6 to 8 inches in diameter; skin golden yellow, tough, wrinkled; flesh thick, white and sweet.

Crenshaw. Requires special handling for shipment and is sold mostly on local markets; plant vigorous, fruit large, somewhat pear shaped, 7 inches by 6 inches; skin rough, dark green when immature, and yellow when ripe; flesh salmon pink, thick, pleasing flavor.

Hale's Best. Outstanding shipping type for West and South; fruits oval, little ribbing but heavy net, 6 by 5 inches; flesh thick, salmon-orange. Other strains are Hale's Best 36, 936, and Jumbo strain.

Hearts of Gold. Grown for local market, fruits almost round, 6 by 6 inches, distinctly ribbed, fine net; flesh thick, salmon.

Honey Ball. Very productive; fruits round, 5 inches in diameter, yellowish white, almost smooth; bright salmon-orange flesh, sweet, good flavor; good shipper and keeper.

Honey Dew. Green-fleshed melon with creamy yellow skin; fruits oval, 7 to 8 inches long; sweet, good flavor and keeper.

Honey Rock. Fruits nearly round, about 6 inches in diameter; skin gray-green, netting coarse and sparse; flesh orange-salmon with a narrow green ring beneath rind.

Persian. Requires long season; 6 to 8 inches diameter; skin dark green and netted; flesh thick, orange, excellent flavor.

Powdery Mildew Resistant No. 6. Fruits almost round with a tendency to be somewhat flattened on the stem and blossom ends, smaller than Hale's Best or No. 45. Sutures shallow, medium heavy netting, orange flesh, very sweet, high quality. Resistant to known strains of powdery mildew in Imperial Valley.

Powdery Mildew Resistant No. 45. Similar to Hale's Best in type; resistant to one strain of powdery mildew; flesh salmon, thick, firm, and of good quality; shape oval with heavy net. Mostly grown outside of Imperial Valley.

Rocky Ford (Netted Gem). Popular east of the Mississippi River. Fruit small, two and one-half pounds; with faint ribs and heavy netting; flesh green with salmon tinge at center.

SR No. 91. A melon which is not resistant to powdery mildew but will tolerate sulfur dust so mildew can be controlled by dusting. The original selections were made by Dr. J. B. Norton who developed rust resistant Mary Washington asparagus. Vines of SR No. 91 (Fig. 87) are vigorous; fruit is large, short-oval, well netted and tough rind; flesh is rich salmon, thick, and pleasing flavor. Used as a shipping melon for Imperial Valley.

Tip Top. Grown for nearby markets in east. Fruits large, six and one-half pounds; rind pale green, turning to yellow at maturity; distinctly ribbed and slightly netted; flesh bright salmon.

Climatic Requirements. Cantaloupes seem best adapted to a mean monthly temperature of 65° to 75° F. The Imperial Valley crop is planted in December under hotcaps and is ready for harvest in May. December to January temperatures are 45° to 55° F. in the open, but under the hotcaps the temperatures are 75° to 80° F. during the day and 40° to 50° F. at night. Mean temperature in March is 60° F. after which there is no need for protection. Low relative humidity, high temperatures, and bright days in the Southwest,

Fig. 87. (*Left*) The SR No. 91 cantaloupe which may be dusted with sulfur to control mildew. This variety is typical of western melons grown for shipment. (Courtesy, Ferry Morse Seed Company.)

(*Right*) Imperial No. 6 cantaloupe. Fruit maturity is indicated by "slip," softness of rind, and yellow color of melons. The melon on the left shows a "no slip," the riper melon on the right "full slip," and above "one-third slip."

probably are responsible for producing cantaloupes high in sugar and with less foliage diseases. The Honey Dew, Honey Ball, and similar types are more susceptible to diseases when grown under conditions of high humidity. Much of this type of acreage is found in the Southwest. Melon seed germinates well at a soil temperature of 75° to 85° F.

Soil. Cantaloupes may be grown on a variety of soils. The crop is grown most extensively on sandy or sandy loam soils. The soil should be fairly fertile, and well drained. Where early production is desired, the soil should be one that warms up rapidly in the spring; good drainage and open texture therefore are required. Heavier loams are better adapted to the later crops than are light soils. Heavy clays and organic soils rarely are used with success. The soil should be free from nematodes and toxic amounts of alkali.

Fertilizers. The kind and quality of fertilizer needed for cantaloupe production depends largely on the type and condition of the soil. In some areas particularly the East, growers emphasize the importance of organic matter as a means of obtaining good growth and yields. The West, however, has been able to obtain good yields without large applications of organic matter through green manures.

Arizona used 200 to 400 pounds of 10-10 or 10-20 in bands at planting time with a side dressing of nitrogen during the season. In some sections of California, especially on light soils, increased yields have been obtained with commercial fertilizers. Growers in Imperial Valley use about 90 pounds of phosphoric acid per acre, while in Fresno, Stanislaus, and Los Angeles counties they use 45 pounds of nitrogen. Growers of Casabas and Honey Dews in Central California use 25 pounds of nitrogen and 45 pounds of phosphoric acid per acre. In California, a second light application of nitrogen, just before the plant begins to send out branches, more than justifies the extra cost. Oregon recommends the use of rotted manure with or without commercial fertilizer. One hundred to 150 pounds of a 4-12-8 is suggested to be applied in bands. In most cases it is desirable to place the fertilizer in bands 3 inches to the side of the row and at a depth of several inches. Growers in Eastern Washington on irrigated soils apply 100 pounds of nitrogen and 50 pounds of phosphoric acid per acre or 80 pounds of nitrogen in addition to 10 tons of manure.

Planting and Spacing. Two general methods are used in planting cantaloupes: the seed is planted in hills by hand, or drilled in the field in rows. After the plants are up, they are thinned to 2 plants per hill or to 3 feet apart in the rows.

Planting dates for commercial areas are as follows:

Arizona: Yuma and Salt River Valley, February 20 to April 10.
California: Imperial Valley, November to April; other areas, March to June.

Colorado: April 15 to May 15.

New Mexico: Dona Ana County, April 1 to 20.

Oregon: Willamette Valley, May.

Utah: North and east areas, April 15 to May 15.

Washington: South and east areas, April to May.

Hills generally are planted 4 feet apart in rows which are spaced 6 feet apart. Drilled rows are generally 6 feet apart. Depth of planting is about one and one-half inches but varies with the type of soil. One pound of seed will plant one acre if planted by hand; 3 pounds are needed if drilled in rows. The same seed treatment is used as was described for summer and winter squash.

Forcing Earliness. Several methods are useful in hastening maturity of the cantaloupe crop. High beds (2 feet or more) are made which slope to the south and expose a large surface to the sun so the ground will warm quickly. Protected plants mature their crops 4 to 10 days earlier than unprotected plants. In the Southwest, the plants are protected by several types of hotcaps, by brush windbreaks on the north side of the row, or by a combination of hotcaps and brush. Davis[4] describes the procedure used in Imperial Valley of preparing a brush or brush and paper windbreak as follows: "A shallow furrow is made along the top of the bed. Posts (grape stakes) are then set at intervals of about 100 feet along the bed. All are slanted over the plants at an angle of about 45° except the two at the end of the bed, which are driven deeper and are usually set erect. One strand of No. eight galvanized wire is attached to the stakes. Brush (chiefly arrowweed) is stuck in the furrow parallel with the grape stakes, six to eight inches apart, and slanted over the plants. Special paper (two and one-half feet wide, sold in rolls about 1,037 feet long) is placed on top of the brush, resting on the single strand of wire. More brush is now set in place on the opposite side of the paper to alternate with that previously set up. At intervals a single stick of brush may be stuck through the paper and then pressed into the soil to add rigidity to the structure. Finally a second strand of wire is stretched between the stakes to hold the brush and paper in place. The cost of putting brush-and-paper cover on one acre of cantaloupes is about $150. Under favorable conditions a total yield of 50 crates per acre may be expected from brushed cantaloupes."

In some areas, transplanting may be used to obtain early melons even though melons are difficult to transplant. This is accomplished by having the roots of the plants make a matted growth in rotted manure so the soil and manure are moved without disturbing the roots of the cantaloupe plant. Hotbeds or some similar structure are used to start the plants. Wooden bands, 3 by 4 by 4 inches, are used commonly. These bands are placed in the bed and about two-thirds filled with well-rotted manure. Soil is added to bring nearer the top that soil in which the seed is to be planted. This procedure permits moving plants with little disturbance and is used successfully to start cucurbits.

Irrigation. Irrigation is essential in practically all the cantaloupe districts of the Southwest, especially in the hot interior valleys where most of the melons are grown. The plants root to a depth of 6 feet. Since cantaloupes are a deep rooted crop their yield is not increased as much from irrigation as shallow rooted crops. Tests made at Davis, California gave increased yields of about 40 per cent from irrigation. Yields from irrigated and nonirrigated plots were about the same for the first third of the harvest season. Most of the decreased yield on the nonirrigated plots occurred in the last third of the picking season. There was little difference in the sugar content of melons from the different treatments but nonirrigated melons tended to be higher. In the above experiments about 15 inches of water were applied in 4 to 6 applications. The total amount of irrigation water suggested for California is 18 inches for inland valleys and 24 inches for Imperial Valley.

Determination of Maturity. Fortunately nature has provided an excellent yardstick to gauge the ripening process. As the cantaloupe approaches maturity a slight crack develops around the stem where it is attached to the fruit. When this crack completely encircles the attachment of the stem, the melon is at the "full slip" stage, ready for harvest. Cantaloupes intended for local market can be left safely on the vine until they have reached "full slip" (Fig. 87, *Right*). For shipment to market, they should be packed at the half to three-quarters slip. Unfortunately, some types of melons like Honey Dews, Crenshaws, and Casaba do not form a definite "slip" upon maturity so the following characteristics must be used, which are applicable to most cantaloupes. As the fruits approach maturity, there are changes in color and netting. The dark green color which indicates an immature melon changes to a yellowish tinge and the net, or corky lines on the fruit, become elevated and very hard. The fruits also tend to decrease in firmness so the melons are slightly soft.

Another method of determining maturity has been by measuring the soluble solids. These constituents contain any material soluble in the juice but are primarily sugars which include sucrose and hexose sugars like dextrose. The usual procedure is to remove the edible flesh with a spoon and place in a piece of cheese cloth so the juice can be obtain by pressing. The soluble solids can be determined by a Brix hydrometer which is graduated in terms of per cent sucrose. A small hand refractometer may be used also for the same purpose and in this case only a few drops of juice are needed. With the latter instrument the sampling technique may be varied and several plugs taken from the melon with a cork borer. Since different parts of a melon vary in soluble solids care should be used to obtain an adequate sample by the last procedure. The flesh of cantaloupes[5] near the seed is higher in soluble solids than the flesh near the rind so the relative depth of flesh used will affect the soluble solids content. The data in Tables 41 and 42 indicate that full slip melons have the highest percentage of soluble solids and that melons of excellent taste are also high in soluble solids and sugar.

Table 41*

SOLUBLE SOLIDS AND SUCROSE CONTENT OF CANTALOUPE JUICE
AT SEVERAL STAGES OF RIPENESS (1916)

California Melons Grown at	*Stage of Ripeness*			
	Field Ripe	*Full Slip*	*Half Slip*	*Immature*
	Per Cent Soluble Solids			
Turlock	11.6	11.9	11.9	9.5
Brawley	12.6	13.1	12.4	10.7
	Per Cent Sucrose†			
Turlock	4.9	5.4	5.1	2.6
Brawley	6.4	6.6	5.5	3.8

* Courtesy, *U.S.D.A. Dept. Bull. 1250, 1924.*
† Cantaloupe juice contains sucrose and other sugars.

Table 42*

SOLUBLE SOLIDS AND SUCROSE CONTENT OF CANTALOUPE JUICE
IN RELATION TO THEIR EATING QUALITY

California Melons Grown at	*Eating Quality of Cantaloupe Fruits*			
	High	*Satisfactory*	*Doubtful*	*Not Marketable*
	Per Cent Soluble Solids			
Tulare County—1920	12.0	11.0	10.0	7.9
Tulare County—1921	11.6	11.9	10.2	8.7
Turlock—1920	11.6	11.0	9.1	7.7
Turlock—1921	12.4	12.2	10.0	7.5
Brawley—1921	12.3	11.9	10.1	8.6
	Per Cent Sucrose†			
Tulare County—1920	6.6	5.3	4.1	2.0
Turlock—1920	6.1	5.4	3.6	1.8

* Courtesy, *U.S.D.A. Dept. Bull. 1250, 1924.*
† Cantaloupe juice contains sucrose and other sugars.

The California Agricultural Code makes use of soluble solids content to regulate the quality of melons shipped. Since the desert areas like Imperial Valley produce a sweeter melon the state standard varies with climatic conditions. Cantaloupes grown south and east of the San Gorgonio Pass must have 10 per cent soluble solids (or have a full slip) in the flesh of the melon to be shipped. Melons grown north and west of this Pass need have only 8 per cent (or full slip) soluble solids. The San Gorgonio Pass is in the area of

Banning, California so the area with the 10 per cent requirement is mainly Imperial Valley. The different kinds of melons have slightly different standards for soluble solids in connection with shipment and the Agricultural Code.

Harvesting. During the peak of the harvest season it is the common practise to go over the fields every third day, or in extremely warm weather, each day. Picking should be completed by 10 or 11 A.M. For harvesting, a type of sack common in the citrus industry is used. This sack may be opened at the bottom by unlatching a hook. Each worker picks the fruit from a single bed and upon reaching the end of the row deposits his load in crates or low-bed wagons used to transport the melons to the packing shed. Upon reaching the packing shed, the melons are placed on a conveyor belt which carries them past the graders and sorters.

Grading. Although there are no rigid standards, cantaloupes usually are graded for size and also as to maturity into "choice", "hard ripe" and "fancy." This system gives the buyer some concrete idea of the fruit he is likely to get. As the melons pass along the conveyor belt they are sorted carefully. Cracked, decayed, bruised, or immature fruits and "slickers" (melons with poor netting) are discarded.

Packing. Melons are graded rigidly according to size. In the trade, cantaloupes are designated by the type of package and by the number of melons a package contains. The standard cantaloupe crate contains either 45, 36, or 27 melons. Each crate contains 3 tiers of 15, 12, or 9 melons each.

After packing, the crates are loaded into refrigerator cars which have been pre-iced. Precooling is a general practise to prevent deterioration of cantaloupe quality. One of the following methods is used: (a) Fans in the upper bunker or floor rack to force air over the ice and through the load; (b) the blowing of air through the load from truck-mounted mechanical refrigerating units driven by a power takeoff from the truck engine; (c) and placing cars on the siding near an ice plant, and blowing cool air into the cars from a brine tower. In recent years top ice also has been used to cool loads of melons.

Storage. The several types of melons differ somewhat as to the most desirable storage temperature and also the maximum storage period. These melons are stored within the range of 34° to 40° F. with cantaloupe having a storage period of 10 days, Honey dews and Honey ball 2 to 4 weeks, and Casabas 4 to 6 weeks. If melons are picked ripe the storage period is somewhat shorter. If Honey Dews are stored for too long a period below 36° F. there will be a breakdown with a watery discoloration of the rind, followed by fungus decay. Casabas may be stored the longest and their quality is best if stored until there is a softening of the fruit.

Quality Characteristics for the Retail Buyer. Selection of melons for quality and flavor is not easy; it often tests the skill of the experienced buyer,

Fig. 88. Chayote is a one-seeded fruit as shown on the left. The plant is a typical vine of the Cucurbitaceae family and may be trained on a fence or other support.

fruits under a suitable climate as well as underground tubers the second year of growth in the tropics. All parts of the plant are usable for food: the young leaves and tender tips are used as greens and the plant is used as forage for livestock. The plant produces best in the tropics where the temperature is cool and the days and nights are of about equal length. In the central plateau of Costa Rica the vines are found growing on fences without any apparent care. Little labor is needed for culture and the primary operation is the harvesting of the fruit. Sometimes the vines grow on trees and make an interesting sight when one or more vines cover a tree 40 to 60 feet high. The crop grows in the warmer parts of the United States such as, California, Louisiana, Georgia. Plants have produced 50 fruits each as far north as Washington, D.C. In these cooler areas the vines are killed by frost and should be given some protection over winter. There is considerable variability in the fruits of different varieties as to color, size, shape, and prickliness. Varieties used in the United States are light green in color, and the fruits weigh 8 to 16 ounces. The surface should be smooth, the fruit should have flesh free from fiber, and possess an agreeable flavor. The plants may be propagated either from cuttings or by placing the entire fruit in the ground. Cuttings are used where specific variety characteristics are desired. If fruits are used, the young plant usually starts growth in storage and the shoot grows out of the blossom end of the fruit. The fruit is placed in the ground on a slant, with the stem end towards the surface, and planted 4 inches deep. Chayote makes a large vine requiring support, and the plants are spaced 12 by 8 feet. In areas like Central California the plants bloom only in the fall when the temperatures are cooler and the days shorter. The fruits develop to maximum size in 25 to 30 days after fruit set. The fruit is used at approximately maximum size but when it is still slightly immature. In warmer climates sometimes it is possible to obtain both a spring and a fall crop, and the year around near the equator. The fruits are stored at about 50° to 55° F. The fruit is cooked in ways similar to those used for summer squash. Chayotes from California are marketed locally and are shipped to eastern markets.

Reference

Hoover, L. G.: The chayote: its culture and uses, *U.S.D.A. Dept. Cir. 286,* 11 p., 1923.

New Zealand spinach (*Tetragonia expansa*) is used as a green, and will grow in hot weather; most of the crops grown for greens, like spinach, can be produced only in cool weather. New Zealand spinach produces a large plant 3 to 4 feet across. Rows are 5 to 6 feet apart, and the culture is similar to that of cucumbers. The plants are thinned to 1 foot apart in the row. The seeds are slow to germinate and, like beets, each so-called seed may produce several plants. The young, tender terminal stems and leaves are harvested for market. These are cut with a knife and marketed loose. After cutting, there is further growth of new, leafy shoots. In a mild climate along the ocean this plant will produce over a period of a year. Adequate water and nitrogen encourage a tender plant growth. Since the crop is harvested repeatedly large yields are obtained per acre.

Pumpkin (*Cucurbita pepo* and *C. moschata*) is used for pie filling and some varieties are baked and used as winter squash. The crop also is used for livestock feed. Cultural and climatic requirements are similar to winter squash. There are several varieties differing in appearance. New England Pie or Sugar is grown commonly in home gardens or for market. Kentucky Field is used for canning and is called Dickinson Field in the Southwest. In Oregon and Washington, Boston Marrow and Golden Delicious varieties of winter squash, are used to produce canned pumpkin.

Reference

Thompson, Ross C.: Production of pumpkins and squash, *U.S.D.A. Leaflet 141,* 8 p., 1943.

Roselle, a member of the Malvaceae family, is grown for the enlarged calyces or flower bases and swollen bracts which are used to make jelly and similar products. The jelly is tart, transparent, and of a bright-red color. Roselle (*Hibiscus sabdariffa*) closely resembles okra in appearance and culture. Most of the production is confined to warmer areas of the southwest and southern states. The plants are started from seed, but cuttings also may be used. Flowering does not occur until short days arrive in the fall of the year. The flowers are large and showy. The fruit is harvested 2 to 3 weeks after flowering and when the calyces are plump, crisp, and of a deep-red color. Harvest should occur before any woody matter has formed in the fruit tissues. The fruits are snapped off the plant; they should be picked at least twice a week. One plant will produce 3 to 10 pounds of calyces or flower bases. The seed capsules are removed in the preparation of the calyx for jelly, jam, or a drink.

Reference

Beattie, J. H.: Production of roselle, *U.S.D.A. Leaflet 139,* 4 p., 1937.

Chapter 19

Group E.   Warm Season Crops Requiring Continuous Warm Weather

Group E. Long season crops, which thrive above 70° F.

WATERMELON

Botany. The watermelon plant (*Citrullus vulgaris*) is a trailing annual and the stems attain a length of 10 to 15 feet. This species includes not only watermelons but also stock melons or citron. The latter also are used for making preserves. Watermelon leaves are cordate at the base and deeply lobed. Most varieties are monoecious but a few have hermaphroditic flowers. The flowers are small and not very showy and occur in the leaf axils. Flowers usually are insect pollinated and bees commonly visit these flowers. Citron cross pollinates readily with watermelons so any citron plantings should be isolated from watermelon seed fields. The pistils remain receptive to pollen for one day, but not all pistillate flowers produce fruits. Watermelon fruits are variable in shape and may weigh from 10 to 60 pounds. Both red and yellow fleshed varieties are grown. The color of the seed varies so some varieties can be identified by the color of the seed.

Origin and History. Watermelons are native to tropical Africa. Livingstone writes that in years of ample rainfall vast tracts of the country are covered with watermelons. The first records of watermelons occur about 1542 but there are numerous descriptions in the next 50 years. Evidently many types occurred in Africa which are not like our present melons. Some melons were reported to weigh 100 pounds. Watermelons varied greatly in size, shape, outside and inside color as well as the color of the seed. The flesh colors reported were red, scarlet, yellow, and white. Most varieties were sweet but others were acid and even bitter. Watermelons are reported as having been grown in Massachusetts as early as 1629. In 1806 McMahon described 4 varieties of this crop. The Florida Indians were known to be growing watermelons in 1664.

Producing Areas. Watermelon production is found in those states with a warm growing season, and those close to large markets. The crop usually is not shipped farther than 800 to 1000 miles. The 1940–1951 statistical data, for yield and marketing of watermelons, follow.

Watermelons for Market

	Acreage	Melons Per Acre	Production Melons	Price Per 1000 Melons Dollars	Farm Value Dollars
United States	254,770	284	72,518,000	$311.27	$22,573,000
Florida	39,250	281	11,047,000	406.98	4,496,000
Georgia	47,250	282	13,364,000	287.26	3,839,000
California	15,333	666	10,217,000	314.67	3,215,000
Texas	55,716	163	9,111,000	309.40	2,819,000
South Carolina	25,166	216	5,456,000	258.24	1,409,000

(Farm value, other Western states: Arizona, $779,000; Washington, $101,000; Oregon, $85,000; Colorado, $29,000.)

The most active harvest season for some of the important market states as well as those in the West are: Florida, June; Georgia, July; California, June to August; Texas, July; South Carolina, July; Arizona, July; Washington, August; Oregon, August; Colorado, September.

Food Value. Watermelons can be recommended for their delicious taste, but they are found in group 4 in food production efficiency. Approximately 46 per cent of the melon is edible. Sometimes watermelon juice has been concentrated to produce a syrup. About 13 volumes of juice are required to produce 1 volume of syrup. Watermelons have been considered also as a source of sugar. Watermelon contains 92.1 per cent water and food value per 100 gm. of edible portion is energy, 31 calories; protein, 0.5 gm.; calcium, 7 mg.; vitamin A, 500 I.U.; ascorbic acid, 7 mg.; thiamine, 0.069 mg.; riboflavin, 0.03 mg.; and niacin, 0.56 mg. The following data give the relative nutrient rank of watermelons.

Pound, rank 31: Nutrient rank is 11 or lower.
Acre, rank 27: Vitamin A, 10.
Man-hour, rank 21: Vitamin A, 10; thiamine, 10.

Varieties. Watermelon varieties vary considerably as to color, shape, and size. Some varieties produce melons 40 to 45 pounds in weight and there is also demand for ice box melons of about 8 to 10 pounds. The following varieties are used in some areas of the West and the fruits weigh 30 pounds or more: Congo, Early Kansas, Florida Giant, Stone Mountain, and Tom Watson. Winter Queen is a medium sized melon which will keep several weeks if properly stored. Most of the acreage in the Southwest is confined to the Klondike varieties (Fig. 89), which are described below.

Cole's Early. Used for home garden and local markets; fruits medium size, 20 pounds, short, oval, with alternating dark and light-green stripes; tender rind, flesh pink-red; seed black.

Blue Ribbon. A striped Klondike, resistant to Fusarium wilt, similar to Klondike, but slightly larger in size (18 to 22 pounds), seed brown with light-tan areas. A nonresistant strain is called Striped Klondike.

Dixie Queen. Popular shipping type. Fruits oval round, light green with dark stripes; rind thin but tough. Flesh red, free from fibre; seeds small and white (30 pounds).

Florida Giant. A very productive variety with dark green fruits which are nearly round. Flesh firm and red; seeds a dark brown flecking on tan ground. A good all-purpose variety, ships well but is a little large for some markets (40 pounds).

Georgia Rattlesnake. Fruits large, elongated, gray-green, with irregular dark green stripes; rind tough. Flesh light red; seeds dull white with black tip (28 pounds).

Klondike R7. Melons medium size, blocky, length one and one-half to one and three-quarter times the diameter; slightly flattened at ends, slightly furrowed; resistant to Fusarium wilt; fine quality; seed, some all black, some similar to Blue Ribbon seed. A non-resistant strain is called Klondike. Improved Peacock is similar to Klondike but with a thicker, tougher, furrowed rind.

Kleckley Sweet. High quality melon for local use. Fruits large, cylindrical; dark bluish green but thin, tender rind. Flesh red and sweet; seed creamy white with traces of brown. Wonder is an improved type of this variety.

Leesburg. A wilt resistant variety similar to Kleckley Sweet. Fruit shorter and blocky ended; rind tough, and not as dark as Kleckley Sweet.

Tom Watson. Standard shipping variety of Southeast. Fruits very large, cylindrical, with deep green, tough rind. Flesh deep red, somewhat coarse; seeds brown (35 pounds).

Fig. 89. Two types of Klondike watermelon are popular in the West. Klondike R7 is on the left and Blue Ribbon on the right. (Courtesy, Ferry Morse Seed Company.)

Climatic Requirements. The watermelon requires a long growing season with high temperatures. Their quality is not affected adversely by high humidity as in the case of cantaloupes. Foliage diseases are usually more destructive under high humidities, and are likely to cause some impairment of quality and reduced yield. Average mean temperatures above 70° F. are desirable for the growth of the plants. There is little demand for watermelons until warm weather arrives. Good seed germination is obtained at soil temperatures of 75° to 85° F.

Soil. Much of this crop is produced on sandy to sandy loam soils. The use of sandy loams is more necessary where the climate is slightly cool, and loams are used more generally in the south. Sandy loams furnish good drainage, which is also desirable. This crop should not be grown on the same soil more than once every 4 or 5 years, and preferably only once in every 6 to 8 years because continuous cropping increases Fusarium wilt, a soil-borne disease. Wilt-resistant strains, however, are grown successfully on Fusarium-infested soil.

Fertilizers. The fertilizer requirement of watermelons on a given soil is similar to that of cantaloupes and, to some extent, summer squash. Since watermelons are spaced widely much of the fertilizer is applied in the hill a week before planting with side dressings after the vines begin to run and spread. Arizona growers use 200 to 300 pounds of ammonium sulphate; or 150 to 200 pounds of ammonium nitrate per acre. Imperial Valley uses about 90 pounds of phosphoric acid per acre, while other areas in California use some 40 pounds of nitrogen. In Eastern Washington on irrigated soils, watermelons are fertilized with 10 tons of manure plus 80 pounds of nitrogen or 100 pounds of nitrogen and 50 pounds of phosphoric acid without manure. Following alfalfa or vetch 40 pounds of nitrogen and 40 pounds of phosphoric acid are applied. The fertilizers in Washington are applied broadcast and incorporated into the soil during seed bed preparation.

Planting and Spacing. Two pounds of seed will plant one acre of watermelons in hills, but more is required where the seed is drilled in rows. In the early districts, watermelons usually are planted on beds about 2 feet high and 9 feet from center to center. Plantings are made on the south or west side of the beds which have been harrowed previously and smoothed with a V drag. In areas where planting dates are later, the seed is planted on the flat in rows 9 feet apart.

Seeds are planted in hills (6 to 9 feet apart in the rows) by hand, and covered with a short-handled hoe; or a hand planter may be used. After the plants are up and established they should be thinned to 2 plants per hill. In the early plantings, maturity is hastened by protecting the young plants for a time with paper caps or brush, or with paper windbreaks. The seed treatments used for summer and winter squash also are applicable for watermelon seed.

The approximate planting dates for commercial areas are:

Arizona: Salt River Valley, March.
California: Imperial Valley, December to March 15; southern part (except Imperial), March to April; central part, April to May.
Colorado: Arkansas Valley, Denver, and Greeley, April 15 to May 15.
Oregon: Northern and eastern areas, May.
Washington: Southern area, April to May.

Irrigation. Irrigation is essential in many watermelon districts, especially in the hot interior valleys where most of the crop is grown. When the seed is planted, the soil should be full of water (at field capacity) from winter rains or preirrigation. Before development of runners, the plant requires relatively small quantities of water because of the limited leaf area or transpiring surface; and if the soil was wet thoroughly before planting, probably no early irrigation will be needed except on extremely light sandy soils. On the heavier soils 3 or 4 irrigations are applied, of 4 to 5 inches each; lighter soils are irrigated more frequently. A minimum of 15 inches of water is required to produce a crop in most areas with slightly more used in Imperial Valley on sandy soils.

Irrigation tests made at Davis, California, where winter rains wet the soil to a depth of 6 to 8 feet, show little effect on the yield, size of melons, days required for the fruit to ripen, or sugar content. Nonirrigated melons are sometimes slightly higher in sugar content. Fig. 26 indicates that the growth of irrigated and nonirrigated watermelons at Davis was the same. This is further evidence that the plants on the nonirrigated plots were receiving sufficient water. Irrigation is essential in areas which are warmer than Davis, or use more water from other causes.

Pruning. Although not a common practise some growers of high grade watermelons find it desirable to thin or "prune" the melons in order to get fruits of shipping size. This does not mean pruning the vines themselves, but reducing the number of melons on each vine. Any cutting back or disturbance of the vine injures the development of the melons. The usual custom is to wait until there is a good set then to remove by cutting all but 2 or 3 of the best melons from each vine. "Pruning" causes all the vigor of the vines to go to the development of the remaining melons and usually results in a high percentage of marketable melons. Melons grown for home use are seldom "pruned", as the question of size is not so important.

Harvesting and Shipping. Maturity tests of watermelons are the color of the ground spot, dryness of tendril near fruit, or sound made by thumping the melon with your fist or knuckles. The ground spot, where the fruit rests on the ground will change from a white background color to a light yellowing at maturity. Tendrils change from a green to a brown, and also have a dry appearance. When a melon is thumped maturity affects the sound. A metallic ringing sound indicates immaturity and a softer somewhat hollow sound indicates maturity. In the final analysis the sugar content of the flesh is the best test (Fig. 90), although this cannot be applied in a practical way; therefore exterior indications are the only ones by which to judge the maturity of the individual melons.

Melons should be cut from the vines, not pulled or broken. Care should be taken to leave the stem as long as possible. As the melons are cut, either they are carried directly to the roadways or turned over so they may be seen easily by loaders following the cutters. Melons should not be stood on end either in the field or trucks. A bed of straw 5 or 6 inches deep should be placed in the bottoms of wagons or trucks. The sides and edges of the body also should be padded with burlap or canvas.

If melons are to be shipped in railroad cars the arrangement in the cars depends on their size and on the type of car being loaded. In general melons weighing 22 to 36 pounds or over usually are loaded in 4 tiers or layers, those weighing 18 to 20 pounds, in 5 tiers—with 14 melons across the car in the bottom layer, 13 in the second, 14 in the third, 13 in the fourth, and 14 in the fifth layer. The stems always are placed toward the doorway. A carload is 12 to 14 tons of melons.

Storage. Watermelons are not stored commonly under refrigeration but a temperature of 36° to 40° F. is desirable with 85 per cent humidity. The storage period is rarely over 2 weeks. While watermelons are shipped they are

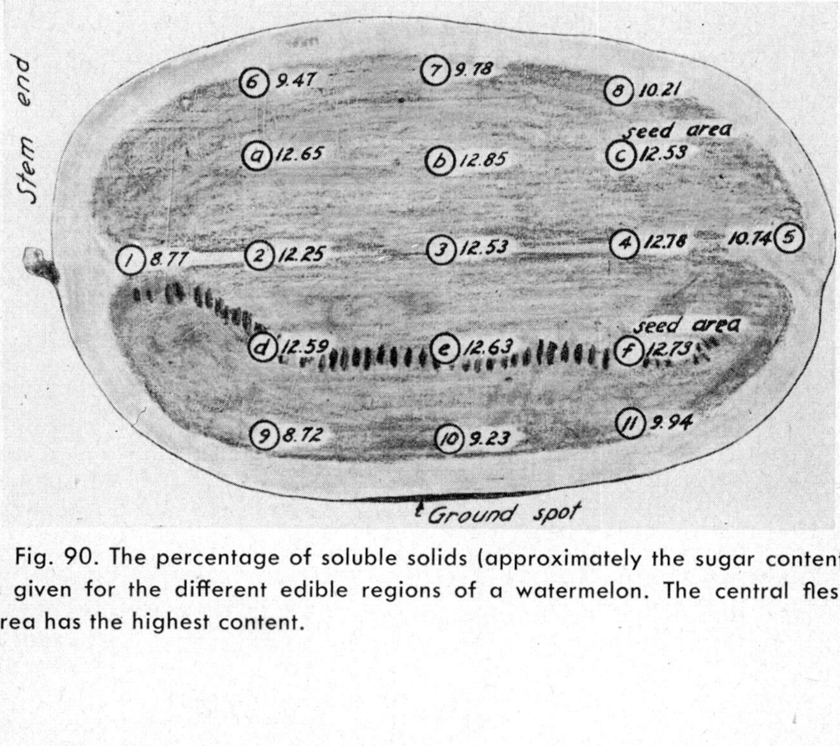

Fig. 90. The percentage of soluble solids (approximately the sugar content) is given for the different edible regions of a watermelon. The central flesh area has the highest content.

not adapted for movement to distant markets. Usually 800 to 1000 miles are the maximum distances for railroad transportation. Some melons are moved by truck. Losses from shipment are so serious and the value may be so low that railroads demand the grower to prepay the freight. Melons are shipped in refrigerator cars with ventilation and rarely with ice in the bunkers. Breakage and decay seem associated and are the most common causes of loss. Some varieties have a thicker and tougher rind, therefore ship better and with less damage to the fruits. Western grown watermelons are consumed in the Pacific and Rocky Mountain states.

Quality Characteristics for the Retail Buyer. Usually, ripe melons of good quality are firm, symmetrical in shape, fresh and attractive in appearance and of good color which may vary from a solid green to a gray according to the variety. A bloom is over the surface of the rind, giving it a somewhat velvety appearance; the lower side of the melon is yellowish in color. Generally such melons will have a crisp, sweet, and juicy flesh. A hollow sound or thumping has been described previously as a test for maturity. Dependence cannot be placed always on this test since the mature melon may prove to be dead-ripe or stale, in which case the flesh usually is dry and mealy, or "slick" and insipid.

Immature melons usually present a hard, greenish, unripe appearance. The underside is usually white or pale green. Overmature or dead ripe melons have a dull, lifeless appearance, and feel soft or springy when pressure is applied with the hand. Ill-shaped melons generally are found in the smaller sizes; the quality of such melons is generally poor. Decay occurs at the stem end and occasionally may be found on the blossom end. It may be seen at the stem end as a discoloration and softening of the stem. This form of decay spreads rapidly soon making the melon unfit for use. Watermelons sometimes have a hard white streak running lengthwise through the flesh which is called "white heart." Such melons are undesirable but cannot be detected without cutting.

Insects: *Aphid (Aphis gossypii)*. The melon aphid is small and very dark green. It builds up rapidly after getting started in a field and it is difficult to control especially after the vines cover the ground. At the first sign of an infestation, apply a 10 per cent nicotine dust and if necessary repeat the applications until the aphids are cleaned up.

Diabrotica (Diabrotica undecimpunctata). The Diabrotica or 12 spotted cucumber beetles gnaw on the stems, leaves, and sometimes on the young fruits. They are most damaging to young plants. The beetles can be repelled by repeated dustings of the plants, with cryolite, calcium arsenate and lime, or ordinary hydrated lime. A 5 per cent DDT or DDD dust also will give good control, but red spiders are likely to increase rapidly after the use of these materials. Also DDT or DDD should be used cautiously on young plants because of the danger of injury.

Flea Beetle (*Epitrix cucumeris,* and Others). These small, black jumping insects can be controlled by the dusting program outlined for Diabrotica.

Red Spiders Mite (*Tetranychus bimaculatus,* and Others). These small, yellowish spiders are a serious pest, particularly in the late summer crops in the central valleys. Effective application of insecticides is difficult because the vines usually are well grown by the time the injury begins to develop. Good weed control, especially of morning glory, in and around the fields helps to reduce red spider infestations by eliminating the host plants. Inadequate irrigation favors the pest. Tetraethylpyrophosphate is effective in spray or dust form, if good coverage of the under sides of the leaves can be obtained. Two applications 10 days apart usually are required to clean up the pest. If a dust of this material is used, it should be prepared freshly.

Diseases: *Curly-Top.* Curly top is a virus disease that sometimes appears on watermelons. Infected plants cease growing, the older leaves turn yellowish green and the new leaves become dark green. The sugar beet leaf hopper carries the disease. There is no control after the plants become infected.

Mosaic. This virus disease, which is transmitted by aphids, causes mottling of the leaves and stunting of the plants. Fruits from diseased plants often are misshapen. The disease is most serious in Imperial Valley. Good control of the aphids and eradication of other cucurbit plants from the vicinity of the fields may help to check the spread of the disease.

Watermelon Wilt. This disease, caused by *Fusarium oxysporum* f. *niveum* attacks the stems and roots, where eventually it blocks the water conducting tissues causing sudden wilting and death of the plant. Roots of infested plants show a dark discoloration of the area just under the skin. The fungus lives in the soil for many years after a watermelon crop has been grown. This particular fungus attacks only watermelons. The use of wilt-resistant varieties or long rotations are the control measures.

References

1. Beattie, W. R.: Watermelons, *U.S.D.A. Farmers' Bull. 1394,* 27 p., 1938.
2. Davis, G. N. and P. A. Minges: Watermelon production in California, *Calif. Agr. Ext. Ser. Leaflet,* 8 p., (Multolith) 1949.

SWEET POTATO

Botany. The sweet potato (*Ipomoea Batatas*) is a tuberous rooted perennial and is a member of the Convolvulaceae family. This family has about 1000 species of plants which are distributed widely around the world, but occur mostly in the tropics. The roots are small and fibrous. Some of these become enlarged near the stem and form an edible root. The plant produces a trailing vine which usually does not produce flowers under field conditions in the United States. In the tropics flowers are produced during the short days of December and January. The leaves are alternate and heart shaped. Leaves vary in shape and this is one characteristic used to identify varieties as is the purple pigment found on the leaves of some varieties. There are 2 types of sweet potatoes which are dry and moist in texture after baking. The moist type frequently but incorrectly is called yams. The true yams are mon-cots and are members of the Dioscoreaceae family which rarely is grown outside of the tropics. Small true yams may be about the size of sweet potatoes, but if the roots have grown for a year or more they may weigh 50 or 100 pounds.

Origin and History. Sweet potatoes are native to the tropics of America where they were an important source of food. In 1514 the Indians of Honduras were growing at least 9 different varieties of this crop. The Indians of the United States did not use the crop except those in the southern states including Florida. Soon after the discovery of America, sweet potatoes were taken to Europe, the islands of the Pacific, as well as Asia. Sweet potatoes were reported grown in Virginia in 1648 and were in general use about the time of the Revolutionary War. Early explorers report finding 4 different colored roots which included red, yellow, brown, and white.

Producing Areas. The sweet potato is a warm season crop and most of the production is south of the Ohio River. California has a few areas of production but it is still an importing state. The 1940–1951 statistical data are given below:

Sweet Potatoes for Market

	Acreage	Bushels* Per Acre	Production Bushels	Price Per Bushel Dollars	Farm Value Dollars
United States	621,367	92	57,465,000	$1.78	$102,310,000
North Carolina	65,167	105	6,866,000	1.86	12,791,000
Louisiana	95,917	91	8,745,000	1.38	12,099,000
Georgia	76,250	78	5,927,900	1.80	10,647,000
Mississippi	52,330	89	4,673,000	1.89	8,834,000
Alabama	61,333	79	4,856,000	1.81	8,784,000

(Farm value, other Western states: California, $3,687,808.)
* Approximately 55 pounds.

The most active harvest season for some of the important market states as well as those in the West are: States east of the Rocky Mountains, September and October; California, October.

Food Value. Sweet potatoes are in group 1 on a food production efficiency. This crop ranks higher than potatoes on nutrients per pound but lower yields per acre and a greater labor requirement place them below potatoes on these items. Sweet potatoes are relatively high in vitamin A. The roots are an excellent source of food and it is unfortunate that storage losses and higher cost to the consumer tend to discourage consumption. Sweet potato contains 68.5 per cent water and the food value per 100 gm. of edible portion is energy, 125 calories; protein, 1.8 gm.; calcium, 33 mg.; vitamin A, 2500 I.U.; ascorbic acid, 24 mg.; thiamine, 0.093 mg.; riboflavin, 0.13 mg.; and niacin, 1.29 mg. The following data give the relative composition of sweet potato as compared to other crops.

Pound, rank 3: Energy, 1; niacin, 1; vitamin A, 2; calcium, 9; riboflavin, 9.

Acre, rank 13: Energy, 4; vitamin A, 5; niacin, 7; riboflavin, 9.

Man-hour, rank 5: Energy, 4; vitamin A, 5; niacin, 5; thiamine, 8; riboflavin, 9.

Varieties. Sweet potatoes may be classified into the dry and moist types, according to their cooking quality, particularly baking. For many years, the dry types were used primarily in the northern states and the moist types in the South. In recent years, the moist types have been popular also in the North. The Yellow Jersey is a typical dry type, and Puerto Rice is a typical moist type. Nancy Hall is a moist type marketed in the East. Maryland Golden sometimes is grown for the early fall market because it reaches market size early. The Ranger variety has been introduced because its heavy yield and good color make it desirable as a canning type. The most important variety is Puerto Rico which is described below with two other varieties.

Hawaiian. This variety was brought from the Pacific Islands about 1920 by Joseph Lial of Merced. Kanaka is another name for this variety. The roots are yellow and the flesh is a light yellow. In early stages of storage, it cooks like a dry potato but later the cooked flesh is more similar to the moist types. This variety keeps well and is stored for the late winter market.

Puerto Rico. Stems coarse, reddish purple in color; leaves with purple stain at base of blade and on veins; roots rose in color; flesh salmon but dark yellow when baked; moist, and of good quality. There are several strains of Puerto Rico being grown in the Southwest. Improved Red or Improved Red Puerto Rico possesses a more uniform red skin color. A second strain called Key West or Velvet possesses a reddish purple skin. Another strain is similar to the last but also has purple pigment below the skin and purple streaks in the flesh. This strain has been called Double Red.

Yellow Jersey. Stems green, slender; leaves without purple stain at base of leaf; roots russet yellow, smooth or veined; flesh yellow and dry when baked.

Climatic Requirements. The sweet potato is a tropical plant that does not thrive in cool weather. A light frost will kill the leaves and soil temperatures of 50° F. or below will result in chilling damage. The commercial crop is grown where the average monthly temperatures are above 70° F. for at least 3 months. The crop is transplanted when the average temperature reaches 70° F. which is about 2 to 3 weeks after the average date for the last killing frost. No other common crop in the United States will stand more heat and very few require as much heat. The crop is not adapted particularly to the deep, heavy, high nitrogen soils of the West so much of the crop is grown on sandy soils. Sweet potatoes grown for stock feed need higher temperatures and longer growing season so higher yields may be obtained. Such conditions also seem to increase the starch content of varieties grown for stock feed.

Propagation. Sweet potatoes are produced commonly by raising the plants or slips from roots bedded in a hotbed. When the roots are placed under the proper temperature conditions, adventitious buds (Fig. 92) develop and form young plants. Sweet potatoes also may be propagated from stem cuttings or by planting sections of the root. The last 2 methods are not practised commonly. Stem cuttings must be obtained from a field and will reduce its yield as well as resulting in late planting of the second field. Using sections of the root increases the amount of roots needed for seed.

The small sized potatoes from healthy plants are stored for the propagation of slips. The roots usually are planted in a hotbed, bedded in sand. The potatoes are laid on the sand so they do not touch each other, and covered with 2 inches of sand. The bed is sprinkled and there should be sufficient heat to produce a temperature of 80° F. soon after bedding, with a temperature of 70° F. to 75° F. after the roots have started to sprout. As the slips start to come through more sand is added so there are 4 to 5 inches to insure a greater area of stems with roots. Two or 3 pullings of slips may be obtained from the same bed for successive plantings. Hotbed covers need to be raised or removed after the plants come through the covering of sand to produce hardened, sturdy plants. To plant 1 acre of sweet potatoes from the first pulling (Fig. 91) requires 350 to 500 pounds of roots. Under favorable propagating conditions plants can be produced in 5 weeks, but with lower temperatures 6 to 10 weeks are required. Good seed should be free from all diseases and nematodes as well as being well cured and properly stored. Care should be used to obtain good seed and unfortunately good seed is more difficult to obtain than for white potatoes.

For the control of black rot, stem rot, and scurf, sweet potatoes for seed should be treated with mercuric chloride or Semesan Bel before bedding. Mercuric chloride (corrosive sublimate) is used at a rate of 1 to 1000 strength (4 ounces to 30 gallons of water); the roots are soaked for 8 to 10 minutes and then bedded without washing. Semesan Bel is mixed with water at one

Fig. 91. A bed of sweet potatoes at the proper stage for pulling slips for field planting.

Fig. 92. A sweet potato root from a plant bed showing the young plants or "slips" arising from the root. A "pulled" slip or plant is shown at right.

pound to seven and one-half gallons; the roots are dipped long enough to wet the surface, then drained and bedded.

Soil. Under ideal climatic conditions, sweet potatoes are grown on a wide range of soils. Thus, in the southern states they are grown on sandy loams and even clay loams where there is good drainage. As the crop is grown in less favorable climates, there is more general use of sands and sandy loams; they warm up more quickly and give more tropical conditions. The lighter soils produce a smoother shaped, and medium sized root which is more desired for market. Where the crop is used for livestock feed, the oversize and poorly shaped roots from a market crop may be disposed of in this way.

Fertilizers. In areas where potash increases yield, as in New Jersey, this element tends to produce shorter, chunkier potatoes. Where potash is low in amount, the potatoes are likely to be long and stringy. Excess of nitrogen in the soil is undesirable since it tends to produce oversized potatoes which must be sold for livestock feed. Most areas in California use 40 to 60 pounds of nitrogen per acre and on some of the poor soils of Merced County an 8-10-12 fertilizer at the rate of 800 pounds per acre is used. The fertilizer should be applied at the time of planting or as a side dressing early in the growing period.

Planting. The crop is planted in the late spring after the danger of frost is over. In the lower end of the San Joaquin Valley, planting begins about April 15 and extends to May 15. In the south coast area, the time is slightly earlier. Planting should occur promptly after the soil is warm enough since length of growing season is an important factor affecting yield. The rows are placed 3 feet apart, with plants 9 to 12 inches apart in the row. Close planting is used to reduce the number of oversized roots. The slips are placed 4 to 6 inches deep with the use of a transplanting machine. In the West, most of the sweet potato plants are set on ridges 6 to 9 inches high (Fig. 93) for the purpose of improving drainage and of increasing the soil temperature. In the South, the crop sometimes is grown without ridges.

Irrigation. The roots of this crop extend into the soil to a depth of 6 feet. Sweet potatoes are grown frequently on sandy soils which contain only a small amount of available water. This crop should not be allowed to suffer for moisture except in the last few weeks before harvest. A relatively dry soil is needed at harvest time so digging equipment can be used. In some areas the crop is grown with little irrigation—cases have been known where growers have irrigated only once or twice. Care should be used to limit water so there is not a large percentage of overgrown roots to be graded into culls. Eighteen inches of water should be ample to produce a maximum crop, if the soil is near field capacity at planting time from winter rains.

Cultural Operations. Cultivation is important in the early part of the season to control weeds; later the vines cover the ground and prevent weed growth. Moving the vines to permit late cultivation has not increased yields,

Fig. 93. Field planting of sweet potatoes by means of transplanting machine. Note that the back wheels are set at an angle to firm the moist soil around the roots.

Garcia[2] in New Mexico studied the effect of vine pruning on yield over a period of 2 years. Vines kept pruned to a length of 12 inches produced 6012 pounds per acre; 24 inches, 8690 pound; 36 inches, 10,857 pounds; and no pruning, 16,520 pounds.

Harvesting. The major portion of the sweet potato crop is stored for various lengths of time before marketing and therefore should be allowed to mature before harvesting. A small portion of the crop is harvested early, to market without storage and these roots may be harvested as soon as they are large enough to be eaten. Maturity of the crop is indicated by a yellowing of the vines. The broken or bruised areas of immature potatoes tend to remain moist, and darken in color, while similar areas on a mature potato tend to be dry.

When the crop is ready for harvest, the first operation is to remove the excess vines and save them to cover the piles of potatoes. There are special vine cutters for this operation, and cultivators with knives set 6 to 8 inches apart also are used. Sometimes the vines are removed by hand, using knives. The roots are plowed out with a double moldboard plow or "middle buster". When the vines have been killed by a light frost, it is customary to remove the vines as soon as possible. During periods of frost there is danger of the roots being affected adversely by low temperatures which may increase the decay of the crop. This effect of low temperature is referred to as chilling injury and usually causes damage to fruit crops. Roots are injured by exposure to temperatures of 50° F. or lower either before or after harvesting.

Freshly dug potatoes are more sensitive to chilling injury than cured potatoes or those removed from storage. Affected potatoes are more subject to rotting and also develop unattractive color and surface depressions. If there is a frost before digging the best policy is to dig and move the potatoes to a warm place as soon as possible. Harvest may start as early as the middle of August in southern California. Most of the crop is gathered during the last half of September to the first half of October.

After digging, the individual hills are laid to dry on the ridge for 2 or 3 hours, but longer exposure to temperatures of 100° F. are likely to cause injury. The potatoes may be gathered into piles and the roots snapped off and graded at the same time. If the roots are going to market they may be packed in the field. Otherwise the roots are taken to the storage house for curing. Vines may be used to cover piles if there is too long a delay from harvesting until placing in the storage house. Sweet potatoes are subject to serious losses due to rots, so every precaution should be taken to harvest the crop with little bruising of the roots. There is less skinning of the roots if the soil is dry at digging time.

Curing and Storage. Freshly harvested potatoes are high in starch and low in sugar. As storage proceeds the starch changes to sugar. Both seed and table stock should be well matured before digging, carefully handled, cured to drive off excess moisture and to heal bruises, and kept at a uniform temperature after they are cured. The small potatoes from good yielding hills may be stored for the next year's seed.

The storage house should be disinfected thoroughly with a fungicide a week before storage takes place. Potatoes usually are stored in bins. After the roots have been placed in storage there should be some method of controlling the temperature and humidity. A temperature of 85° to 95° F. for 10 to 14 days with high humidity is desirable to cure the roots and cause the healing or suberization of any cut surfaces. Growers frequently refer to desirable curing conditions as a "double 85"—or 85° F. and 85 per cent relative humidity.

Storage. After sweet potatoes have passed through a curing process they should be stored at 55° F., 85 per cent humidity for a period of about 8 to 24 weeks. A few hours storage at a temperature lower than 50° F. will not cause great harm, but prolonged periods should be avoided, since such conditions are likely to cause decay. Sweet potatoes should be well matured and free from mechanical damage and decay when put in storage. The roots should be handled as little as possible during storage. Storage losses may be considerable due to decay, sprouting, and shrinkage so the market price needs to increase to cover these losses.

Quality Characteristics for the Retail Buyer. Good sweet potatoes are smooth, well-shaped, firm, and of bright appearance. The most common defects are decay, misshapen potatoes, growth cracks, and wireworm injury.

Badly misshapen roots and those with growth cracks and wireworm injury are undesirable only from the viewpoint of waste in preparation. Sweet potatoes affected by decay are objectionable, because the decay usually spreads rapidly and usually imparts a disagreeable flavor to the potato even if the decayed portion is removed before cooking. Decay may appear either as a soft, wet rot or as a dry, shriveled, discolored, sunken area, usually at the ends of the potato; but it may appear anywhere on the surface. Another form of decay may appear as greenish (almost black) circular spots, varying in size from small to large. At times the spots are irregular and occur in bruised and injured places.

Sweet potatoes sometimes are marked with small, dark, clay-colored spots which may unite and form large dark blotches. These spots are only skin deep, and affect the appearance but not the flesh. Roots that appear damp should be examined carefully—they may have been badly handled or frozen, or decayed specimens may be present.

Insects. The common insects are cutworm, wireworm, and rootknot nematode which are discussed in Chapter 14.

Diseases: *Black Rot (Ceratostomella fimbriata)*. Affected roots when dug show large, circular, almost black spots on the surface. Under these spots is a rather dry, shallow, very black fungus decay of the flesh. The disease may develop or increase in storage. Young plants also show this disease as a black discoloration at the lower end of the stem. All potatoes showing these symptoms should be discarded at digging time, sorting, or planting. Treat roots as described for stem rot.

Dry End Rot. This trouble, common on stored potatoes in California apparently is due to drying of the tissues under the broken ends of the potatoes. Secondary organisms then enter the affected tissues and proceed to cause decay when the potatoes are placed in moist conditions. Proper curing is the best control for this disorder.

Scurf (Monilochaetes infuscans). Irregular patches of a brown russeting appear on the skin of affected potatoes, sometimes covering most of the surface with a uniform discoloration. The fungus causes no decay or injury to the flesh, but appearance is affected. For control select disease-free seed.

Soft Rot (Rhizopus nigricans). Potatoes in storage or transit often are attacked by a soft, mushy, dripping, fast-spreading rot, which entirely destroys the root. The rot attacks mostly potatoes which have been bruised in digging or handling, injured by low or high temperatures, insufficiently cured, or stored with poor ventilation. Sound, well-cured potatoes, held at proper temperatures and with good ventilation, are not likely to be affected.

Stem Rot or Wilt (Fusarium oxysporum, F. batatas). Plants wither and die before starting to grow. Others develop more or less, then die, and the leaves turn black. Many plants have the main stem partially discolored, some of the shoots are alive and some dead. If the stem is split lengthwise, dark-colored streaks will be seen in the inner woody tissue. These streaks run down into the potatoes and form, in cross section, a dark-brown ring in the flesh near the stem end. Diseased plants are inclined to produce many small potatoes about the size used for seed. Only disease free potatoes should be used in the seed bed for propagation. Crop rotation and seed treatments are of minor benefit in reducing stem rot losses. Most infection comes from soil through wounds, not from seed roots.

Surface Rot (Fusarium oxysporum). Surface rot lesions are circular, regular in shape, hard, sunken and grayish-brown in color. By the end of the storage season the lesions pretty well cover the surface and the potatoes are shrunken, dry and sometimes mummified. The causal fungus belongs to the *Fusarium* group, but is not the one that causes stem rot. Potatoes put into storage while the surfaces are still wet and not cured are most likely to develop this disease.

Control of Storage Diseases. A program of precautionary measures should be followed to control storage diseases. This program includes (1) careful harvesting to avoid bruising and skinning, (2) allowing the surface of the potatoes to dry in the field, (3) avoiding chilling of the potatoes both before and after digging, (4) sorting out all diseased potatoes (including scurf) while harvesting, (5) sanitation in the storages, (6) proper curing, and (7) good storage conditions.

Storages should be cleaned of all refuse immediately following the storage season in the spring. In the fall, before the potatoes are brought in, the storage room may be fumigated with formaldehyde or sprayed with copper sulfate to kill spores of the storage diseases.

References

1. Boswell, Victor R.: Commercial growing and harvesting of sweet potatoes, *U.S.D.A. Farmers' Bull. 2020,* 38 p., 1950.
2. Garcia, Fabian: Sweet potato culture, *N.M. Agr. Exp. Sta. Bull. 70,* 35 p., 1909.
3. Minges, P. A., and L. L. Morris: Sweet potato production in California, *Calif. Agr. Ext. Ser. Leaflet,* 20 p., (Multolith) 1948.

GROUP E. MINOR CROPS

Eggplant *(Solanum Melongena)* is more tender to low temperatures than either tomatoes or peppers, although similar to them in culture. The plant is not grown commonly in the cooler sections of the north, although New Hampshire Hybrid is adapted to a short growing season. The plants grow to a height of 2 to 4 feet and bear a few large purple fruits which are oval-shaped or an elongated oval. The Black Beauty and Improved Long Purple

Fig. 94. Three eggplant varieties which are, from left to right, Black Beauty, Fort Meyers Market, and Improved Long Purple (New York Spineless). (Courtesy, Ferry-Morse Seed Co.)

varieties produce 4 to 6 fruits per plant. Fort Myers Market (Fig. 94) has a more elongated fruit which the tall plant holds off the ground, thus reducing soil-borne rots. Seed is planted in a hotbed and grown for 8 to 12 weeks before setting in the field, which occurs after danger from frost, and when the soil is warm. Plants are spaced 3 by 4 feet. The fruits are harvested after they have reached sufficient size to produce a good yield and before the seeds begin to harden. As fruits become mature, the flesh softens so if it is pressed with the thumb it will leave an indentation indicating advancing maturity. In more immature fruits this indentation will spring back to its original shape. The stem of the fruit is tough and may be severed readily from the plant by means of a pruning shears or a sharp knife. The crop is marketed with a short stem attached to the fruit. Care should be used in packing crates to prevent the stems from bruising other fruits.

Reference

Beattie, J. H.: Production of eggplant, *U.S.D.A. Leaflet 131,* 4 p., 1937.

Okra (*Hibiscus esculentus*) is a member of the Malvaceae Family. Cotton belongs to this same family and okra produces a somewhat similar plant, which grows to a height of 4 to 5 feet and is spaced about 2 by 3 feet. The seed germinates slowly, and the process may be hastened by soaking the seed 24 hours in water. Common varieties are Clemson Spineless and Green Velvet. Okra is a warm season crop and thrives best in the southern states where it is grown primarily for home use. The crop also is canned and in some countries it is dried in large amounts. The taste for okra is probably an acquired one; the sliced pod imparts a "slick" taste which is desired in many southern soups. It is also fried and cooked in other ways.

The flower, which is large and showy, appears in the axil of each leaf above the bottom leaves. The flowers remain open only a few hours of one day. The pod grows rapidly; in 4 or 5 days they have made about one-fourth of their maximum growth. The pods should be harvested at this immature stage and used almost immediately. The pods become tough as they increase in age on the plant or are stored for any considerable length of time. A tender crisp pod can be snapped like snap beans while older pods tend to bend without breaking. Regular harvest is essential for maximum production which may reach yields of 300 bushels per acre. Sometimes harvesting causes a stinging or itching sensation of the tender parts of the skin; this may be removed by washing the hands or may be prevented by wearing gloves.

Reference

Beattie, W. R.: Culture and uses of okra. *U.S.D.A. Farmers' Bull. 232*, 12 p., 1940.

Peppers (Hot). Types of tabasco and chili peppers prefer a warmer climate than the sweet type. Tabasco is grown primarily in Louisiana and the chili types in the Southwest. Culture is very similar to that given for sweet peppers.

Index